HOW TO USE THIS [BOOK]

G000152562

Ireland is divided into four ancient Provin[ces which] are applied in the administration of golf b[y the] Union of Ireland. **Golf Days** has adopt[ed this] geographical division. The courses in t[his book are] grouped in Provinces, sub-divided into C[ounties and] then listed alphabetically. The Province appears on the top left hand corner and the County name at the top right of each page.

COURSE INFORMATION

This information has been provided by each club and readers are advised to check details in advance as the publishers cannot guarantee the accuracy. Most clubs will be only too glad to answer queries and telephone numbers for all the courses listed have been included for this purpose.
A telephone call can save a wasted journey.
There are different area dialing codes when calling from the Republic of Ireland to Northern Ireland and vice versa. From N.Ireland dial 00 353 & then the code omitting the first zero. From the Republic of Ireland dial 08 then the code including the first zero.

CURRENCY

All green Fees for Northern Ireland *(Counties: Down, Armagh, Antrim, Londonderry, Fermanagh and Tyrone)* are in £ Sterling. Those for the Republic of Ireland are in IR £ (punts). The currencies tend to be within 10% of each other.

SCORE CARD

Some course cards are marked in metres, some in yards and some have both. Whatever method of distance that is currently used by each course, the same has been adopted in **Golf Days** to maintain the same standard of measurement. Some course lengths differ in text from course cards depending on whether Championship or Medal lengths are on the score card.

COURSE MAP

These are for general information and to provide a layout of the course. They are not intended for interpretation for scoring or competition purposes.

Published by	Original Editorial Committee	Sales & Distribution
Tudor Journals Ltd	Leinster:	Alan Looby
97 Botanic Avenue,	Kenneth W. Haughton	
Belfast BT7 1JN. N. Ireland.	Ulster:	**Production**
Telephone (01232) 320088.	Brendan Edwards.	Paula McVeigh.
Fax (01232) 323163.	Munster:	Bill Jordan.
Also at:	J. Percy Shannon.	Roger Campbell.
77 Grand Parade, Cork.	Connacht:	
Tel/Fax (021) 279666.	Michael P. O'Donoghue.	**Publisher**
		Bill Campbell.

Provincial Introductions:
Jack Magowan.

Printed by Universities Press Ltd.
All contents of this publication are copyright and may not be reproduced in any form whatsoever or stored in any retrieval system without the prior written permission of the publishers.
Copyright Tudor Journals Ltd. April 1998. ISBN 0-907520-45-6

THE NUMBERS ABOVE ARE COLOUR CODED IN PROVINCES FOR GEOGRAPHICAL LOCATION ON THE MAP (OPPOSITE).
FOR PAGE NUMBERS OF EACH CLUB REFER TO ALPHABETICAL INDEX ON PAGES 379 – 382.

The popular Grange Golf Club in the Sylvian setting of South Dublin

Two of Ireland's great courses – Ballybunion (above) and Royal County Down.

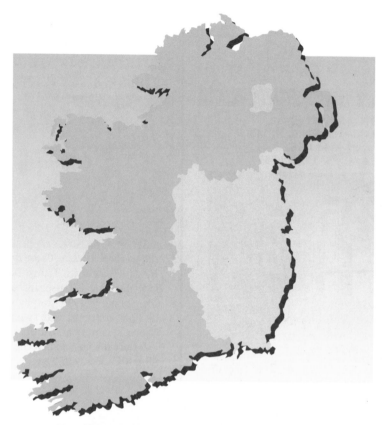

LEINSTER

BY JACK MAGOWAN

Jack Smith was his name, and nobody ever heard of him again. Clearly, the shock of leading a championship field by eight strokes must have been too much for this nervous young Londoner. While George Duncan, his boss at Wentworth, signed for a gale-lashed final-round 74 at Portmarnock, Smith needed seventeen shots more for a butter-fingered score of 91, and fretted all the way home.

This was 1927, the year of the first-ever Irish Open over a course made famous some years before by a couple of high-fliers who glided, in a Vickers-Vimy on to Portmarnock Strand, both fuel tanks empty, after taking off from Newfoundland the day before.

Overnight, the flagship of Leinster

MOUNT HERBERT HOTEL

BEST VALUE IN THE ♥ OF DUBLIN

**Herbert Road,
Lansdowne Road, Dublin 4.
Tel: +353 1 668 4321.
Fax: +353 1 660 7077**

MOUNT HERBERT is a fine Victorian Residence in picturesque gardens. Once the family home of Lord Robinson, it is just south of the city centre in Ballsbridge, Dublin's most exclusive area, where most diplomatic embassies are based.
The Loughran family have been welcoming guests to Mount Herbert for over 40 years, and it is renowned for its superb value, and its warm and friendly atmosphere.

FOR THE MORE ACTIVE
We will be delighted to arrange tee off times at one of the city's many fine golf courses. For example; Druid's Glen, European Club, Milltown with many more to choose from.

FACILITIES INCLUDE:
- Private Car Park
- Sauna/Sunbed
- Gift Shop
- 200 Modern Bedrooms
- Restaurant/Bar
- Conference Centre

NEARBY ATTRACTIONS:
- Temple Bar
- Trinity College
- Point Concert Venue
- RDS Exhibition Centre
- Grafton Street Shopping
- Lansdowne Road Stadium

ABOVE PAR ACCOMMODATION AT THE REGENCY HOTEL GROUP

The Royal Hotel & Leisure Centre Bray, Co. Wicklow.
RAC, AA and Irish Tourist Board graded 3***. Five local courses including Druid's Glen, home of 1996 Murphy's Irish Open. Full leisure centre with swimming pool, sauna, steam-room, whirlpool, massage, beauty therapy, and creche facilities.
Tel: (01) 286 2935. Fax: (01) 286 7373.

The Esplanade Hotel, Bray, Co. Wicklow.
Combines old world charm with modern day facilities. RAC 3*** with spectacular sea views. Leisure facilities include a gym, sauna, steam room and 10 seater jacuzzi.
Golf available 7 days a week on a choice of five challenging local courses.
Convenient to Dublin by DART (30 minutes).
Tel: (01) 286 2056. Fax: (01) 286 6496.

A jewel in the Leinster crown is the famous Portmarnock course.

golf had an exciting new identity. Maggie Leonard's cow was no more, but the quickest way to get to this great links was across the estuary from Baldoyle in a row boat or horse and trap, depending on the tide. In those days, no stranger ever left Portmarnock. He may have arrived as a stranger, but by closing time he was a friend. They would ring a ship's bell to signal to signal the departure of the last boat back to the mainland, then came the motor-car and Duncan and Mitchell and Easterbrook and Bobby Locke, all championship over the longest, sometimes toughest links course in Europe.

The face of Portmarnock hasn't changed a great deal. Without wind it may be like Samson shorn of his hair, yet how often do we ever get this Dublin Bay pearl bereft of wind? Even when Sandy Lyle beat a 30 year-old record with a staggering 64 on day one of the 1989 Irish Open, the burly

Scot was in a cashmere sweater and cords. In Duncan's day, they usually wore oil-paper under plus-fours as protection against rain or cold.

Locke always waxed eloquent about Portmarnock, and not without reason. Wasn't it there at the age of 21, and in his first season as a professional, that 'Old Muffin Face' won the Irish championship. Two years later (1940) he was flying bombing missions against Rommel in North Africa and didn't touch a golf club again until the War ended. Half-a-century later, the tournament revived by Carrolls Tobacco, and rescued by Murphy's Stout, royally hosts nearly all the game's top players before some of the biggest galleries in Europe.

The Irish love to watch golf as well as play it, and nobody was surprised when Portmarnock had to put up 'house full' notices at the first Walker Cup match ever staged here. That was in 1991 and part of the Golfing Union's

The 1st and 7th tees at Finnstown.

centenary celebrations, and you can be certain this glamour fixture will be back in the Emerald Isle before long. If not at Portmarnock, then maybe Royal County Down, Mount Juliet or the K-Club. Out of nearly 20 Irish courses ranked among *Golf World's* choice of the top 100 in Britain, seven now wear the Leinster label.

Arnold Palmer's baby at Naas, the fashionable K-Club, only comes in at No.93, but don't hold that against it. This is nothing short of a superb course, tailored to a tee and possibly boasting more five-star holes than any other new course in the country. As club pro Ernie Jones said recently,

borrowing a phrase from the most celebrated Jones-boy of all.

"There's not a hole here that can't be birdied if you just think. And there's not a hole that can't be double-bogied if you stop thinking!"

What a boost for Michael Smurfit, and Irish golf, it would be if the Ryder Cup comes to the K-Club in 2005, as well it might.

County Louth, Royal Dublin, The Island, Rosslare — all welcoming hosts and courses that have few equals in a links context. And the same can be said for Pat Ruddy's wonderful new creation at Brittas Bay, the European Club. This course was only played for the first time

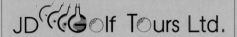

ACKNOWLEDGEMENTS

GOLF DAYS WOULD LIKE TO RECORD ITS THANKS AND APPRECIATION TO THE MANY GOLF CLUBS AND STAFF WHO GREATLY ASSISTED THE PUBLISHERS IN COMPILING THIS BOOK. THE PUBLISHER'S ALSO ACKNOWLEDGE THE SUPPORT OF THE MANY ADVERTISERS THROUGHOUT THE JOURNAL AND WOULD RECOMMEND THEIR SERVICES TO READERS.

13

in the summer of '94 and, like Portmarnock Links of Langer fame, needs time to mature. Once it does, we'll be talking about a roller coaster gem in the same breath as Baltray, Portstewart, Ballyliffin, Sligo and others of merit.

Water, in my view, adds greatly to the charm and magnetism of a golf course, and there's an abundance of it at St Margaret's, near Dublin Airport. The eighth there is one of the most genuine par-5's in the business, an exhileratingly difficult long hole that top-girl Laura Davies clearly treated with respectful caution, even in the '95 championship she won there by a runaway 16 strokes. Laura was in orbit that week, surrendering only one shot to par in 72 holes for a World record tally of 25 – under (267) that may never be bettered in a ladies' tourament in Ireland.

St. Margaret's is the brainchild of Ruddy and designer, Tom Caddock, whose eye for what's best in golfing architecture has also put a hideaway hamlet in County Wicklow called Newtownmountkennedy firmly on the map.

Who said Valderrama was the toughest course in Europe?.

It's a pussy-cat (almost) compared to Druid's Glen, where the key is not to play all four short holes in par, but without getting that Titleist wet!

The 17th to an Island green is a spectacle hole, a carbon copy of No.17 on Florida's famous Tournament Players' course, only longer.

Druid's Glen is not for everybody, not at an entrance fee of £25,000 + plus, or annual sub. of £1,500, but for sheer drama and challenge, it's something special, an examination in golf for sure.

"Our brief was to build the best inland course in the country," says Craddock, once a Walker Cup player. " Clearly, there can't be many better than this."

Golf's magnetism is like the

Elm Park Golf Club in Dublin – popular city parkland course with many mature trees adding to the test of golf.

common cold – everybody gets it, but nobody can explain why. There are many permutations for a rewarding, if not inexpensive, tour of Ireland's South-East region, but for one lovely lady from Baltinglass it would begin with a round at the European Club and end at Rathsallagh. Sandwiched between the – two would be a visit to Woodenbridge (Arklow), Rosslare, St Helens Bay, Faithlegg, Mount Juliet and Carlow.

Eight different courses in ten days? Sheer exhaustion, but it would be a never-to-be-forgotten experience!

Every year, nearly 60 top people in golf are invited to rank in merit order Ireland's thirty greatest courses. Portmarnock seems to have found a permanent place at No. 1, followed by Royal Portrush and or Ballybunion and Royal County Down.

And how are the others rated? Mount Juliet, which carries the Nicklaus signature, is currently at No.7 and the K-Club at No.10, just in front of Killarney.

Not surprisingly, Druid's Glen won unstinted applause from the winner of the first two Irish Opens there, Colin Montgomerie, and so will Portmarnock Links when the pros are invited for a closer look. It, too, is a wonderful test of shot-making and should be played again and again!

Here is how Ireland's top courses, North and South, are ranked at home:

1) Portamarnock; 2) Royal Portrush; 3) Royal Co. Down; 4) Ballybunion Old; 5) Waterville; 6) The European Club; 7) Mount Juliet; 8) Co. Louth; 9) Druid's Glen; 10) The K-Club; 11) Lahinch; 12) Killarney (Killeen); 13) Co Sligo; 14) Portmarnock Links; 15) Royal Dublin; 16) Malone; 17) Portstewart; 18) Carlow; 19) Connemara; 20) The Island; 21) St Margaret's; 22) Tralee; 23) Donegal; 24) Slieve Russell; 25) Rathsallagh; 26) Luttrellstown; 27) Cork; 28) Killarney (Mahoney); 29) Enniscrone, and 30) Fota Island.

**Borris Golf Club,
Deerpark, Borris,
Co. Carlow.
Tel: (0503) 73143/73201.**

LOCATION: Outskirts of the town on the road to New Ross.
SECRETARY: Richard Long.

Picturesque nine hole course, sited in wooded land with an attractive backdrop of hills and mountains.

COURSE INFORMATION

Par 70; SSS 69; Length 5,572 metres.
Visitors: Welcome Mon – Fri.
Opening Hours: 9.30am – 5.30pm.
Avoid: Thursday afternoons, Saturdays and Sundays.
Ladies: Welcome.
Green Fees: £10. (With Members Sun Only).

Juveniles: Welcome. Caddy service available by prior arrangements.
Clubhouse Hours: 10.00am – 11.00pm.
Clubhouse Dress: Casual.
Clubhouse Facilities: Bar food.

NO.	METRES	PAR	S.I.	NO.	METRES	PAR	S.I.
1	297	4	10	10	312	4	7
2	345	4	5	11	311	4	9
3	274	4	16	12	293	4	15
4	117	3	18	13	151	3	14
5	450	5	12	14	346	4	6
6	323	4	8	15	355	4	4
7	152	3	13	16	132	3	17
8	393	4	3	17	430	4	1
9	414	4	2	18	477	5	11
OUT	2,765	35		IN	2,807	35	
				TOTAL	5,572	70	
STANDARD SCRATCH		69					

BORRIS CLUBHOUSE

NO.	MEDAL YARDS	GEN. YARDS	PAR	S.I.	NO.	MEDAL YARDS	GEN. YARDS	PAR	S.I.
1	401	393	4	4	10	279	276	4	11
2	292	269	4	14	11	393	376	4	3
3	131	122	3	17	12	344	335	4	7
4	354	342	4	9	13	152	147	3	16
5	503	460	5	15	14	416	411	4	5
6	165	162	3	12	15	354	340	4	10
7	398	389	4	1	16	401	377	4	2
8	397	390	4	6	17	139	132	3	18
9	373	334	4	8	18	482	467	5	13
OUT	3,014	2,861	35		IN	2,960	2,861	35	
					TOTAL	5,974	5,722	70	
	STANDARD SCRATCH					70	70		

Deerpark, Dublin Road, Co. Carlow.
Tel: (0503) 31695.

LOCATION: Two miles north of Carlow Town on main Dublin Road (N9).
SECRETARY: Margaret Meaney.
Tel: (0503) 31695. Fax: (0503) 40065.
PROFESSIONAL: Andrew Gilbert.
Tel: (0503) 41745.

Considered one of the best inland courses with fair but tight fairways and good greens. Its fine springy turf earns the reputation of "inland links". The course has extensive mature woods and many scenic views.

COURSE INFORMATION

Par 70; SSS 71; Length 5,974 metres.
Visitors: Welcome.
Opening Hours: Sunrise – Sunset.
Avoid: Tuesday, Saturday and Sunday.
Ladies: Welcome.
Green Fees: Mon –Fri £22; Groups (12+) £20; Weekends £27. Groups (12+) £20 & £25.
Juveniles: Restricted. Lessons available by prior arrangements. Caddy service available by prior arrangement. Handicap certificate required.
Clubhouse Hours: 9.30am – 11.30pm. Full Clubhouse Facilities.
Clubhouse Dress: Casual.
Clubhouse Facilities: Breakfast (summer), lunches, evening meals, snacks all day. Menu available on request.
Open Competitions: Open Week: 29th May – 6th June; Midland Scratch Cup: 26th – 27th Sept.

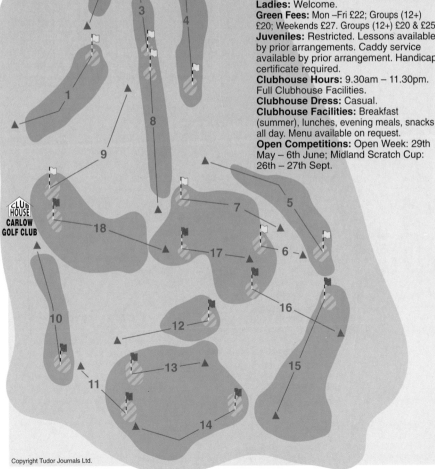

CLUB HOUSE
CARLOW GOLF CLUB

Mount Wolseley Golf & Country Club, Tullow, Co. Carlow.
Tel: (0503) 51674.
Fax: (0503) 52123.

Location: Adjacent to Tullow town on the Ardattin Road.
Secretary / Manager: Kathy Walsh.
Tel: (0503) 51674.
Professional: Jimmy Bolger.
Captain: Bernard Byrne.

A testing 18 hole course with plenty of water hazards and bunkers. Incorporated is a good practice area consisting of finished fairways and greens situated right beside the Clubhouse.

COURSE INFORMATION

Par 72; SSS 74; Length 7,106 yards.
Green Fees: £25 Mon – Fri. £30 Weekends. Club hire availablefrom fully stocked pro shop.
Clubhouse Facilities:
Catering facilities available: Bar food from 10.30am, full bar menu from 12.30pm.

Restaurant a la carte from 6pm – 10pm (summer) & 6pm – 9pm (winter). Breakfast for groups.
Open Competitions:
Fourball Stableford Competitions. 14th & 15th April: 3rd & 31st May: 1st June: 3rd August: 26th October. Entry fee £20 p.p.

NO.	CHAMP METRES	MEDAL METRES	PAR	S.I.	NO.	CHAMP METRES	MEDAL METRES	PAR	S.I.
1	411	383	4	9	10	592	571	5	6
2	447	417	4	5	11	207	191	3	10
3	447	435	4	1	12	519	504	5	18
4	273	267	4	15	13	427	409	4	14
5	499	483	5	7	14	339	319	4	12
6	210	187	3	13	15	466	438	4	2
7	542	521	5	11	16	226	204	3	16
8	440	418	4	3	17	457	397	4	4
9	191	177	3	17	18	413	394	4	8
OUT	3,460	3,288	36		IN	3646	3,427	36	
					TOTAL	7,106	6,715	72	
					STANDARD SCRATCH	74	73		

Bunker & tree positions indicated.

MOUNT WOLSELEY CLUBHOUSE

Blackhall, Balbriggan, Co. Dublin.
Tel: 8412229 or 8412173.

LOCATION: 1 mile south of Balbriggan on Dublin / Belfast road.
SECRETARY / MANAGER: Michael O'Halloran.
Tel: 8412229.

Expanded to eighteen holes in 1985 and has been developed using an additional 32 acres that the club purchased which allowed for a new clubhouse to be built in 1991 adding to the club's many attractive features. The new layout has made the course more of a formidable challenge.

COURSE INFORMATION

Par 71; SSS 71; Length 5,922 metres.
Visitors: Welcome Monday, Wednesday, Thursday and Friday.
Opening Hours: 8.00am – sunset.
Avoid: Weekends and Tuesday (Ladies day).

Juveniles: Open Week, August.
Green Fees: £16 Mon – Fri. £10 early bird green fee weekdays (except Tuesdays) before 10.00am.
Clubhouse Hours: 8.00am – 11.00pm.
Clubhouse Dress: Casual.
Clubhouse Facilities: Snacks and meals available from noon.
Open Competitions: Open Week June.

NO.	METRES	PAR	S.I.	NO.	METRES	PAR	S.I.
1	365	4	6	10	417	5	15
2	504	5	16	11	184	3	7
3	357	4	4	12	368	4	3
4	321	4	18	13	308	4	13
5	384	4	2	14	358	4	5
6	180	3	10	15	392	4	1
7	339	4	14	16	130	3	11
8	171	3	12	17	323	4	9
9	360	4	8	18	461	5	17
OUT	2,981	35		IN	2,941	36	
				TOTAL	5,922	71	
		STANDARD SCRATCH				71	

BALBRIGGAN
CLUBHOUSE
CLUB HOUSE

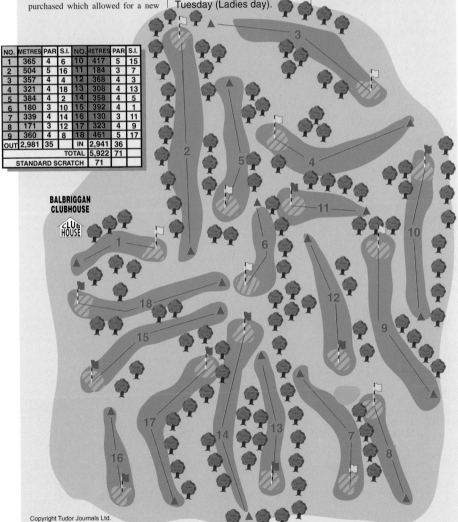

**Balcarrick Golf Club,
Corballis, Donabate,
Co. Dublin.**

Secretary: Patrick Dillon.
Tel: (01) 843 6957 / 843 6228.
Course Designer: Barry Langan.

A relatively new club, founded in
1992. In 1995 it was converted to a
fine 18 hole course featuring deceptive
holes and water hazards creating quite
a challenge. In 1997 a clubhouse was
built situated on course.

COURSE INFORMATION

**Par 73; SSS 72; Length
5,940 metres.
Visitors:** Welcome.
Opening Hours:
Sunrise – sunset.
Ladies: Welcome.
Green Fees: Weekdays £13;
weekends £20.
Juveniles: Must be accompanied
by an adult.
Clubhouse Hours:
12am –11pm.

Clubhouse Dress: Neat &
Tidy. No denims or trainers on
course or in clubhouse.
Clubhouse Facilities:
Full catering facilities. Fully
licenced.
Open Competitions:
Every Thursday and Bank
Holidays,
Open Week 26th July – 2nd
Aug.

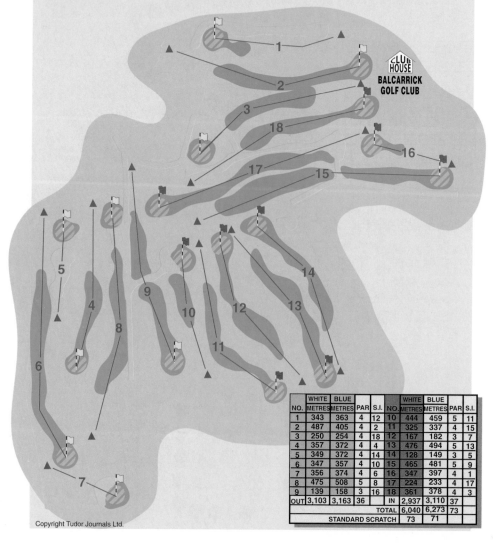

NO.	WHITE METRES	BLUE METRES	PAR	S.I.	NO.	WHITE METRES	BLUE METRES	PAR	S.I.
1	343	363	4	12	10	444	459	5	11
2	487	405	4	2	11	325	337	4	15
3	250	254	4	18	12	167	182	3	7
4	357	372	4	4	13	476	494	5	13
5	349	372	4	14	14	128	149	3	5
6	347	357	4	10	15	465	481	5	9
7	356	374	4	6	16	347	397	4	1
8	475	508	5	8	17	224	233	4	17
9	139	158	3	16	18	361	378	4	3
OUT	3,103	3,163	36		IN	2,937	3,110	37	
					TOTAL	6,040	6,273	73	
					STANDARD SCRATCH	73	71		

Ballinascorney, Tallaght, Dublin 24, Co. Dublin. Tel: 4512775.

LOCATION: Approx. ten miles south west of Dublin.
MANAGER: Mr Tom Bagnall. Tel: 4516430.

Flat picturesque course in the foothills of the Dublin Mountains. The area has scenic views of the mountains, forests and lakes and overlooks Dublin city and Dublin bay. The course itself offers a varied selection of terrain from level parkland to gentle rolling slopes and some optional terrain of a more difficult nature. The newer section has some interesting water hazards and features holes.

COURSE INFORMATION

Par 71; SSS 67; Length 5,464 metres.
Visitors: Welcome (phone in advance) – societies welcome.
Opening Hours: Sunrise – sunset.
Avoid: Weekends.
Ladies: Welcome Tuesdays.

Green Fees: £12 (weekdays) £15 (weekends).
Juveniles: Welcome.
Clubhouse Hours: 8.00am – 11.00pm.
Clubhouse Dress: Smart / casual (no denim).
Clubhouse Facilities: Snacks and full catering available.

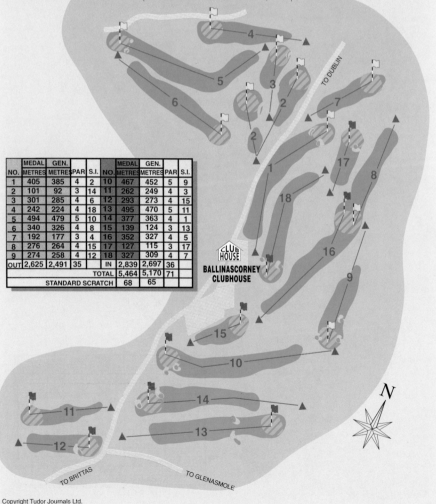

NO.	MEDAL METRES	GEN. METRES	PAR	S.I.	NO.	MEDAL METRES	GEN. METRES	PAR	S.I.
1	405	385	4	2	10	467	452	5	9
2	101	92	3	14	11	262	249	4	3
3	301	285	4	6	12	293	273	4	15
4	242	224	4	18	13	495	470	5	11
5	494	479	5	10	14	377	363	4	1
6	340	326	4	8	15	139	124	3	13
7	192	177	3	4	16	352	327	4	5
8	276	264	4	15	17	127	115	3	17
9	274	258	4	12	18	327	309	4	7
OUT	2,625	2,491	35		IN	2,839	2,697	36	
					TOTAL	5,464	5,170	71	
					STANDARD SCRATCH	68	65		

BALLINASCORNEY CLUBHOUSE

Beaverstown, Donabate, Co. Dublin.
Tel: (01) 8436439.
Fax: (01) 8436721.

LOCATION: 6 miles north of Dublin Airport.
MANAGER: Sean Flavin
Tel: (01) 8436721.
ARCHITECT: Eddie Hackett.

Beaverstown is sited in an attractive orchard setting. The main feature of the course is its proximity to deep water which is a hazard on as many as ten of the eighteen holes.

COURSE INFORMATION

Par 71; SSS 70; Length 5,874 metres.
Visitors: Welcome.
Opening Hours: 8.00am – sunset.
Avoid: Wed, Sat and Sun.
Ladies: Welcome.
Juveniles: Must be accompanied by an adult. Prior arrangement required;

Caddy service available by prior arrangements.
Green Fees: £20 Mon – Fri; £25 Sat / Sun.
Clubhouse Hours: 8.00am to closing time.
Clubhouse Dress: Neat dress essential, no blue jeans allowed.
Clubhouse Facilities: Bar and restaurant from 10.30am.
Open Competitions: As per list published by G.U.I. (1st weekend in April / last week in May / 1st weekend in September).

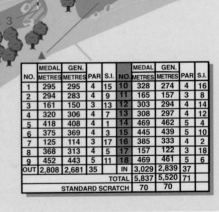

NO.	MEDAL METRES	GEN. METRES	PAR	S.I.	NO.	MEDAL METRES	GEN. METRES	PAR	S.I.
1	295	295	4	15	10	328	274	4	16
2	294	283	4	9	11	165	157	3	8
3	161	150	3	13	12	303	294	4	14
4	320	306	4	7	13	308	297	4	12
5	418	408	4	1	14	469	462	5	4
6	375	369	4	3	15	445	439	5	10
7	125	114	3	17	16	385	333	4	2
8	368	313	4	5	17	157	122	3	18
9	452	443	5	11	18	469	461	5	6
OUT	2,808	2,681	35		IN	3,029	2,839	37	
					TOTAL	5,837	5,520	71	
					STANDARD SCRATCH	70	70		

Johnstown, Rathcoole, Co. Dublin.
Tel: 4580100 / 4580522.

LOCATION: 2 miles from Rathcoole village on Kilteel Road.
SECRETARY / MANAGER: Joe Deally.
ARCHITECT: Eddie Hackett.

The course is in a setting of natural beauty with mature beech trees in abundance. Holes 9, 10, 11, 12 & 13 have a combination of mature trees and water providing difficulty, particularly in the drives.

COURSE INFORMATION

Par 72; SSS 70; Length 6,268 yds; 5,730 metres.
Visitors: Welcome Mon, Thurs & Fri.
Opening Hours: 8.00am – Sunset.
Avoid: Tues, Wed, and weekends.
Ladies Day: Tuesday.
Juveniles: Must be accompanied by an adult.

Green Fees: £22 all week; Juveniles £6.
Clubhouse Hours: 9.00am – midnight.
Clubhouse Dress: Collar and tie after 8.00pm. No jeans or sneakers.
Clubhouse Facilities: 11.30am – 10.30pm.
Open Competitions: Open Week June.

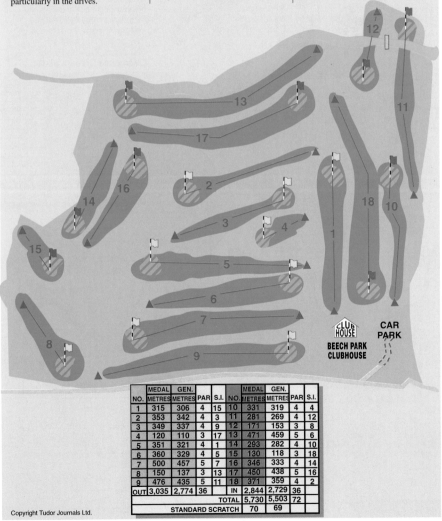

NO.	MEDAL METRES	GEN. METRES	PAR	S.I.	NO.	MEDAL METRES	GEN. METRES	PAR	S.I.
1	315	306	4	15	10	331	319	4	4
2	353	342	4	3	11	281	269	4	12
3	349	337	4	9	12	171	153	3	8
4	120	110	3	17	13	471	459	5	6
5	351	321	4	1	14	293	282	4	10
6	360	329	4	5	15	130	118	3	18
7	500	457	5	7	16	346	333	4	14
8	150	137	3	13	17	450	438	5	16
9	476	435	5	11	18	371	359	4	2
OUT	3,035	2,774	36		IN	2,844	2,729	36	
					TOTAL	5,730	5,503	72	
					STANDARD SCRATCH	70	69		

**Citywest Golf Course,
Saggart, Co. Dublin.
Tel: (01) 458 8566.
Fax: (01) 458 8565.**

LOCATION: 15 minutes from Dublin's City centre (N7 Saggart Village).
SECRETARY / MANAGER: Eddie Jones.
Tel: (01) 458 8566.

GOLF DIRECTOR: Peter O'Hagan.
ARCHITECT: Christy O'Connor Jnr.

The careful construction of the course using the latest technology in drainage and irrigation systems has resulted in a superb playing surface which almost guarantees all year round golf.

COURSE INFORMATION

Par 71; Length 6,822 yards.
Visitors: Always welcome.
Opening Hours: 7.00am – sunset.
Green Fees: £27 weekdays; £30 weekends / Bank Holidays. Residents £15.
Juveniles: Golf clubs, trolleys, buggies, locker and caddies available. Professional tuition and golf schools available.
Clubhouse Facilities: First class restaurant open 7 days a week, bar food and banqueting / conference facilities available for 400 people. Steam room, sauna, gym and 50 luxurious bedrooms. Driving Range.
Clubhouse Dress: Casual.

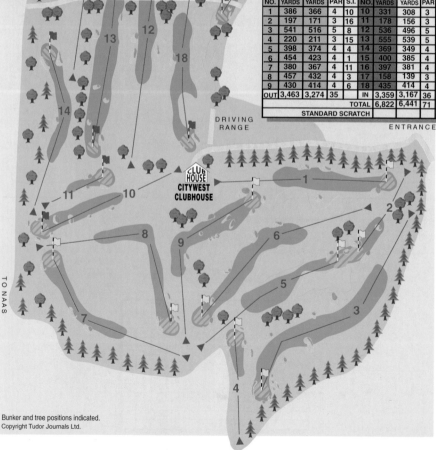

CITYWEST CLUBHOUSE

DRIVING RANGE

ENTRANCE

TO DUBLIN

TO NAAS

NO.	CHAMP YARDS	MEDAL YARDS	PAR	S.I.	NO.	CHAMP YARDS	MEDAL YARDS	PAR	S.I.
1	386	366	4	10	10	331	308	3	14
2	197	171	3	16	11	178	156	3	17
3	541	516	5	8	12	536	496	5	7
4	220	211	3	15	13	555	539	5	9
5	398	374	4	4	14	369	349	4	12
6	454	423	4	1	15	400	385	4	13
7	380	367	4	11	16	397	381	4	5
8	457	432	4	3	17	158	139	3	18
9	430	414	4	6	18	435	414	4	2
OUT	3,463	3,274	35		IN	3,359	3,167	36	
					TOTAL	6,822	6,441	71	
					STANDARD SCRATCH				

Bunker and tree positions indicated.
Copyright Tudor Journals Ltd.

NO.	YARDS	PAR	S.I.	NO.	YARDS	PAR	S.I.
1	155	3	12	10	132	3	15
2	251	4	18	11	374	4	9
3	465	4	2	12	405	4	3
4	155	3	16	13	264	4	17
5	389	4	4	14	191	3	11
6	183	3	6	15	196	3	5
7	188	3	8	16	392	4	1
8	264	4	14	17	140	3	13
9	494	5	10	18	333	4	7
OUT	2,544	33		IN	2,427	32	
				TOTAL	4,971	65	
	STANDARD SCRATCH			64			

Corballis Public Golf Course, Donabate, Co. Dublin.
Tel: 8436583.

LOCATION: North County Dublin on the coast.
MANAGER: P. J. Boylan.
Tel: 8436583/8436781.
ARCHITECT: Dublin County Council.

A links course situated adjacent to Corballis Beach, Donabate. Aquired and redeveloped by Dublin County Council in 1973. A very popular and challenging Par 65 course which attracts large numbers of golfers particularly during the winter months.

COURSE INFORMATION

Par 65; SSS 64; Length 4,971 yards.
Visitors: Welcome.
Opening Hours: Weekends 7.00am; Weekdays 8.00am.
Ladies: Welcome.
Green Fees: £9 Mon – Fri; £12 Sat/Sun; Juveniles, Senior Citizens & unemployed £6 (Mon–Fri before 2.30pm).
Juveniles: Welcome.
Clubhouse Hours: Open normal hours.
Clubhouse Dress: Casual/neat.

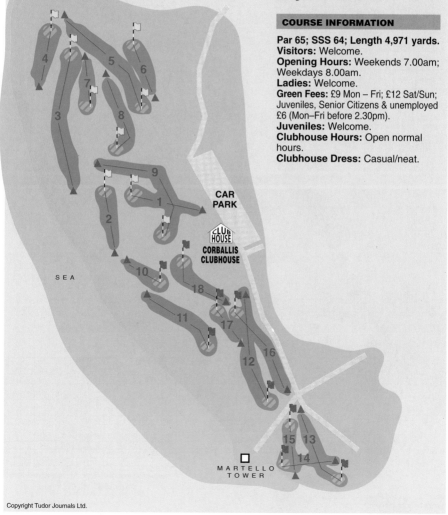

CAR PARK

CLUB HOUSE
CORBALLIS CLUBHOUSE

SEA

MARTELLO TOWER

**Corrstown Golf Club,
Kilsallaghan, Co Dublin.
Tel: (01) 8640533.**

LOCATION: North West Dublin
Airport - 6 minutes.
SECRETARY: Jason Kelly. (Admin)
Tel: (01) 864 0533.
Fax: (01) 864 0537.
PROFESSIONAL: Pat Gittens.
ARCHITECT: Eddie Connaughton
B. Sc. – Designer Agronomist.
Course: Grass Technology
International.

27 holes – 9 hole course (Orchard
Course) 18 hole course (River Course).
Both parkland courses. 18 hole course
contains a river with island green and
water features throughout the course.

COURSE INFORMATION

**Par 72; SSS 71; Length; 6,298
metres (River Course); 5,584
metres (Orchard Course).**
Visitors: Welcome weekdays
before 3pm (ring for booking).
Opening Hours: 7.00am.
Avoid: Wednesdays.

Ladies: Full members.
Green Fees: Mon – Fri £17
(£10 with a member).
Juveniles: Usually
accompanied with an adult.
Clubhouse Hours:
11.30am – 11.30pm; pub hours
in summer.
Clubhouse Dress: Informal.
Clubhouse Facilities: Full
catering and bar facilities.
Open Competitions:
Intermediate Scratch Cup.

NO.	GENTS Metres	PAR	S.I.	NO.	LADIES Metres	PAR	S.I.
1	298	4	16	1	278	4	16
2	356	4	2	2	326	4	2
3	125	3	18	3	105	3	18
4	323	4	12	4	300	4	12
5	387	4	4	5	365	5	4
6	140	3	8	6	130	3	8
7	448	5	10	7	400	5	10
8	332	4	14	8	310	4	14
9	383	4	6	9	318	4	6
OUT	2,792	35		IN	2,532	36	
				TOTAL	5,324	72	
				STANDARD SCRATCH	71		

ORCHARD COURSE

PRACTICE AREA

CORRSTOWN HOUSE

CLUB HOUSE CORRSTOWN CLUBHOUSE

NO.	MEDAL METRES	GEN. METRES	PAR	S.I.	NO.	MEDAL METRES	GEN. METRES	PAR	S.I.
1	144	138	3	10	10	319	314	4	15
2	518	504	5	2	11	538	526	5	5
3	372	361	4	12	12	476	463	5	17
4	507	497	5	6	13	415	387	4	1
5	454	446	5	16	14	178	169	3	13
6	153	144	3	18	15	410	384	4	7
7	395	388	4	4	16	421	395	4	9
8	292	286	4	14	17	174	163	3	11
9	150	141	3	8	18	382	371	4	3
OUT	2,985	2,905	36		IN	3,313	3,172	36	
					TOTAL	6,298	6,077	72	
					STANDARD SCRATCH	72	71		

RIVER COURSE

Bunker and tree positions indicated.

DONABATE

Balcarrick, Donabate, Co. Dublin.
Tel: (01) 8436346

LOCATION: 12 miles north of Dublin city.
SECRETARY / MANAGER: Brian Judd.
Tel: (01) 8436346.
PROFESSIONAL: Hugh Jackson.
Tel: (01) 8436346.

Flat parkland course in a rural setting, best described as a good holiday course.

COURSE INFORMATION

Par 70; SSS 69; Length 5,704 yards.
Visitors: Welcome Mon – Fri.
Opening Hours: 7.30am – sunset.
Avoid: Wednesday, Saturday, Sunday and Bank Holidays.
Ladies: Welcome.
Green Fees: £20 daily (£10 with member); Sat, Sun & Bank Hols.
Juveniles: Welcome if accompanied by an adult. Club Hire and Caddy carts available by prior arrangements.
Clubhouse Hours: 8.00am – 11.30pm.
Clubhouse Dress: Casual / neat (no jeans or trainners).
Clubhouse Facilities: Snacks available at all times; a la carte from 5pm, bar also.
Open Competitions: Cutter Cup singles 18th July. Open Week 2nd – 9th August

NO.	MEDAL YARDS	GEN. YARDS	PAR	S.I.	NO.	MEDAL YARDS	GEN. YARDS	PAR	S.I.
1	162	147	3	9	10	375	366	4	2
2	444	435	5	13	11	191	176	3	6
3	375	356	4	3	12	315	296	4	12
4	408	380	4	1	13	322	309	4	15
5	325	314	4	11	14	359	334	4	8
6	356	342	5	5	15	173	164	3	14
7	272	251	4	18	16	316	309	4	10
8	330	315	4	7	17	375	340	4	4
9	154	145	3	16	18	452	438	5	17
OUT	2,826	2,685	35		IN	2,878	2,732	35	
					TOTAL	5,704	5,417	70	
					STANDARD SCRATCH	69	67		

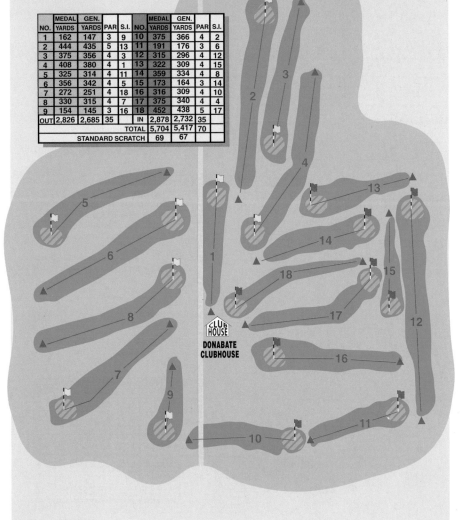

DONABATE CLUBHOUSE

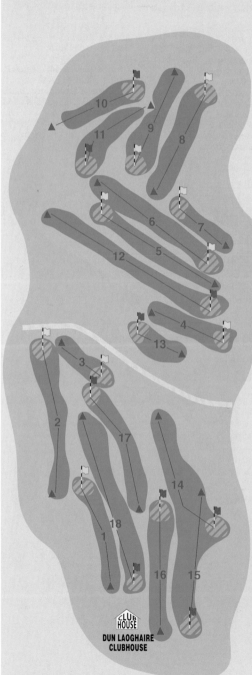

**Dun Laoghaire Golf Club,
Eglinton Park, Tivoli Road,
Dun Laoghaire.
Tel: (01) 2803916.
Fax: (01) 2804868.**

LOCATION: 7 miles South of Dublin.
SECRETARY: Terry Stewart.
Tel: (01) 2803916.
PROFESSIONAL: Owen Mulhall.
Tel: (01) 2801694.

Generally speaking a short course in the quiet suburbs of Dun Laoghaire, but with some interesting holes requiring accurate club selection.

COURSE INFORMATION

Par 68; SSS 67; Length 5,161 metres.
Visitors: Welcome Mon, Tues, Wed, Friday & Sun.
Opening Hours: 8.00am – sunset.
Ladies: Welcome.
Green Fees: £26 each day.
Juveniles: Welcome.
Lessons available by prior arrangements. Club Hire available.
Clubhouse Hours: 10.00am – 11.00pm.
Clubhouse Dress: Casual. Jacket and tie after 8.00pm.
Clubhouse Facilities: 10.00am – 10.00pm snack service April – Oct; 6.00pm – 10.00pm Restaurant April – Oct; 10.00am – 6.00pm Snack service Nov – March.

NO.	METRES	PAR	S.I.	NO.	METRES	PAR	S.I.
1	306	4	11	10	183	3	9
2	333	4	5	11	344	4	6
3	148	3	8	12	438	5	17
4	240	4	18	13	148	3	7
5	392	4	1	14	371	4	2
6	281	4	15	15	343	4	12
7	110	3	14	16	336	4	4
8	368	4	3	17	313	4	13
9	345	4	10	18	479	5	16
OUT	2,523	34		IN	2,955	36	
				TOTAL	5,161	68	
STANDARD SCRATCH		67					

**DUN LAOGHAIRE
CLUBHOUSE**

**Castleknock,
Dublin 15.
Tel: (01) 8200 797.**

LOCATION: Situated just off the Navan Road, a minutes drive from Castleknock roundabout.
SECRETARIES: Gerry Carr.
Tel: (01) 8200 797.
PROFESSIONAL: Paul McGahan/Arnold O'Connor.

Located 15 minutes from Dublin City. This is a very pleasant parkland course. The 17th hole Par 3 is an exceptional hole played against the backdrop of the Wicklow Mountains.

COURSE INFORMATION

Par 71; SSS 68; Length 5,796 Yards.
Visitors: Welcome anytime. Telephone for booking.
Opening Hours: Dawn 'till Dusk.
Ladies: Welcome Anytime.
Green Fees: £12 Weekdays. £17 Weekends.
Juveniles: Welcome anytime.

Clubhouse Facilities:
Changing Rooms / Showers. Coffee Shop.
Open Competitions: Varied contact club.

NO.	YARDS	PAR	S.I.	NO.	YARDS	PAR	S.I.
1	269	4	9	10	300	4	10
2	476	5	13	11	121	3	18
3	118	3	17	12	350	4	12
4	383	4	11	13	401	4	2
5	478	5	5	14	332	4	14
6	308	4	7	15	337	4	8
7	397	4	1	16	509	5	6
8	153	3	15	17	177	3	16
9	289	4	3	18	398	4	4
OUT	2,871	36		IN	2,925	35	
				TOTAL	5,796	71	
	STANDARD SCRATCH				68		

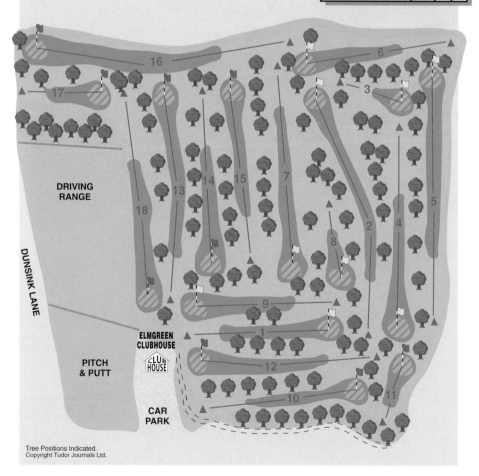

DRIVING RANGE

DUNSINK LANE

ELMGREEN CLUBHOUSE

CLUB HOUSE

PITCH & PUTT

CAR PARK

Tree Positions Indicated.
Copyright Tudor Journals Ltd.

Finnstown Country House Hotel, Newcastle Road, Lucan, Co. Dublin.
Tel: (01) 628 0644.
Fax: (01) 628 1088.
E-mail: http://WWW.

LOCATION: Newcastle Road, Lucan – off the N4.
SECRETARY: Paula Smith.
MANAGER: Elizabeth Duffy.
Tel: (01) 628 0644.
ARCHITECT: Robert Browne.

A parkland 9 hole course where many mature trees have skillfully been brought into play. Claimed by locals to be a little gem in the Irish Golfing crown.

It is certainly a challenging course, providing even the best of players with a tough test of golf.

COURSE INFORMATION

Par 66; SSS 66; Length 5,190 metres.
Visitors: Welcome anytime.
Opening Hours: Sunrise – sunset.
Green Fees: £15-£19 Mon – Fri; £23 Sat / Sun / Bank Holidays.
Juveniles: Welcome at certain times. Lessons and Club Hire available by prior arrangements.

Clubhouse Dress: Neat (no denims allowed).
Clubhouse Facilities: 'Home' to Finnstown Country House Hotel. Changing room, bar and restaurant within Finnstown Hotel. Full catering facilities available 7.30am – 9.00pm (booked in advance if possible). Golf buggys available. Indoor swimming pool.

NO.	YARDS	PAR	S.I.	NO.	YARDS	PAR	S.I.
1	278	4	11	10	278	4	12
2	313	4	5	11	313	4	6
3	334	4	13	12	334	4	14
4	178	3	15	13	178	3	16
5	165	3	17	14	165	3	18
6	419	4	1	15	419	4	2
7	483	5	9	16	483	5	10
8	230	3	3	17	230	3	4
9	195	3	7	18	195	3	8
OUT	2,595	33		IN	2,595	33	
				TOTAL	5,190	66	
STANDARD SCRATCH				66			

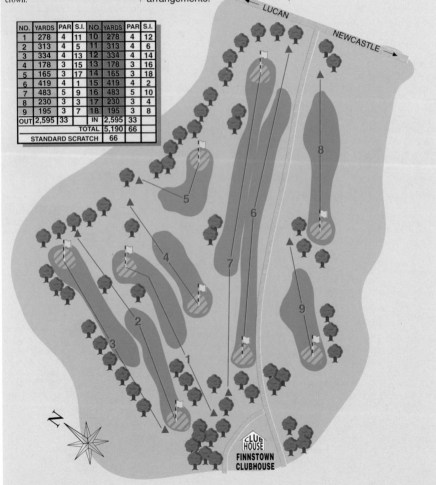

Tree positions indicated.

Cloghran.
Co. Dublin.
Tel: (01) 8401183 / 8401763.

LOCATION: Beside Dublin Airport.
SECRETARY / MANAGER: A. J. Greany.
Tel: 8401763.
PROFESSIONAL: Tony Judd.
Tel: 407670.

One of the pre-qualifying courses for the Irish Open. A parkland course sited close to Dublin Airport.

NO.	MEDAL METRES	GEN. METRES	PAR	S.I.	NO.	MEDAL METRES	GEN. METRES	PAR	S.I.
1	291	278	4	7	10	349	334	4	12
2	377	353	4	5	11	160	143	3	8
3	354	342	4	11	12	324	309	4	4
4	413	374	4	1	13	351	335	4	16
5	171	156	3	9	14	183	170	3	10
6	460	446	5	15	15	450	432	5	18
7	149	126	3	17	16	346	332	4	6
8	400	386	4	3	17	320	304	4	14
9	349	338	4	13	18	418	402	4	2
OUT	2,964	2,799	35		IN	2,901	2,761	35	
					TOTAL	5,865	5,560	70	
		STANDARD SCRATCH	70	69					

COURSE INFORMATION

Par 70; SSS 70; Length 5,865 metres.
Visitors: Welcome Mon – Fri.
Societies Mon – Thur.
Opening Hours:
8.00am – sunset.
Green Fees: £20 daily.
Avoid: Weekends, Wed & Fri afternoons. Telephone appointment required.
Ladies & Juveniles: Welcome. Handicap Certificate required. Lessons, Club Hire and caddy cars available. Ladies day Tuesday. Juveniles must be off the course by 3.00pm.
Clubhouse Hours:
8.00am – midnight.
Clubhouse Dress:
Casual (no jeans).
Clubhouse Facilities: Tues & Wed evenings & weekends, full catering and bar.
Open Competitions: Open Week; 7th – 14th June.

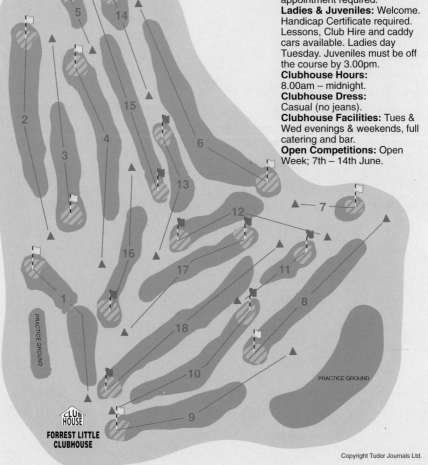

FORREST LITTLE
CLUBHOUSE

HERMITAGE

**Ballydowd, Lucan,
Co. Dublin.
Tel: 6268491.**

LOCATION: 8 miles from Dublin city on main Galway Road.
SECRETARY / MANAGER: Tom Spelman. Tel: 6268491.
PROFESSIONAL: Ciaran Carroll.
Tel: 6268072.

This course has a fairly flat front nine and an undulating back nine. The 10th hole is the most scenic, followed by an extremely difficult par 5, bordered on right by the River Liffey and on the left by woodland. Modern sand based greens will be put into use this year.

COURSE INFORMATION

Par 71; SSS 71; Length 6,032 metres.
Visitors: Welcome Monday – Friday mornings (except Tuesday).
Opening Hours: 8.00am – Sunset.
Avoid: Weekends.
Ladies: Ladies day Tuesday.

Juveniles: Must be accompanied by an adult, tel. appointment required. Caddy service available; club hire and lessons available by prior arrangement.
Green Fees: £32 Mon – Fri.
Clubhouse Hours: 9.00am – midnight.
Clubhouse Dress: Casual. No jeans or shorts.
Clubhouse Facilities: Snacks from 10.00am; full restaurant from 12.30pm – 9.30pm everyday.

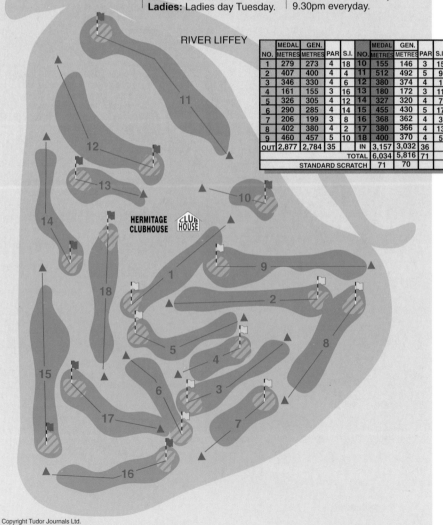

RIVER LIFFEY

NO.	MEDAL METRES	GEN. METRES	PAR	S.I.	NO.	MEDAL METRES	GEN. METRES	PAR	S.I.
1	279	273	4	18	10	155	146	3	15
2	407	400	4	4	11	512	492	5	9
3	346	330	4	6	12	380	374	4	1
4	161	155	3	16	13	180	172	3	11
5	326	305	4	12	14	327	320	4	7
6	290	285	4	14	15	455	430	5	17
7	206	199	3	8	16	368	362	4	3
8	402	380	4	2	17	380	366	4	13
9	460	457	5	10	18	400	370	4	5
OUT	2,877	2,784	35		IN	3,157	3,032	36	
					TOTAL	6,034	5,816	71	
					STANDARD SCRATCH	71	70		

HERMITAGE CLUBHOUSE

Hollystown Golf, Hollystown, Hollywood Rath, Dublin 15.
Tel: (01) 8207444
Fax: (01) 8207447

LOCATION: 10km from Dublin City.
MANAGER: Oliver Barry.
PROFESSIONAL: Adam Whiston.
ARCHITECT: Eddie Hackett.

An inviting green fees only policy gives this new, superb golfing facility a novel attraction. Set in rich natural parkland, well endowed with stately trees, gurgling streams and pleasant ponds, the course has a graceful maturity to please the most discerning golfer. Three testing par 5's, a tricky combination of par 4's and three varying 3's, can make the par 72 an elusive target for those without the right balance of skill, subtlety and aggression.

COURSE INFORMATION

Par 72; SSS 70; Length 5,764 metres.
Visitors: Welcome.
Opening Hours: Daylight Hours.
Ladies: Welcome Wednesdays.
Green Fees: £14 Weekdays; £18 Weekends.
Juveniles: Welcome.
Clubhouse Hours: Daylight Hours.
Clubhouse Dress: Casual.
Clubhouse Facilities: Temporary facilities until Aug / Sept as clubhouse is under reconstruction. Coffee Shop available.

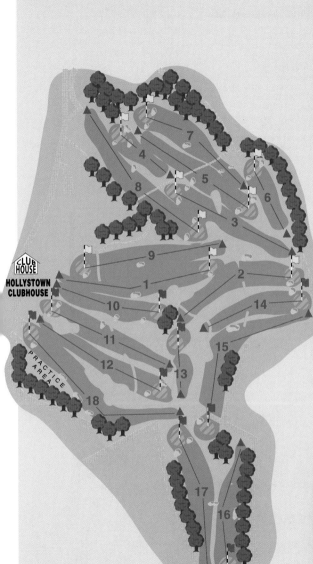

NO.	METRES	PAR	S.I.	NO.	METRES	PAR	S.I.
1	369	4	3	10	291	4	18
2	324	4	11	11	356	4	12
3	307	4	5	12	356	4	2
4	214	3	7	13	147	3	14
5	373	4	1	14	291	4	16
6	134	3	17	15	446	5	6
7	317	4	15	16	322	4	10
8	440	5	9	17	345	4	4
9	283	4	13	18	449	5	8
OUT	2,761	35		IN	3,003	37	
				TOTAL	5,764	72	
				STANDARD SCRATCH		70	

Bunker and tree positions indicated.

Hollywood Lakes Golf Club, Ballyboughal, Co.Dublin.
Tel: (01) 8433407, (01) 8433002.

LOCATION: 12 miles north of Dublin Airport.
SECRETARY: A.C. Brogan
Tel: (01) 8433407.
ARCHITECT: M. Flanagan

Parkland course featuring many lakes, large greens and the longest par 5 in Ireland at 581 meters. A long course demanding accuracy from the tee.

COURSE INFORMATION

Par 72; SSS 72; Length 6,870 yards.
Visitors: Welcome.
Opening Hours: Dawn – dusk.
Avoid: Weekends before 11.30am / Wed after 5.00pm.
Ladies: Welcome.
Green Fees: Weekdays £17 & weekends £21.
Juveniles: Welcome.
Clubhouse Hours: 12.00noon – 11.30pm.

Clubhouse Dress: Casual – no denim.
Clubhouse Facilities: Bar / Lounge / Restaurant.
Open Competitions: July 1997.

NO.	CHAMP YARDS	MEDAL YARDS	PAR	S.I.	NO.	CHAMP YARDS	MEDAL YARDS	PAR	S.I.
1	321	299	4	8	10	365	345	4	3
2	379	373	4	4	11	166	158	3	11
3	358	330	4	12	12	337	323	4	17
4	129	120	3	14	13	366	360	4	9
5	449	431	5	18	14	581	534	5	7
6	166	156	3	10	15	481	465	5	15
7	373	364	4	2	16	389	381	4	5
8	350	318	4	6	17	185	164	3	13
9	438	429	5	16	18	413	359	4	1
OUT	2,963	2,820	36	36	IN	3,283	3,089	36	
					TOTAL	6,246	5,909	72	
					STANDARD SCRATCH				

Bunker and tree positions indicated.

CAR PARK

CLUB HOUSE

HOLLYWOOD CLUBHOUSE

PRACTICE AREA & DRIVING RANGE

Island Golf Club, Corballis, Donabate, Co. Dublin
Tel: (01) 8436462.
Fax: (01) 8436860.

LOCATION: Corballis.
SECRETARY: John Finn.
Tel: (01) 8436205.
ARCHITECT: 1990 Redesign, F. Hawtree & E. Hackett.

Enveloped on three sides by the sea, this is a naturally true links course. The 1st, 3rd and 7th are probably the best holes on the outward nine but the most spectacular are to be found on the inward half. The 12th needs an excellent drive while the 13th is a superb par 3 of 190 metres, requiring a long iron or wood shot to reach a naturally well protected green. The 425 metre par 4 18th offers an excellent challenge with imposing sandhills on both sides.

COURSE INFORMATION

Par 71; SSS 72; Length 6,053 metres.
Visitors: Welcome Mon, Tues, Wed mornings & Fridays.
Opening Hours:
6.00am – sunset.
Ladies: Welcome Thursdays.
Green Fees: £40 Mon – Fri.

Juveniles: Welcome.
Clubhouse Hours: 7.00am – 12.00 midnight (summer); 8.00am – 12.00 midnight (winter).
Clubhouse Dress: Casual. No denims or training shoes.
Clubhouse Facilities: 10.30am – 8.30pm winter. 8.00am - 11.30pm summer.
Competitions: Irish Close Championship in 1998.

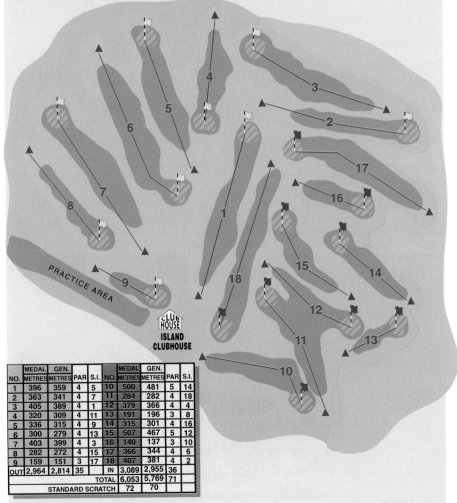

NO.	MEDAL METRES	GEN. METRES	PAR	S.I.	NO.	MEDAL METRES	GEN. METRES	PAR	S.I.
1	396	359	4	5	10	500	481	5	14
2	363	341	4	7	11	284	282	4	18
3	405	389	4	1	12	379	366	4	4
4	320	309	4	11	13	191	196	3	8
5	336	315	4	9	14	315	301	4	16
6	300	279	4	13	15	507	467	5	12
7	403	399	4	3	16	140	137	3	10
8	282	272	4	15	17	366	344	4	6
9	159	151	3	17	18	407	381	4	2
OUT	2,964	2,814	35		IN	3,089	2,955	36	
					TOTAL	6,053	5,769	71	
					STANDARD SCRATCH	72	70		

Killiney Golf Club,
Balinclea Road,
Killiney,
Co. Dublin.
Tel: (01) 2851027/2852823.

LOCATION: Killiney.
SECRETARY: Hugh Keegan.
Tel: (01) 2852823.
PROFESSIONAL: Paddy O'Boyle.
Tel: (01) 2856294.

This parkland course is on the southern side of Killiney Hill, the most scenic area of Co. Dubin. The local terrain while hilly is not too difficult.

COURSE INFORMATION

Par 70; SSS 70; Length 5,656 metres.
Visitors: Welcome Monday and Tuesday morning; Wednesday, Friday and Sunday afternoons.
Opening Hours: 8.30am – sunset.
Avoid: Thursdays, Saturdays, Sunday mornings and Tuesday pm.
Ladies: Welcome Thursdays.
Green Fees: £20 Mon – Fri: £20 Sat / Sun (£10 with member).

Juveniles: Welcome. Must be accompanied by an adult. Lessons available by prior arrangements; Club Hire available; Caddy service available by prior arrangement.
Clubhouse Hours: 10.00am – 11.00pm. Full clubhouse facilities.
Clubhouse Dress: Casual / Neat (no jeans, T-shirts or trainers).
Clubhouse Facilities: Bar snacks 10.00am – 11.00pm everyday.

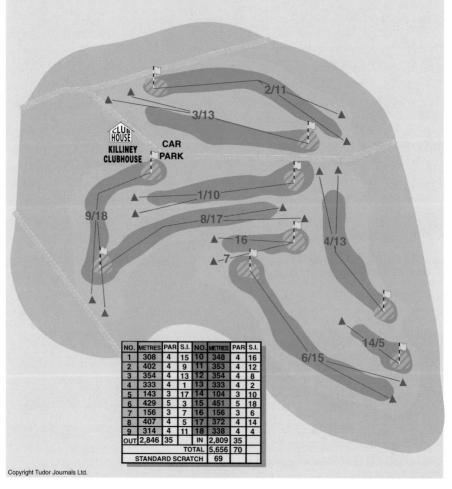

NO.	METRES	PAR	S.I.	NO.	METRES	PAR	S.I.
1	308	4	15	10	348	4	16
2	402	4	9	11	353	4	12
3	354	4	13	12	354	4	8
4	333	4	1	13	333	4	2
5	143	3	17	14	104	3	10
6	429	5	3	15	451	5	18
7	156	3	7	16	156	3	6
8	407	4	5	17	372	4	14
9	314	4	11	18	338	4	4
OUT	2,846	35		IN	2,809	35	
				TOTAL	5,656	70	
				STANDARD SCRATCH	69		

Kilternan Golf & Country Club Hotel, Enniskerry Road, Kilternan, Co. Dublin.
Tel: (01) 2955542
Fax: (01) 2955670.

LOCATION: Kilternan, Co. Dublin.
SECRETARY: Mr Jimmy Kinsella.
Tel: (01) 2955542.
PROFESSIONAL: Gary Hendley.

A challenging course with spectacular views over Dublin Bay, "Offers every golf shot in the book."

COURSE INFORMATION

Par 68; SSS 68; Length 4,952 metres.
Visitors: Welcome by booking any time outside competition hours.
Opening Hours: Operates on time sheet only.
Ladies: Welcome.
Green Fees: Mon – Fri £16; Sat / Sun £20. Hotel residents 50% discount.
Juveniles: Welcome. Lessons available by prior arrangement. Club Hire /

Buggy Hire available by prior arrangements.
Clubhouse Hours: Monday – Sunday 8.00am – 11.00pm. Full clubhouse facilities.
Clubhouse Dress: Smart / casual, no jeans or training shoes.
Clubhouse Facilities: Food available everyday – 8am to 9.30pm.

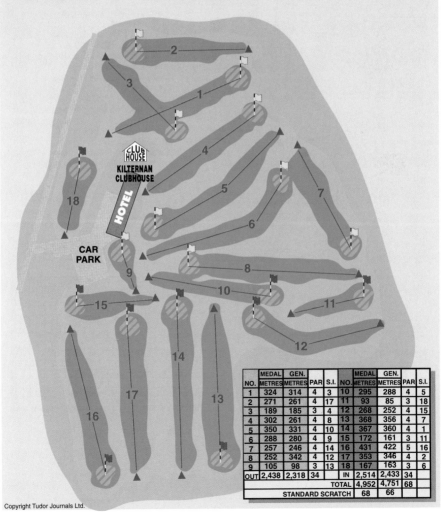

NO.	MEDAL METRES	GEN. METRES	PAR	S.I.	NO.	MEDAL METRES	GEN. METRES	PAR	S.I.
1	324	314	4	3	10	295	288	4	5
2	271	261	4	17	11	93	85	3	18
3	189	185	3	4	12	268	252	4	15
4	302	261	4	8	13	368	356	4	7
5	350	331	4	10	14	367	360	4	1
6	288	280	4	9	15	172	161	3	11
7	257	246	4	14	16	431	422	5	16
8	252	342	4	12	17	353	346	4	2
9	105	98	3	13	18	167	163	3	6
OUT	2,438	2,318	34		IN	2,514	2,433	34	
					TOTAL	4,952	4,751	68	
					STANDARD SCRATCH	68	66		

Lucan, Co. Dublin.
Tel: (01) 6282106.

LOCATION: 10 miles from Dublin City
on Cellbridge Road.
SECRETARY / MANAGER: Tom O'Donnell.
Tel: (01) 6282106.
CADDYMASTERS: Maurice Brown &
Christy Dobbs. Tel: (01) 6280246.

Lucan Golf Course has an undulating first
nine. The first and seventh providing a good
test. The back nine which was added in
1988 is fairly flat and has a fine finishing
18th hole of 530 metres.

COURSE INFORMATION

Par 71; SSS 71; Length
5,888 metres.
Visitors: Monday, Tuesday, Fridays,
Wednesdays to 1.00pm.
Opening Hours: Sunrise – sunset.
Avoid: Weekends.
Ladies: Welcome Thursdays.
Green Fees: £20.
Juveniles: Must be accompanied
by an adult. Telephone appointment
required; Club Hire available; Caddy
service available by prior
arrangements.
Clubhouse Hours: 9.00am – 12.00
midnight. Full clubhouse facilities.
Clubhouse Dress: No denims on
Course or in Clubhouse.
Clubhouse Facilities: Full bar &
restaurent facilities. Bar food
available.

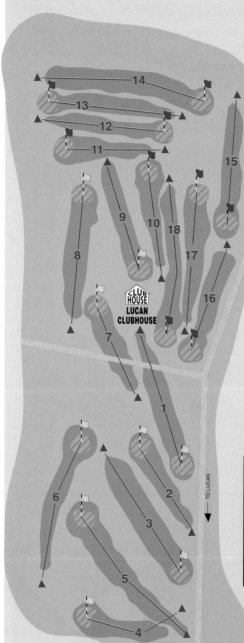

LUCAN
CLUBHOUSE

NO.	MEDAL METRES	GEN. METRES	PAR	S.I.	NO.	MEDAL METRES	GEN. METRES	PAR	S.I.
1	364	369	4	6	10	358	371	4	3
2	304	332	4	8	11	156	169	3	7
3	411	416	4	4	12	279	292	4	15
4	143	107	3	12	13	317	330	4	11
5	431	435	5	16	14	402	415	4	1
6	268	279	4	18	15	321	334	4	13
7	124	138	3	10	16	172	185	3	9
8	346	366	4	2	17	426	439	5	17
9	310	344	4	14	18	518	531	5	5
OUT	2,701	2,786	35		IN	2,949	3,066	36	
					TOTAL	5,650	5,852	71	
					STANDARD SCRATCH	71	70		

Beechwood, The Grange, Malahide, Co. Dublin.

LOCATION: Malahide.
SECRETARY/MANAGER: Mr Tom Gallagher.
Tel: (01) 8461611 / 8461270 8461642 Fax: 8461270.
PROFESSIONAL: David Barton.
Tel: 01 8460002.
ARCHITECT: E. Hackett.

A championship standard course, which opened to 27 holes in 1990. This parkland course has water as a feature of a number of the holes.

COURSE INFORMATION

Par 71; SSS 72; Length 6,066 metres
Visitors: Welcome.
Opening Hours: Sunrise – sunset.
Ladies: Welcome. Telephone appointment required.
Green Fees: £30 Mon – Fri; (£10 with member). Weekends & Holidays £40 (£10 with member).
Clubhouse Hours: 9.00am – 12.30am.

Clubhouse Facilities: Full catering and bar facilities.
Clubhouse Dress: Dining room – jacket and tie after 7.30pm; Lounge and bar – casual but neat.
Open Competitions: August Bank Holiday week.

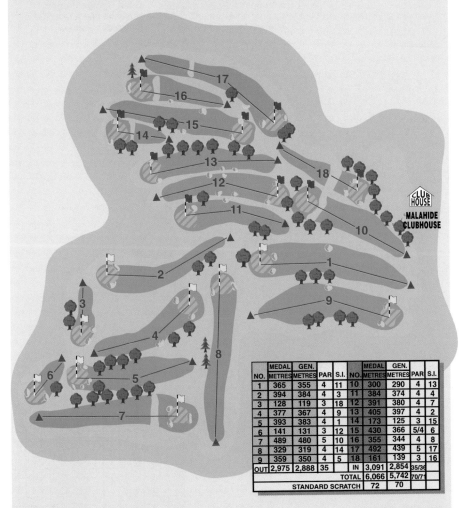

	MEDAL	GEN.				MEDAL	GEN.		
NO.	METRES	METRES	PAR	S.I.	NO.	METRES	METRES	PAR	S.I.
1	365	355	4	11	10	300	290	4	13
2	394	384	4	3	11	384	374	4	4
3	128	119	3	18	12	391	380	4	7
4	377	367	4	9	13	405	397	4	2
5	393	383	4	1	14	173	125	3	15
6	141	131	3	12	15	430	366	5/4	6
7	489	480	5	10	16	355	344	4	8
8	329	319	4	14	17	492	439	5	17
9	359	350	4	5	18	161	139	3	16
OUT	2,975	2,888	35		IN	3,091	2,854	35/36	
					TOTAL	6,066	5,742	70/71	
					STANDARD SCRATCH	72	70		

Bunker and tree positions indicated.

**Clondalkin,
Dublin, 22.
Tel: 4592903/4593157.
Fax: 4593498.**

LOCATION: Dublin.
SECRETARY / MANAGER:
A.T. O'Neill.
Tel: 4593157/4593498.
ARCHITECT: James Braid.
PROFESSIONAL: Karl O'Donnell.

Attractive, mature parkland course. The careful placing of trees, bunkers and other hazards soon dispels any feeling of complacency, even with the most accomplished of players.

COURSE INFORMATION

Par 71; SSS 70; Length 5,714 metres.
Visitors: Welcome Monday, Wednesday (am), Thursday, Friday.
Opening Hours: 9.00am – Sunset.
Avoid: Tuesday, Saturday, Sunday.
Ladies: Welcome Tuesdays.
Juveniles: Welcome. Must be accompanied by an adult after 6pm. Lessons available by prior arrangement; club hire available; telephone

appointment required.
Green Fees: £30 Mon – Fri (£12 with member). Societies £27.
Clubhouse Hours: 7.30am – 12.30pm. Full clubhouse facilities.
Clubhouse Dress: Casual. Jacket and tie in Dining Room after 8.00pm.
Clubhouse Facilities: Full catering and bar; Summer 10.00am – 9.30pm; Winter 10.00am – 6.00pm.
Open Competitions: Husband and wife mixed foursomes – June.

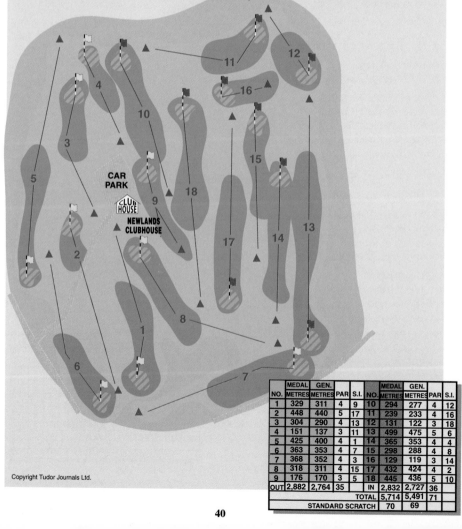

NO.	MEDAL METRES	GEN. METRES	PAR	S.I.	NO.	MEDAL METRES	GEN. METRES	PAR	S.I.
1	329	311	4	9	10	294	277	4	12
2	448	440	5	17	11	239	233	4	16
3	304	290	4	13	12	131	122	3	18
4	151	137	3	11	13	499	475	5	6
5	425	400	4	1	14	365	353	4	4
6	363	353	4	7	15	298	288	4	8
7	368	352	4	3	16	129	119	3	14
8	318	311	4	15	17	432	424	4	2
9	176	170	3	5	18	445	436	5	10
OUT	2,882	2,764	35		IN	2,832	2,727	36	
					TOTAL	5,714	5,491	71	
					STANDARD SCRATCH	70	69		

**Old Conna Golf Club,
Ferndale Road, Bray,
Co Wicklow.
Tel: (01) 2826055/2826766.
Fax: (01) 2825611.**

LOCATION: Two miles north of Bray.
SECRETARY: Dave Diviney.
Tel: (01) 2826055/2826766.
PROFESSIONAL: Paul McDaid.
Tel: (01) 2720022.
ARCHITECT: E. Hackett

Situated twelve miles south of Dublin in the Bray area, Old Conna is a testing 18 hole parkland course with panoramic views of the Irish Sea and Wicklow mountains. Set in wooded terrain, otralegically placed hazards and mature trees ensure a challenging round for even the most accomplished golfer.
This attractive layout should become one of the regions premier inland courses in the not too distant future.

COURSE INFORMATION

Par 72; SSS 71; Length 6,551 yards.
Visitors: Welcome Mon – Fri 9.00am – 4.00pm (closed 12.30pm – 2.00pm).
Opening Hours: Sunrise – sunset.
Avoid: Tuesday, Wednesday, Saturday & Sunday.
Ladies: Welcome Tuesdays.
Green Fees: £22.50 weekdays. £30 at weekends.

Juveniles: Must be over 12 yrs old. Lessons available by prior arrangement; Caddy Service / Cars and Club Hire available by prior arrangement.
Clubhouse Hours: 10.30am – 11.30pm; Full clubhouse facilities.
Clubhouse Dress: Neat attire essential (no jeans / T-shirts).
Clubhouse Facilities: Bar snacks and full catering everyday. Menu available 12.00 noon – 9.30pm. Phone: Mr. P Coleman (01) 2820038.
Open Competitions: Junior Scratch Cup: 31st July. Intermediate Scratch Cup: 12th July. Minor Scratch Cup: 30th August.

NO.	MEDAL YARDS	GEN. YARDS	PAR	S.I.	NO.	MEDAL YARDS	GEN. YARDS	PAR	S.I.
1	376	362	4	10	10	354	334	4	15
2	236	221	3	4	11	351	339	4	5
3	320	305	4	12	12	163	149	3	11
4	546	532	5	14	13	565	551	5	7
5	582	568	5	2	14	292	278	4	13
6	373	354	4	8	15	470	461	4	1
7	382	358	4	6	16	434	424	4	3
8	112	98	3	18	17	160	146	3	9
9	346	332	4	16	18	500	476	5	17
OUT	3,264	3,130	36		IN	3,289	3,158	36	
					TOTAL	6,553	6,288	72	
					STANDARD SCRATCH	72	71		

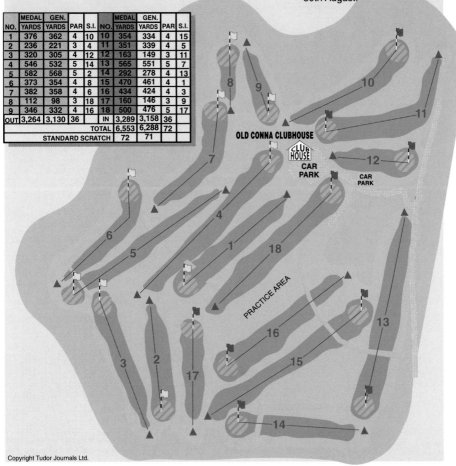

OLD CONNA CLUBHOUSE
CLUB HOUSE
CAR PARK
CAR PARK
PRACTICE AREA

**Newtown House,
St. Margaret's, Co. Dublin.
Tel: (01) 8640324.**

LOCATION: Between Derry Rd,
N2 and the St. Margaret's Rd,
by Dublin Airport.
SECRETARY / PROFESSIONAL: Mr
R. Yates.
Tel: (01) 8640324.
ARCHITECT: Martin Hawtree.

Parkland course with large well
guarded greens. Driving range and
large tuition staff – excellent pro shop.
Full range of hire equipment and full
tee time reservation system.

COURSE INFORMATION

**Par 71; SSS 70; Length
6,532 yards.**
Visitors: Welcome at any
time. Bookings may be made
48hrs in advance by telephone.

Ladies: Welcome at any time.
Juveniles: Welcome at any
time.
Green Fees: £8.50 – 18 hole
& £6.50 – 9 hole (mid week).
£12.50 – 18 holes & £9.00 – 9
holes (weekends & Bank
Holidays).
Clubhouse Dress: Casual.
Clubhouse Facilities: Golf
shop & coffee shop.

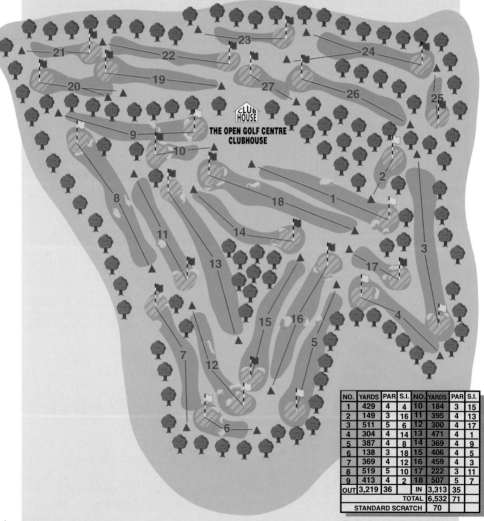

THE OPEN GOLF CENTRE
CLUBHOUSE

NO.	YARDS	PAR	S.I.	NO.	YARDS	PAR	S.I.
1	429	4	4	10	184	3	15
2	149	3	16	11	395	4	13
3	511	5	6	12	300	4	17
4	304	4	14	13	471	4	1
5	387	4	8	14	369	4	9
6	138	3	18	15	406	4	5
7	369	4	12	16	459	4	3
8	519	5	10	17	222	3	11
9	413	4	2	18	507	5	7
OUT	3,219	36		IN	3,313	35	
				TOTAL	6,532	71	
				STANDARD SCRATCH		70	

Bunker & tree positions indicated.

PORTMARNOCK LEINSTER DUBLIN

Portmarnock, Co. Dublin.
Tel: 8462968/Fax: 8462601.

LOCATION: North east of Dublin city.
GOLF DIRECTOR: Moira Cassidy.
Tel: 8462968.
DESIGNER: Bernhard Langer.
Tel: 8462634.
ARCHITECT: Stan Eby.

One of the premium links courses in the country. Venue for the Irish Open Championship and given world championship ranking by many critics. The sandy soil of the Portmarnock peninsula makes it ideal for golf. Now has 27 holes with room for more. Its potential as a golf links was realised in 1894. Within two years of the opening of the 18 hole course, Portmarnock hosted its first tournament, the Irish Open Amateur Championship and has hosted the prestigious Irish Open Championship many times since then and was also host for the Walker Cup. New computerised irrigation system.

COURSE INFORMATION

Par 72; SSS 74; Length 7,321 metres.
Visitors: Welcome.
Opening Hours: 7.30am – sunset.
Ladies: Welcome. Lessons available on weekdays by prior arrangements. Caddy service available by prior arrangement. Handicap Certificate required. Prior arrangement preferred.
Green Fees: Mon – Fri £65 (not Wednesday); Sat, Sun & Bank Holidays £80.
Clubhouse Hours: 7.00am – 11.30pm.
Clubhouse Dress: Jacket and tie for dining room and members bar. Casual attire for Harry Bradshaw Room.
Clubhouse Facilities: Changing rooms and showers.

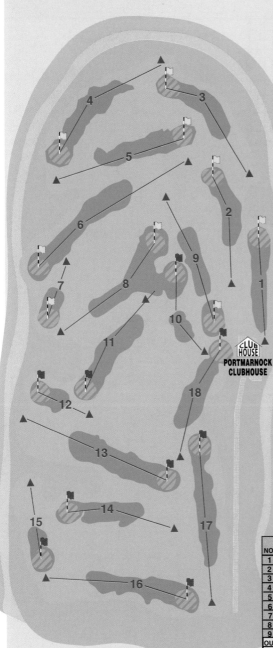

PORTMARNOCK
CLUBHOUSE

NO.	MEDAL METRES	GEN. METRES	PAR	S.I.	NO.	MEDAL METRES	GEN. METRES	PAR	S.I.
1	304	320	4	14	10	467	484	5	15
2	305	329	4	10	11	406	419	4	1
3	172	178	3	12	12	316	329	4	5
4	512	527	5	6	13	135	137	3	17
5	409	431	4	2	14	312	317	4	13
6	462	486	5	18	15	352	364	4	7
7	405	412	4	4	16	354	371	4	11
8	323	342	4	8	17	171	185	3	9
9	139	156	3	16	18	365	408	4	3
OUT	3,031	3,181	36		IN	2,878	3,014	35	
					TOTAL	7,321	6,175	72	
					STANDARD SCRATCH	74	73		

NO.	CHAMP METRES	MEDAL METRES	PAR	S.I.	NO.	CHAMP METRES	MEDAL METRES	PAR	S.I.
1	354	320	4	14	10	484	467	5	15
2	360	350	4	10	11	419	406	4	1
3	178	172	3	12	12	329	316	4	5
4	527	512	5	6	13	137	135	3	17
5	431	409	4	2	14	317	312	4	13
6	486	462	5	18	15	364	352	4	7
7	412	405	4	4	16	371	354	4	11
8	342	323	4	8	17	185	171	3	9
9	156	139	3	16	18	408	365	4	3
OUT	3,246	3,092	36		IN	3,014	2,878	35	
					TOTAL	6,260	5,970	71	
	STANDARD SCRATCH					73	72		

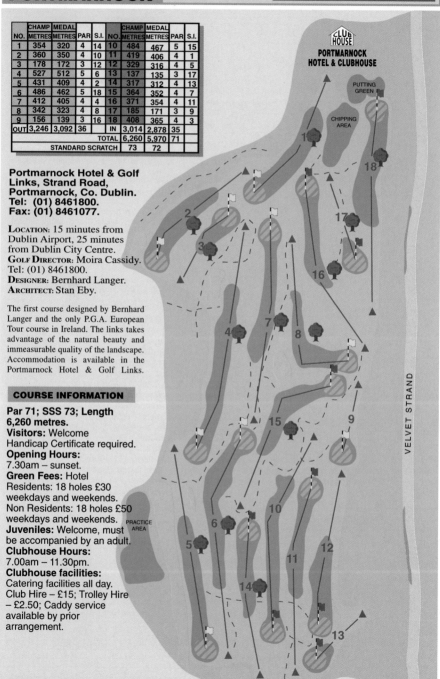

PORTMARNOCK
HOTEL & CLUBHOUSE

PUTTING GREEN

CHIPPING AREA

VELVET STRAND

PRACTICE AREA

Portmarnock Hotel & Golf Links, Strand Road, Portmarnock, Co. Dublin.
Tel: (01) 8461800.
Fax: (01) 8461077.

LOCATION: 15 minutes from Dublin Airport, 25 minutes from Dublin City Centre.
GOLF DIRECTOR: Moira Cassidy.
Tel: (01) 8461800.
DESIGNER: Bernhard Langer.
ARCHITECT: Stan Eby.

The first course designed by Bernhard Langer and the only P.G.A. European Tour course in Ireland. The links takes advantage of the natural beauty and immeasurable quality of the landscape. Accommodation is available in the Portmarnock Hotel & Golf Links.

COURSE INFORMATION

Par 71; SSS 73; Length 6,260 metres.
Visitors: Welcome Handicap Certificate required.
Opening Hours:
7.30am – sunset.
Green Fees: Hotel Residents: 18 holes £30 weekdays and weekends.
Non Residents: 18 holes £50 weekdays and weekends.
Juveniles: Welcome, must be accompanied by an adult.
Clubhouse Hours:
7.00am – 11.30pm.
Clubhouse facilities:
Catering facilities all day. Club Hire – £15; Trolley Hire – £2.50; Caddy service available by prior arrangement.

Rush, Dublin.
Tel: 01 8437548.
Fax: 01 8438177.

Location: Seaside.
Secretary: B. Clear
Tel: 01 8438177.

Links course which is playable all year round. Good greens protected by pot bunkers, with undulating fairways. Alternate tees except on two par 3's.

COURSE INFORMATION

Par 70; SSS 69; Length 5,598 metres.
Visitors: Welcome Monday, Tuesday, Friday.
Opening Hours: 8.00am – sunset.
Avoid: Wednesday, Thursday, weekends.
Ladies: Welcome.

Green Fees: £15 (£6 with member).
Juveniles: Welcome.
Clubhouse Hours: 11.00am – 11.00pm.
Clubhouse Dress: Casual. No jeans or shorts allowed.
Clubhouse Facilities: Available on request.
Open Competitions: Seniors only on fourth Friday in May each year.

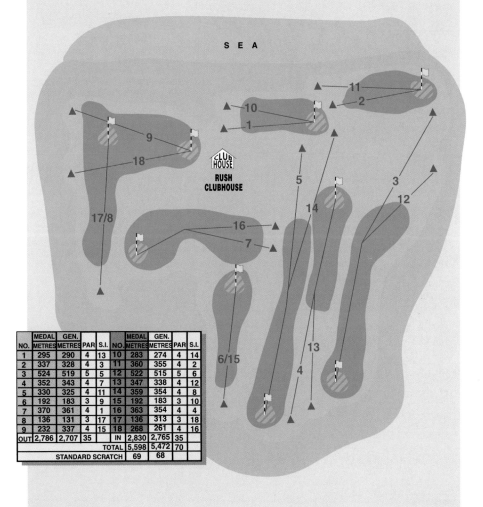

NO.	MEDAL METRES	GEN. METRES	PAR	S.I.	NO.	MEDAL METRES	GEN. METRES	PAR	S.I.
1	295	290	4	13	10	283	274	4	14
2	337	328	4	3	11	360	355	4	2
3	524	519	5	5	12	522	515	5	6
4	352	343	4	7	13	347	338	4	12
5	330	325	4	11	14	359	354	4	8
6	192	183	3	9	15	192	183	3	10
7	370	361	4	1	16	363	354	4	4
8	136	131	3	17	17	136	313	3	18
9	232	337	4	15	18	268	261	4	16
OUT	2,786	2,707	35		IN	2,830	2,765	35	
					TOTAL	5,598	5,472	70	
				STANDARD SCRATCH		69	68		

NO.	MEDAL METRES	GEN.	PAR	S.I.	NO.	MEDAL METRES	GEN.	PAR	S.I.
1	370	369	4	3	10	354	346	4	6
2	154	147	3	15	11	267	256	4	18
3	393	386	4	1	12	131	122	3	16
4	419	410	5	17	13	366	357	4	4
5	393	383	4	5	14	449	438	5	14
6	470	465	5	7	15	144	133	3	12
7	144	135	3	13	16	372	362	4	8
8	479	470	5	9	17	485	481	5	10
9	320	311	4	11	18	371	362	4	2
OUT	3,142	3,076	37		IN	2,939	2,857	36	
					TOTAL	6,081	5,933	73	
					STANDARD SCRATCH	72	71		

**Hacketstown, Skerries,
Co. Dublin.
Tel: 8491567/8491204. Fax: 8491591.**

LOCATION: 20 miles north of Dublin.
MANAGER: Aiden Burns.
Tel: 8491567.
PROFESSIONAL: Jimmy Kinsella.
Tel: 8490925.

A rolling parkland course with splendid views of the coastline. Many of the holes demand accuracy from the tee to the green. The 12th (par 3) and 18th (par 4) are particularly attractive holes. The newer 4th (par 5), 6th (par 5) and 7th (par 3) have enhanced the course as a good test of golf.

COURSE INFORMATION

**Par 73; SSS 72; Length
6,113 metres.
Visitors:** Welcome Mon – Fri.
Avoid: Wednesday afternoons, weekends, Tuesday after 4.30pm. Members hour 1.00pm – 2.00pm.
Opening Hours: Sunrise – sunset.
Ladies: Welcome.
Green Fees: £20 weekdays & £25 weekends (reduction before 8.30am).
Juveniles: Must be accompanied by an adult.
Clubhouse Hours: 9.00am – 11.30pm.
Clubhouse Dress: Casual.
Clubhouse Facilities: Snacks lunches, dinner available daily.
Open Competitions: Junior Scratch Cup – May; Intermediate Scratch Cup – June; Open Week – July.

SKERRIES
CLUBHOUSE

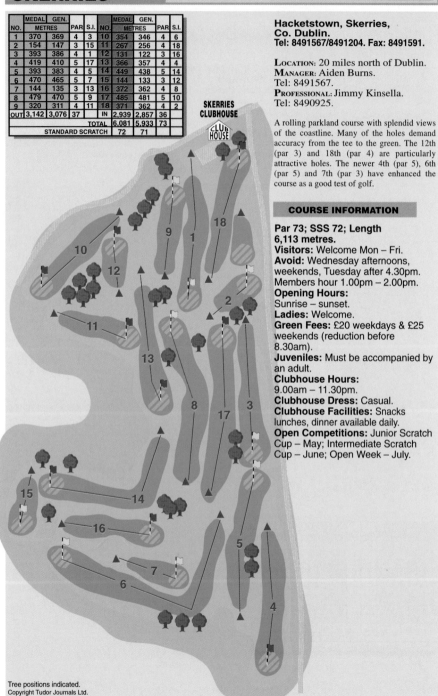

Tree positions indicated.
Copyright Tudor Journals Ltd.

SLADE VALLEY — L E I N S T E R — DUBLIN

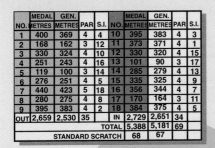

NO.	MEDAL METRES	GEN. METRES	PAR	S.I.	NO.	MEDAL METRES	GEN. METRES	PAR	S.I.
1	400	369	4	4	10	395	383	4	3
2	168	162	3	12	11	373	371	4	1
3	330	324	4	10	12	330	320	4	15
4	251	243	4	16	13	101	90	3	17
5	119	100	3	14	14	285	279	4	13
6	276	251	4	5	15	335	325	4	9
7	440	423	5	18	16	356	344	4	7
8	280	275	4	8	17	170	164	3	11
9	395	383	4	2	18	384	375	4	5
OUT	2,659	2,530	35		IN	2,729	2,651	34	
					TOTAL	5,388	5,181	69	
					STANDARD SCRATCH	68	67		

Lynch Park, Brittas,
Co. Dublin.
Tel: 01 4582207/4582183.

SECRETARY: Pat Maguire.
Tel: 01 4582183.
ARCHITECT: W. Sullivan &
D. O'Brien.
PROFESSIONAL: John Dignam.

Not a particularly demanding course, but the scenic views make for a very pleasant and relaxing game with some interesting holes. A "take it easy" course.

COURSE INFORMATION

Par 69; SSS 68; Length 5,388 Metres.
Visitors: Welcome Monday, Thursday, Friday.
Opening Hours: Sunrise – Sunset.
Avoid: Weekends.
Ladies: Welcome.
Ladies Day: Tuesday.
Green Fees: Weekdays – £17 (£7.50 with a member).
Juveniles: Welcome.
Clubhouse Hours: 8.30am – 12.00 midnight; Full clubhouse facilities.
Clubhouse Dress: Neat dress.
Clubhouse Facilities: All day.

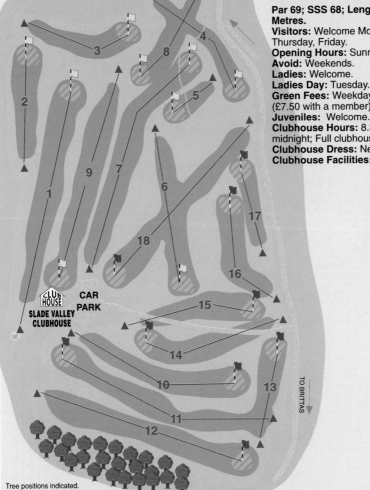

Tree positions indicated.
Copyright Tudor Journals Ltd.

47

Kilternan, Co. Dublin.
Tel: (01) 2952859.

Location: Eight miles south of Dublin City.
Secretary: Jim Wheelan.
Tel: (01) 2952859.
Architect: E. Hackett.

This course was constructed in 1981 by the joint efforts of the Dublin County Council and G.U.I. who contributed to the construction costs of the course. It is popular both from the availability and the standard of the course.

COURSE INFORMATION

Par 74; SSS 70; Length 5,848 metres.
Visitors: Welcome.
Opening Hours:
8.00am – sunset.
Ladies: Welcome.
Green Fees: £9 Mon – Fri; £12 Sat / Sun. Senior Citizens, Students and unemployed £5.
Juveniles: Welcome.
Clubhouse Hours:
8.00am – sunset.

Clubhouse Dress: Casual.
Clubhouse Facilities:
Snacks available.

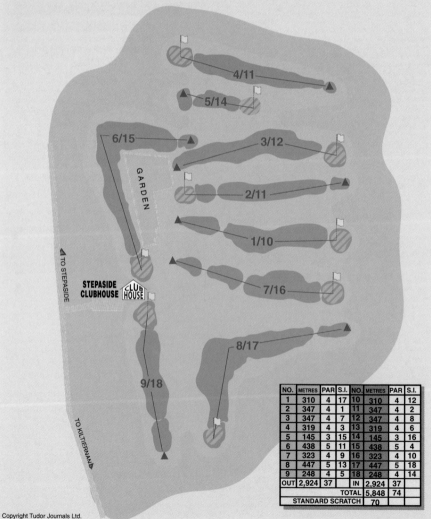

NO.	METRES	PAR	S.I.	NO.	METRES	PAR	S.I.
1	310	4	17	10	310	4	12
2	347	4	1	11	347	4	2
3	347	4	7	12	347	4	8
4	319	4	3	13	319	4	6
5	145	3	15	14	145	3	16
6	438	5	11	15	438	5	4
7	323	4	9	16	323	4	10
8	447	5	13	17	447	5	18
9	248	4	5	18	248	4	14
OUT	2,924	37		IN	2,924	37	
				TOTAL	5,848	74	
				STANDARD SCRATCH	70		

**Blanchardstown Golf Centre,
Tyrrelstown House,
Mulhuddart, Co. Dublin.
Tel: (01) 821 3206.**
LOCATION: 2 miles
Blanchardstown town centre, off
N3 near Mulhuddart Cemetary.
SECRETARY: Noelle McClenahan
PROFESSIONAL: Johnny Young &
Kevin Garvey.
ARCHITECT: Johnny Young.

North Leinsters longest par 3 (which
has not been parred). Set in mature
parkland around a beautiful all
timber public golf practice range,
which is floodlit with white lighting.
Includes excellent practice bunkers.

We specalise in group lessons for adult
& juniors (during school holidays) and
corporate groups which include clinic
and round of golf.

COURSE INFORMATION

**Par 54; SSS 56; Length
2,663 yards; 2,453 metres.
Visitors:** Public pay & play all
welcome.
Opening Hours:
9am – 10pm Mon – Fri. All year.
9am – 8pm. Sat & Sun
Summertime. 9am – 6pm. Sat &
Sun Wintertime.
Avoid: No restrictions.

Green Fees: Mon – Fri £5; Sat
& Sun £6; Bank Hols £7.
Juveniles: Welcome.
Clubhouse Hours:
Up to 10pm midweek; 8pm
weekends and 6pm weekends
in Wintertime.
Clubhouse Dress: Casual.
Clubhouse Facilities:
Coffee Shop, sandwich bar.
No alcohol.

NO.	METRES	PAR	S.I.	NO.	METRES	PAR	S.I.
1	94	3	18	10	186	3	1
2	121	3	8	11	157	3	15
3	113	3	14	12	160	3	11
4	156	3	4	13	146	3	5
5	157	3	2	14	91	3	17
6	136	3	10	15	135	3	9
7	120	3	12	16	175	3	3
8	138	3	6	17	159	3	7
9	111	3	16	18	176	3	13
OUT	1,146	27		IN	1,385	27	
				TOTAL	2,531	54	
	STANDARD SCRATCH					56	

Bunker and tree positions indicated.

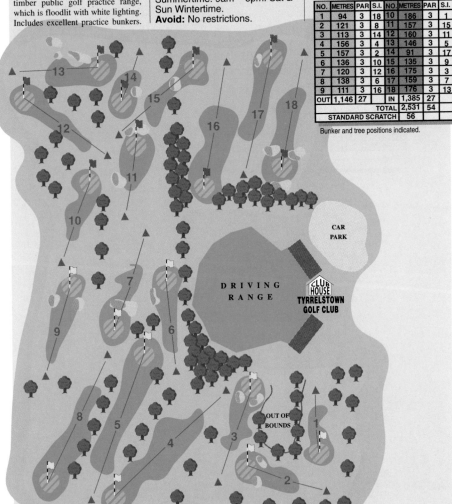

Copyright Tudor Journals Ltd.

Westmanstown, Clonsilla, Dublin 15.
Tel: (01) 8205817.
Fax: (01) 8207891.

LOCATION: Two miles from Lucan Village.
HON. SECRETARY: Ronan Monaghan.
Tel: (01) 8210562.
ARCHITECT: Mr Eddie Hackett.

Short flat parkland course which has recently undergone additional development.

COURSE INFORMATION

Par 71; SSS 70; Length 5,848 metres.
Visitors: Welcome except Sat and Sun.
Opening Hours: 8am – Sunset.
Ladies: Welcome Tuesdays.
Green Fees: Weekdays £18; Sat, Sun & Bank Hols £22.
Clubhouse Hours: 7.30am – 12.30pm.
Clubhouse Dress: Neat dress essential on course.

Clubhouse Facilities: Full bar and catering facilities all year round.
Open Competitiions: Invitation Four Ball every Wednesday.
Open week: 27th July – 3rd August.

NO.	CHAMP METRES	MEDAL METRES	PAR	S.I.	NO.	CHAMP METRES	MEDAL METRES	PAR	S.I.
1	285	285	4	6	10	462	462	4	3
2	333	333	3	14	11	263	263	4	15
3	140	140	4	18	12	170	170	3	9
4	437	437	4	8	13	493	485	5	13
5	368	368	3	10	14	426	415	3	7
6	132	132	4	2	15	400	374	4	11
7	486	477	5	4	16	178	116	3	1
8	393	393	5	16	17	368	355	4	5
9	176	176	4	12	18	338	328	5	17
OUT	2,750	2,656	36		IN	3,098	2,974	35	
					TOTAL	5,848	5,630	71	
					STANDARD SCRATCH	70	69		

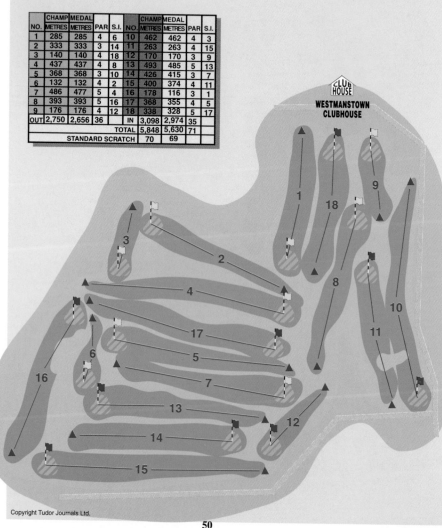

WESTMANSTOWN CLUBHOUSE

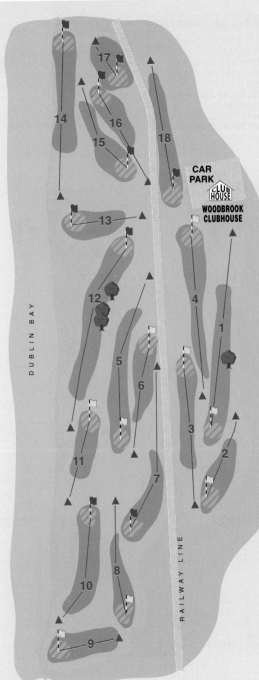

Woodbrook Golf Club, Dublin Road, Bray, Co. Wicklow Tel: 2824799.

LOCATION: Eleven Miles south of Dublin City on N11.
GENERAL MANAGER: Bryan O'Neill. Tel: 2824799 Fax: 2821950.
PROFESSIONAL: Billy Kinsella.

Newly constructed layout with 18 new sand based greens and whilst beside the sea it is not a links course. The return of the course to Championship status will offer an excellent test of golf for all handicaps and with its traditional heritage, atmosphere and ambience, it is the perfect location for golf and hospitality.

COURSE INFORMATION

Par 72; SSS 72; Length 6,863 yards.
Visitors: Welcome weekdays and occasional weekends.
Opening Hours: Sunrise – Sunset.
Avoid: Tuesdays and Bank Holidays.
Ladies: Welcome.
Green Fees: £35 Mon - Fri; £40 Sat/Sun & Public Holidays.
Juveniles: Welcome. Lessons available by prior arrangement; Club hire available; Caddy service available by prior arrangement; Letter of introduction required (if possible); Handicap certificate required; Telephone appointment required.
Clubhouse Hours: 8.00am - 12 midnight.
Clubhouse Dress: Jacket and tie in restaurant after 5.00pm.
Clubhouse Facilities: 10.00am - 9.00pm (with some exceptions in winter); Full restaurant facilities.

NO.	YARDS	PAR	S.I.	NO.	YARDS	PAR	S.I.
1	506	5	17	10	443	4	4
2	194	3	9	11	175	3	10
3	383	4	11	12	542	5	14
4	392	4	3	13	230	3	6
5	576	5	7	14	551	5	12
6	401	4	13	15	447	4	2
7	467	4	1	16	507	5	16
8	385	4	5	17	136	3	18
9	157	3	15	18	371	4	8
OUT	3,461	36		IN	3,402	36	
					TOTAL	6,863	72
	STANDARD SCRATCH				72		

**Carrickmines,
Dublin 18.
Tel: 2955972/2955941.**

LOCATION: Carrickmines.
SECRETARY: A. N. McEachern.
Tel: 2893183.

Nine hole inland course situated on hilly country approximately six miles from Dublin. Alternate tees are used in summer.

COURSE INFORMATION

**Par 71; SSS 69; Length 6,103 yards.
Visitors:** Welcome.
Opening Hours: 8.30am – Sunset.
Avoid: Saturday and Wednesday.
Ladies: Welcome.
Green Fees: £20 week days; £23 Sundays.

Juveniles: Must be accompanied by a responsible adult.
Clubhouse Hours: 8.30am – 11.30pm.
Clubhouse Dress: Casual.
Clubhouse Facilities: Limited.

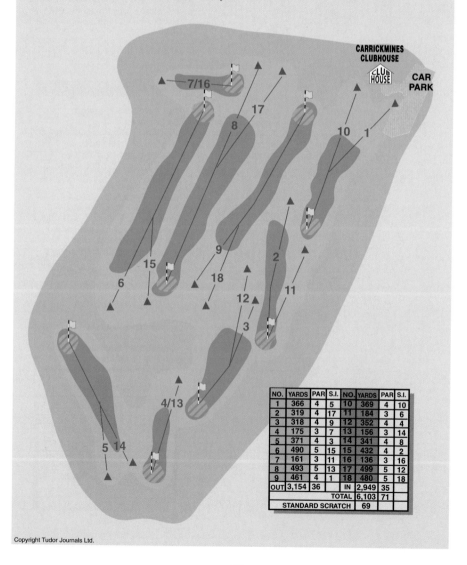

NO.	YARDS	PAR	S.I.	NO.	YARDS	PAR	S.I.
1	366	4	5	10	369	4	10
2	319	4	17	11	184	3	6
3	318	4	9	12	352	4	4
4	175	3	7	13	156	3	14
5	371	4	3	14	341	4	8
6	490	5	15	15	432	4	2
7	161	3	11	16	136	3	16
8	493	5	13	17	499	5	12
9	461	4	1	18	480	5	18
OUT	3,154	36		IN	2,949	35	
				TOTAL	6,103	71	
				STANDARD SCRATCH		69	

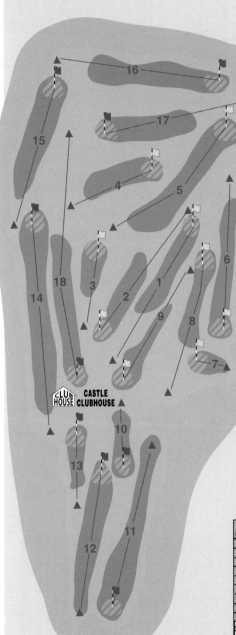

Castle Golf Club, Woodside Drive, Rathfarnham, Dublin 14. Tel: 4904207.

LOCATION: Between Rathfarnham & Churchtown.
SECRETARY: L. Blackburne.
Tel: 4905835.
PROFESSIONAL: D. Kinsella.
Tel: 4920272.
ARCHITECT: Barcroft Pickman & Hood.

Very tight fairways – the Par 4 6th hole regarded as one of the most difficult and yet attractive golf holes. Spectacular views from the Clubhouse.

COURSE INFORMATION

Par 70; SSS 69; Length 5,653 metres.
Visitors: Welcome Monday, Thursday, Friday.
Opening Hours: Sunrise – Sunset.
Avoid: Tuesday, Wednesday afternoons and weekends.
Ladies: Tuesdays. Lessons available by prior arrangements; Caddy trolleys available; telephone appointment required 01 492 2000.
Green Fees: £35.
Juveniles: As Visitors. Lessons available by prior arrangements; Caddy trolleys available; telephone appointment required 01 492 2000.
Clubhouse Hours: 8.30am – 11.30pm; Full clubhouse facilities.
Clubhouse Dress: Jacket and tie in Dining Room, otherwise casual.
Clubhouse Facilities: 10.00am – 10.30pm, lunch, dinner, snacks & bar everyday.
Open Competitions: Ladies Opens; April, July & Aug; Father & Son – July.

NO.	MEDAL YARDS	GEN. YARDS	PAR	S.I.	NO.	MEDAL YARDS	GEN. YARDS	PAR	S.I.
1	492	482	5	9	10	234	216	3	6
2	433	420	4	5	11	401	391	4	2
3	149	130	3	17	12	348	333	4	14
4	317	307	4	13	13	132	122	3	18
5	372	362	4	7	14	371	358	4	8
6	418	401	4	1	15	187	180	3	10
7	177	157	3	15	16	529	509	5	12
8	347	326	4	11	17	500	487	5	16
9	452	440	4	3	18	411	403	4	4
OUT	3,157	3,025	35		IN	3,113	2,999	35	
					TOTAL	6,270	6,024	70	
					STANDARD SCRATCH	68	67		

**Clontarf Golf Club,
Donnycarney House,
Malahide Road, Dublin 3.
Tel: (01) 8331892.**

LOCATION: Two miles from city
Centre.
PROFESSIONAL: Joe Craddock.
Tel: (01) 331877.
HON. SECRETARY: Brian Cuitan.
ARCHITECT: Harry Colt.

A pleasant parkland course with a
quarry hole as a special feature.
Convenient city course with good
access.

COURSE INFORMATION

**Par 69; SSS 68; Length
5,459 metres.**
Visitors: Welcome Mon – Fri
(telephone first).
Avoid: Monday.
Ladies: Welcome.
Ladies Day: Monday.
Green Fees: £17 winter, £36
weekends. £26 summers, £36
weekends.
Juveniles: Must be
accompanied by an adult
member if not before
10.00am.
Clubhouse Hours:
9.00am – 12.00pm; full
clubhouse facilities.
Clubhouse Dress:
Casual (no jeans / sneakers).
Collar and tie for dining room
after 8.00pm.
Clubhouse Facilities:
Catering facilities: meals and
snacks every day.
Open Competitions: Mixed
Foursomes (Matchplay) May;
AIB Lord Mayors Cup (Junior
Matchplay) August.

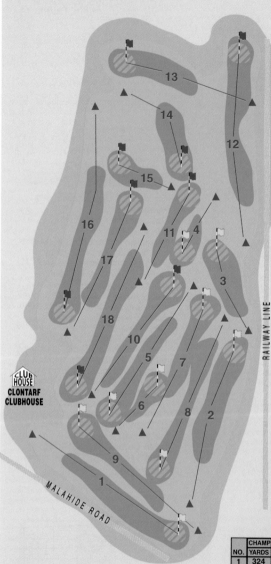

NO.	CHAMP YARDS	MEDAL YARDS	PAR	S.I.	NO.	CHAMP YARDS	MEDAL YARDS	PAR	S.I.
1	324	294	4	10	10	365	351	4	7
2	414	404	4	2	11	187	169	3	11
3	287	272	4	14	12	301	377	4	1
4	151	139	3	12	13	267	361	4	15
5	338	327	4	6	14	329	299	4	3
6	122	112	3	18	15	145	130	3	17
7	339	309	4	8	16	351	336	4	5
8	356	347	4	2	17	358	340	4	9
9	295	272	4	16	18	452	439	5	13
OUT	2,626	2,476	34		IN	2,833	2,702	35	
					TOTAL	5,459	5,178	69	
					STANDARD SCRATCH	68	67		

DEERPARK

**Deer Park Hotel,
Howth, Co. Dublin.
Tel: 8322624.**

LOCATION: Howth Head.
SECRETARY: David Tighe.

A busy course with both visitors and holiday makers, especially during August, well served by the adjacent Deer Park Hotel – another 18 hole and a course are also included as part of the Hotel facilities.

COURSE INFORMATION

Par 72; SSS 73; Length 6,174 Metres.
Visitors: Welcome.
Opening Hours: 7.30am – Sunset (weekdays) & 6.30 – Sunset (weekends).
Ladies: Welcome.
Green Fees: £9.50 Mon – Fri; £11.50 Sat / Sun (18 holes).

Juveniles: Welcome. Club Hire and caddy trolleys available.
Clubhouse Hours: Sunrise – Sunset.
Clubhouse facilities: Full catering and bar facilities available at Hotel – other leisure facilities also.

NO.	METRES	PAR	S.I.	NO.	METRES	PAR	S.I.
1	382	4	9	10	399	4	2
2	203	3	5	11	178	3	12
3	322	4	17	12	360	4	8
4	335	4	13	13	292	4	16
5	372	5	3	14	510	5	4
6	190	3	7	15	153	3	18
7	467	4	11	16	312	4	10
8	395	4	1	17	393	4	14
9	477	5	15	18	595	5	6
OUT	3,143	36		IN	3,787	36	
				TOTAL	6,930	72	
	STANDARD SCRATCH				73		

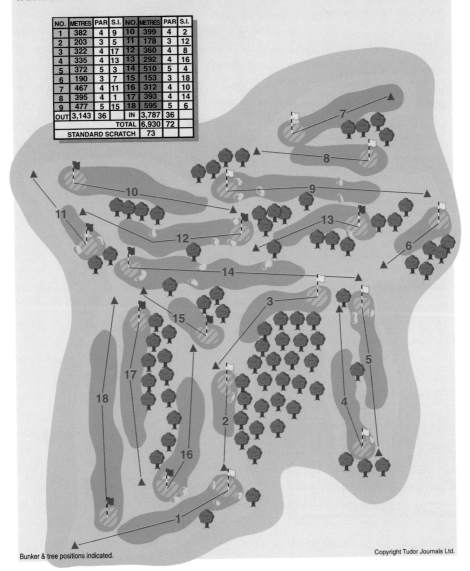

Bunker & tree positions indicated.

Copyright Tudor Journals Ltd.

55

Edmondstown Golf Club, Edmondstown, Dublin 16.
Tel: (01) 4932461.

MANAGER: Selwyn S. Davies.
HON: SECRETARY: Sean
Blennane.
Tel: (01) 4931082.
PROFESSIONAL: A. Crofton.
Tel: (01) 4941049.

An elevated parkland course with a
fair but testing reputation, situated in
the Dublin suburbs.

COURSE INFORMATION

**Par 70; SSS 70; Length
6,195 yards; 5,663 metres.**
Visitors: Welcome to play
Monday – Friday.
Opening Hours:
8.00am – 11.30pm.
Ladies: Welcome.
Green Fees: Mon – Fri £25;
Sat / Sun £30 (by
appointment). Lessons and
caddy service available by
prior arrangement. Second
week in July is Festival Week.
Juveniles: Welcome. Must be
accompanied by an adult.
Clubhouse Hours:
8.00am – 11.30pm.
Clubhouse Dress: Collar and
tie in restaurant. Neat casual
dress on course.
No denims.
Clubhouse Facilities:
Coffee and snacks available
9.00am onwards.
Lunch: 12.30pm – 2.00pm.
Dinner: 6.30pm –
11.00pm, to order if later.

EUROPEAN
CLUBHOUSE

NO.	MEDAL YARDS	GEN. YARDS	PAR	S.I.	NO.	MEDAL YARDS	GEN. YARDS	PAR	S.I.
1	295	280	4	16	10	375	360	4	1
2	339	324	4	8	11	268	253	4	17
3	130	115	3	18	12	143	128	3	15
4	507	492	5	6	13	367	352	4	5
5	391	376	4	2	14	321	306	4	7
6	368	353	4	4	15	319	304	4	11
7	462	447	5	14	16	139	124	3	13
8	181	166	3	12	17	326	311	4	9
9	314	299	4	10	18	418	403	4	3
OUT	2,987	2,852	36		IN	2,676	2,541	34	
					TOTAL	5,663	5,393	70	
					STANDARD SCRATCH	70	70		

Bunker & tree positions indicated.
Copyright Tudor Journals Ltd.

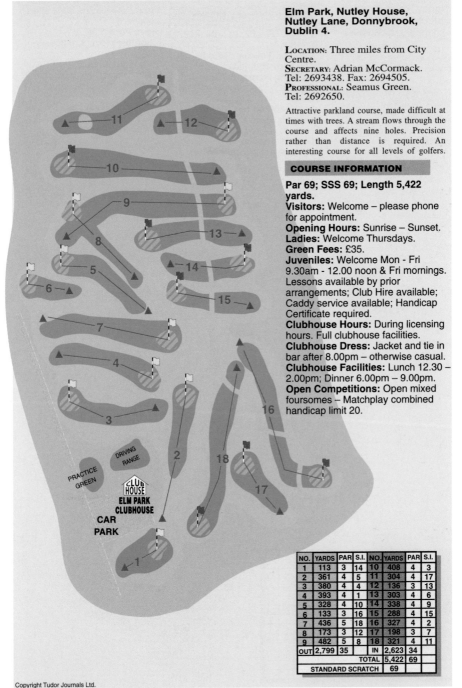

Elm Park, Nutley House, Nutley Lane, Donnybrook, Dublin 4.

LOCATION: Three miles from City Centre.
SECRETARY: Adrian McCormack.
Tel: 2693438. Fax: 2694505.
PROFESSIONAL: Seamus Green.
Tel: 2692650.

Attractive parkland course, made difficult at times with trees. A stream flows through the course and affects nine holes. Precision rather than distance is required. An interesting course for all levels of golfers.

COURSE INFORMATION

Par 69; SSS 69; Length 5,422 yards.
Visitors: Welcome – please phone for appointment.
Opening Hours: Sunrise – Sunset.
Ladies: Welcome Thursdays.
Green Fees: £35.
Juveniles: Welcome Mon - Fri 9.30am - 12.00 noon & Fri mornings. Lessons available by prior arrangements; Club Hire available; Caddy service available; Handicap Certificate required.
Clubhouse Hours: During licensing hours. Full clubhouse facilities.
Clubhouse Dress: Jacket and tie in bar after 8.00pm – otherwise casual.
Clubhouse Facilities: Lunch 12.30 – 2.00pm; Dinner 6.00pm – 9.00pm.
Open Competitions: Open mixed foursomes – Matchplay combined handicap limit 20.

NO.	YARDS	PAR	S.I.	NO.	YARDS	PAR	S.I.
1	113	3	14	10	408	4	3
2	361	4	5	11	304	4	17
3	380	4	4	12	136	3	13
4	393	4	1	13	303	4	6
5	328	4	10	14	338	4	9
6	133	3	16	15	288	4	15
7	436	5	18	16	327	4	2
8	173	3	12	17	198	3	7
9	482	5	8	18	321	4	11
OUT	2,799	35		IN	2,623	34	
				TOTAL	5,422	69	
				STANDARD SCRATCH		69	

Torquay Road, Foxrock, Dublin 18.
Tel: 2893992/2895668.

LOCATION: South Dublin.
SECRETARY / MANAGER: William Daly.
Tel: 2893992. Fax: 2894943.
PROFESSIONAL: David Walker.
Tel: 2893414.

Foxrock is a very flat course but it nonetheless provides a reasonable test of golf ability.

COURSE INFORMATION

Par 70; SSS 69; Length 5,667 metres.
Visitors: Welcome Monday, Thursday and Friday mornings.
Opening Hours: 8.00am – Sunset.
Avoid: Tues, Wed, weekends.
Ladies: Welcome Tuesdays. Lessons and Caddy service available by prior arrangement; Club Hire available.
Juveniles: Welcome. Must be accompanied by an adult after 5.00pm.
Green Fees: £30.
Clubhouse Hours: 8.30am – 11.30pm.
Clubhouse Dress: Smart /Casual. Jacket and tie after 7.00pm in the Dining Room.
Clubhouse Facilities: Snacks in the bar; meals on Wednesdays and Saturdays.

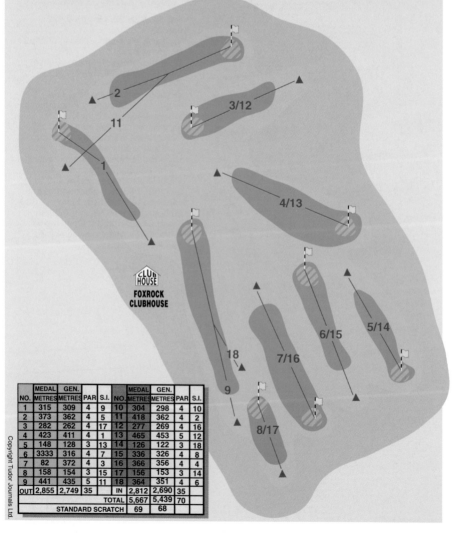

FOXROCK CLUBHOUSE

NO.	MEDAL METRES	GEN. METRES	PAR	S.I.	NO.	MEDAL METRES	GEN. METRES	PAR	S.I.
1	315	309	4	9	10	304	298	4	10
2	373	362	4	5	11	418	362	4	2
3	282	262	4	17	12	277	269	4	16
4	423	411	4	1	13	465	453	5	12
5	148	128	3	13	14	126	122	3	18
6	3333	316	4	7	15	336	326	4	8
7	82	372	4	3	16	366	356	4	4
8	158	154	3	15	17	156	153	3	14
9	441	435	5	11	18	364	351	4	6
OUT	2,855	2,749	35		IN	2,812	2,690	35	
					TOTAL	5,667	5,439	70	
					STANDARD SCRATCH	69	68		

Copyright Tudor Journals Ltd.

GRANGE

LEINSTER **DUBLIN CITY**

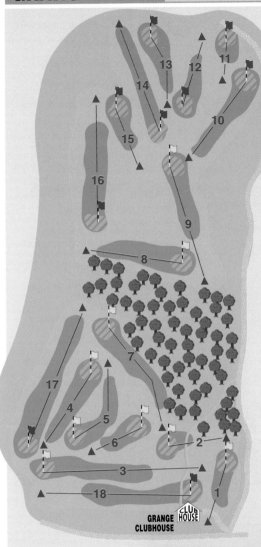

**Whitechurch Road,
Rathfarnham, Dublin 16.
Tel: (01) 4932889.**

LOCATION: South West of Dublin
City, four miles from City Centre.
SECRETARY: J. A. O'Donaghue.
Tel: (01) 4932889.
PROFESSIONAL: Barry Hamill.
Tel: (01) 4932299.

Interesting and popular parkland course,
with tree-lined fairways being a major
feature, which is both attractive yet
challenging.

COURSE INFORMATION

**Par 68; SSS 69; Length
5,517 metres.**
Visitors: Welcome to play during
the week.
Opening Hours: Sunrise –
sunset.
Avoid: Weekends.
Ladies: Welcome Tuesdays.
Green Fees: £35 Mon – Fri. £40
Weekends.
Juveniles: Welcome. Must be
accompanied by an adult after
12.00 noon. Lessons available by
prior arrangement; Caddy service
available by prior arrangement;
telephone appointment advisable.
Clubhouse Hours: 8.00am –
12.30 noon.
Clubhouse Facilities: Full bar
and catering facilities.
Clubhouse Dress: Casual / neat
(summer). Collar and tie (winter).

NO.	MEDAL METRES	GEN. METRES	PAR	S.I.	NO.	MEDAL METRES	GEN. METRES	PAR	S.I.
1	203	195	3	7	10	390	385	4	2
2	122	111	3	17	11	182	177	3	8
3	389	384	4	1	12	292	287	4	16
4	383	378	4	5	13	329	324	4	10
5	306	301	4	13	14	487	483	5	14
6	170	165	3	15	15	150	145	3	18
7	388	383	4	3	16	385	380	4	4
8	193	188	3	9	17	467	462	5	12
9	319	315	4	11	18	362	357	4	6
OUT	2,473	2,240	32		IN	3,044	3,000	36	
					TOTAL	5,517	5,420	68	
					STANDARD SCRATCH	69	68		

GRANGE CLUBHOUSE

Copyright Tudor Journals Ltd.

59

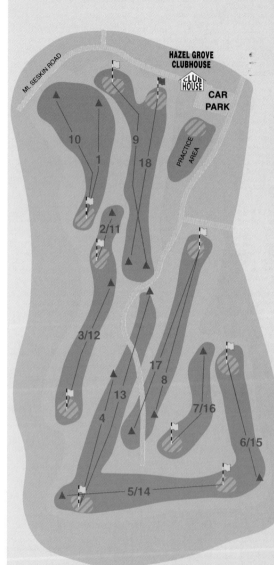

HAZEL GROVE CLUBHOUSE

CLUB HOUSE

CAR PARK

PRACTICE AREA

Mt. SESKIN ROAD

10
1
9
18
2/11
3/12
17
8
13
4
7/16
6/15
5/14

Mount Seskin Road, Jobstown, Tallaght, Dublin 24.
Tel: 4520911/4512010.

LOCATION: Tallaght, Blessington Road.
SECRETARY / MANAGER: Mr. Foley. Tel: 4520911.
ARCHITECT: Watty Sullivan & Eddie Hackett.

One of the few courses in Dublin which will give you a full panoramic view of the city. This is a course that appears easy on first sight but can be unexpectedly difficult.

COURSE INFORMATION

Par 69; SSS 67; Length 5,077 metres.
Visitors: Welcome Mon – Fri.
Opening Hours: 8.30am – Sunset.
Green Fees: Mon – Fri £8 (£6 with member any day); Sat, Sun & Bank Holidays £10.
Avoid: Sat, Sun, Tues mornings and Thur afternoons.
Juveniles: Welcome. Lessons available by prior arrangement; telephone appointment required.
Clubhouse Hours: 8.30am – 11.30pm.
Clubhouse Dress: Neat / Casual.
Clubhouse Facilities: Full clubhouse facilities. Catering facilities by prior arrangement – Bar snacks throughout the day.
Open Competitions: Tuesday, Fourballs from April – Sept; Open Week June.

NO.	METRES	PAR	S.I.	NO.	METRES	PAR	S.I.
1	306	4	10	10	292	4	11
2	81	3	18	11	110	3	17
3	300	4	7	12	300	4	8
4	352	4	2	13	390	4	1
5	144	3	9	14	322	4	4
6	200	3	12	15	206	3	13
7	242	4	15	16	242	4	16
8	371	4	5	17	431	4	3
9	507	5	14	18	429	4	6
OUT	2,503	34		IN	2,722	34	
				TOTAL	5,225	69	
				STANDARD SCRATCH	67		

**St. Fintan's, Carrickbrack Road, Sutton, Dublin 13.
Tel: 8323055.**

LOCATION: Nine miles north east of city centre, two miles from Sutton Cross on Sutton side of hill of Howth.
SECRETARY: Ann MacNeice. Tel: 8323055.
PROFESSIONAL: John McGuirk. Tel: 8393895.
ARCHITECT: James Braid.

Moorland course with scenic views of Dublin Bay. Very hilly – a challenge for the athletic golfer.

COURSE INFORMATION

Par 71; SSS 69; Length 6,202 yards, 5,672 metres.
Visitors: Welcome weekdays except Wednesday.
Opening Hours: 8.30am – 4.00pm.
Avoid: 1.00pm – 2.00pm; All day Wednesday, Thursday afternoons.
Ladies: Welcome. Lessons available by prior arrangements; Club Hire available; Caddy service available by prior arrangements.
Green Fees: £20 Mon -Thur; £22 Fri.
Clubhouse Hours: 8.30am – 11.00pm.
Clubhouse Dress: Informal. No denim, training shoes or shorts in Clubhouse.
Clubhouse Facilities: Bar snacks from 11.00am.

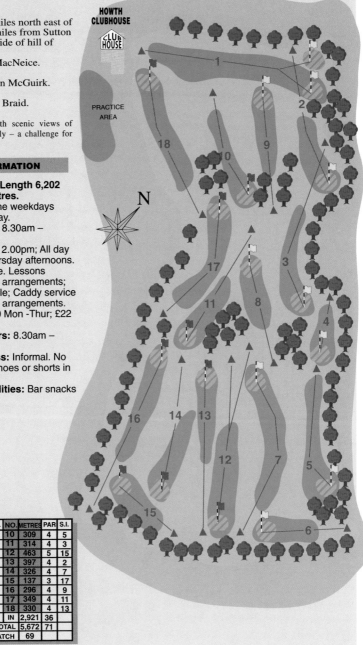

NO.	METRES	PAR	S.I.	NO.	METRES	PAR	S.I.
1	306	4	10	10	309	4	5
2	321	4	4	11	314	4	3
3	408	4	1	12	463	5	15
4	155	3	12	13	397	4	2
5	355	4	6	14	326	4	7
6	269	4	14	15	137	3	17
7	486	5	8	16	296	4	9
8	134	3	18	17	349	4	11
9	252	4	16	18	330	4	13
OUT	2,686	35		IN	2,921	36	
				TOTAL	5,672	71	
	STANDARD SCRATCH				69		

Tree positions indicated.

MILLTOWN

Lower Churchtown Road, Dublin 14.
Tel: (01) 4976090.
Fax: (01) 4976008.

LOCATION: South Dublin three miles from the city centre.
SECRETARY/MANAGER: William Johnston.
Tel: (01) 4976090.
PROFESSIONAL: John Harnett.
Tel: (01) 4977072.
ARCHITECT: Freddie Davis.

Well established parkland course on the suburbs of Dublin. One of the many Dublin clubs that provide convenient locations.

COURSE INFORMATION

Par 71; SSS 69; Length 5,638 metres.
Visitors: Welcome.
Opening Hours: Sunrise – Sunset.
Avoid: Weekends.
Ladies: Welcome.
Green Fees: £35 Mon – Fri.
Juveniles: Welcome.
Lessons available by prior arrangement; club hire available; caddy service

available by prior arrangement. Telephone appointment advisable.
Handicap Certificate required.
Clubhouse Hours: 9.00am – 11.30pm.
Clubhouse Dress: Casual. Jacket & tie required for evening dining.
Clubhouse Facilities: Full clubhouse and catering facilities.

NO.	MEDAL METRES	GEN. METRES	PAR	S.I.	NO.	MEDAL METRES	GEN. METRES	PAR	S.I.
1	230	223	4	16	10	375	364	3	5
2	307	301	4	10	11	302	285	4	13
3	315	307	4	6	12	130	121	4	15
4	109	106	3	18	13	347	343	3	7
5	450	427	5	12	14	434	433	5	17
6	336	332	4	4	15	330	325	4	9
7	300	293	4	8	16	181	171	3	11
8	370	353	4	2	17	415	404	5	1
9	306	299	4	14	18	401	400	4	3
OUT	2,723	2,641	36		IN	2,915	2,846	35	
					TOTAL	5,638	5,487	71	
					STANDARD SCRATCH	69	69		

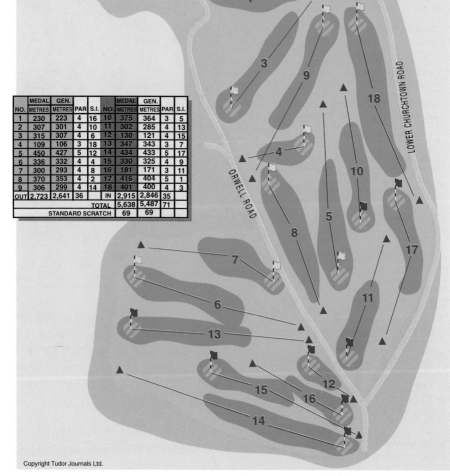

RATHFARNHAM   L E I N S T E R   DUBLIN CITY

**Newtown, Rathfarnham,
Dublin 16
Tel: (01) 4931201.**

LOCATION: Two miles from Rathfarnham
Village.
SECRETARY/MANAGER: Mr. D. Tipping.
PROFESSIONAL: Brian O'Hara.
Tel: (01) 4931201.
ARCHITECT: John Jacob.

Parkland course, with attractive
scenery, mature trees and spinneys.
Greens are built on the natural lie of
the ground.

COURSE INFORMATION

**Par 71; SSS 70; Length
5,824 metres.**
Visitors: Welcome Monday,
Wednesday & Friday.
Opening Hours: 8.30am –
Sunset.
Avoid: Tues, Sat, Sun & Bank
Holidays.
Ladies: Welcome (Handicap
Certificate required).
Green Fees: £11.50 Mon –
Fri (£22.50 without member);
£28 Sun (with a member).
Juveniles: Welcome with
member only. Lessons
available by prior
arrangements.
Clubhouse Hours: 10.30am
– 11.00pm.
Clubhouse Dress: Jacket
and tie after 7.30pm.
Clubhouse Facilities: Light
snacks daily; meals by prior
arrangements.

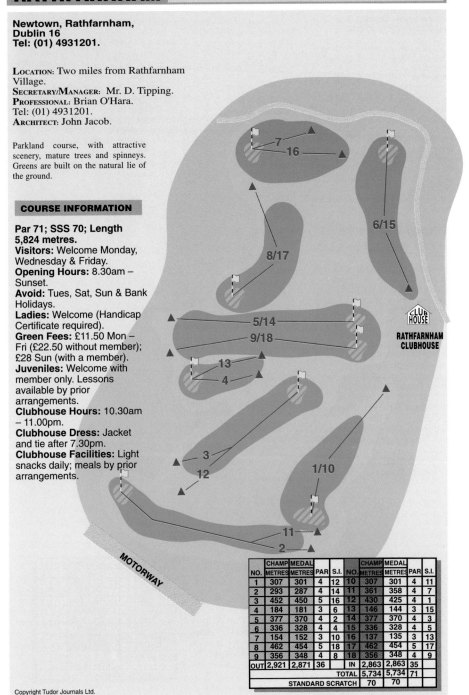

NO.	CHAMP METRES	MEDAL METRES	PAR	S.I.	NO.	CHAMP METRES	MEDAL METRES	PAR	S.I.
1	307	301	4	12	10	307	301	4	11
2	293	287	4	14	11	361	358	4	7
3	452	450	5	16	12	430	425	4	1
4	184	181	3	6	13	146	144	3	15
5	377	370	4	2	14	377	370	4	3
6	336	328	4	4	15	336	328	4	5
7	154	152	3	10	16	137	135	3	13
8	462	454	5	18	17	462	454	5	17
9	356	348	4	8	18	356	348	4	9
OUT	2,921	2,871	36		IN	2,863	2,863	35	
					TOTAL	5,734	5,734	71	
					STANDARD SCRATCH	70	70		

RATHFARNHAM
CLUBHOUSE

Dollymount, Dublin 3.
Tel: 8336346/8331262.

LOCATION: Three miles north east
from the city centre along the
coast road.
SECRETARY: John A. Lambe.
Tel: 8336346.
PROFESSIONAL: Leonard Owens.
Tel: 8336477.
ARCHITECT: H. S. Colt.

The links is 6,922 yards (6,330 metres) in
length and is laid out in the old traditional
links style resembling St Andrews. Fine
fescue grasses provide an ideal basis for
greens and fairways and a wandering wind
adds that extra hazard. Fine bunkers, close
lies and subtle trapping are all features of
Royal Dublin.

COURSE INFORMATION

Par 72; SSS 73; Length 6,330
Metres.
Visitors: Welcome Monday,
Tuesday, Thursday & Friday.
Please telephone for availability.
Opening Hours: 8.30am – Sunset.
Avoid: Wed. and weekends.
Ladies: Welcome. Lessons
available by prior arrangements;
Club Hire available; Caddy
service available by prior
arrangements. Telephone
appointment required.
Green Fees: £50 Mon – Fri; £60
Sat/Sun.
Clubhouse Hours: 8.00am –
midnight.
Clubhouse Dress: Jacket and
tie in Clubhouse; Casual in Grill
Room.
Clubhouse Facilities: Every
day except Monday.

NO.	METRES	PAR	S.I.	NO.	METRES	PAR	S.I.
1	361	4	7	10	427	4	3
2	445	5	17	11	493	5	13
3	363	4	4	12	188	3	10
4	163	3	12	13	425	4	1
5	423	4	2	14	455	5	15
6	180	3	16	15	397	4	6
7	338	4	9	16	245	4	18
8	465	5	11	17	345	4	8
9	164	3	14	18	453	4	5
OUT	2,902	35		IN	3,428	37	
				TOTAL	6,330	72	
				STANDARD SCRATCH		73	

ROYAL DUBLIN
CLUBHOUSE

Copyright Tudor Journals Ltd.

Bunker positions indicated.

64

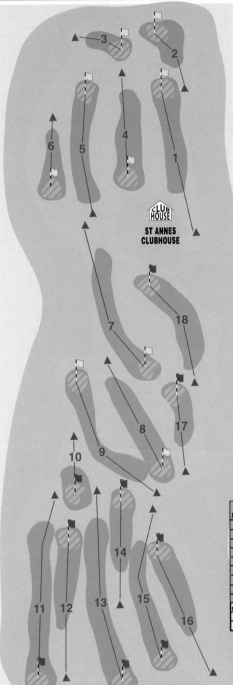

North Bull Island, Dollymount, Dublin, 5. Tel: 8336471/8332797.

LOCATION: Five miles north east of Dublin.
SECRETARY: Wally Bornemann. Tel: 8336471.
PROFESSIONAL: P. Skerritt. Tel: 8314138.
ARCHITECT: E. Hackett and Committee.

This is a links course that has recently undergone the transition from nine holes to eighteen, which enjoys a very pleasant seaside location.

COURSE INFORMATION

Par 70; SSS 70; Length 5,797 metres.
Visitors: Welcome any time except during Gents or Ladies Competitions.
Opening Hours: 9.00am – 7.00pm.
Avoid: Days of Competitions.
Ladies: Welcome. Lessons available by prior arrangements; Telephone appointment required.
Green Fees: Weekdays – £25 & weekends and Bank Holidays – £30.
Clubhouse Hours: 8.30am – 11.00pm.
Clubhouse Dress: Casual.
Clubhouse Facilities: Snacks 10.30am – 6.30pm; Meals and snacks 6.30pm - 9.30pm. Bar and Catering Tel: 332797.
Open Competitions: Open weeks – June, July & August.

NO.	CHAMP METRES	MEDAL METRES	PAR	S.I.	NO.	CHAMP METRES	MEDAL METRES	PAR	S.I.
1	463	458	5	15	10	148	140	3	16
2	354	349	4	9	11	506	479	5	10
3	150	144	3	13	12	347	339	4	6
4	364	359	4	3	13	440	436	5	8
5	343	335	4	11	14	214	204	3	12
6	144	140	3	17	15	377	369	4	2
7	430	426	4	1	16	284	276	4	18
8	372	360	4	7	17	177	168	3	14
9	360	353	4	5	18	378	366	4	4
OUT	2,926	2,875	35		IN	2,871	2,777	35	
					TOTAL	5,797	5,652	70	
					STANDARD SCRATCH	70	69		

Copyright Tudor Journals Ltd.

65

St Margarets Golf & Country Club, St. Margarets, Co. Dublin.
Tel: (01) 864 0400.
Fax: (01) 864 0289.

LOCATION: Eight miles north of city centre.
SECRETARY: Mr Denis Kane.
RESERVATIONS MANAGER: Gillian Harris.
ARCHITECT: Tom Craddock & Pat Ruddy

Home to the Women's Irish Open and the PGA Irish Seniors Open, St Margaret's measures just under 7,000 yards off the back tees and the modern design approach makes use of water hazards and sculptured mounding on a level new to Irish golf. Every effort has been made to make the course a challenge full of variety and drama but very playable by all standards of player.

COURSE INFORMATION

Par 73; SSS 73; Length 6,917 yards.
Visitors: Welcome everyday.
Opening Hours: Sunrise – Sunset.

Ladies: Welcome.
Green Fees: £40 all days.
Juveniles: Welcome.
Clubhouse Hours: 8.30am – 11.00pm.
Clubhouse Dress: Neat.
Clubhouse Facilities: Full catering facilities available.

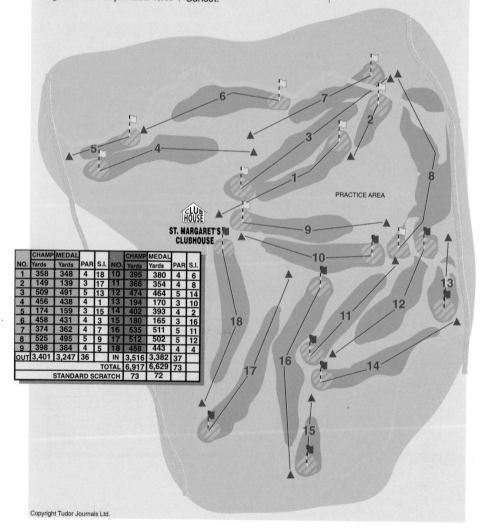

NO.	CHAMP Yards	MEDAL Yards	PAR	S.I.	NO.	CHAMP Yards	MEDAL Yards	PAR	S.I.
1	358	348	4	18	10	395	380	4	6
2	149	139	3	17	11	366	354	4	8
3	509	491	5	13	12	474	464	5	14
4	456	438	4	1	13	194	170	3	10
5	174	159	3	15	14	402	393	4	2
6	458	431	4	3	15	180	165	3	16
7	374	362	4	7	16	535	511	5	11
8	525	495	5	9	17	512	502	5	12
9	398	384	4	5	18	458	443	4	4
OUT	3,401	3,247	36		IN	3,516	3,382	37	
					TOTAL	6,917	6,629	73	
					STANDARD SCRATCH	73	72		

STACKSTOWN

**Kellystown Road,
Rathfarnham, Dublin 16.
Tel: (01) 494 2338.**

LOCATION: South West Dublin, six miles from City Centre.
SECRETARY: Kieran Lawler.
Tel: (01) 494 1993.
ARCHITECT: Shaffreys.

An attractive course on the side of Ticnock Mountain, with marvellous views of Dublin and the Bay.

COURSE INFORMATION

**Par 72; SSS 68; Length 5,952 metres.
Visitors:** Welcome weekdays.
Opening Hours: Sunrise – Sunset.
Avoid: Weekends and Bank holidays.
Ladies: Welcome.
Green Fees: £16 Mon – Fri; £20 Sat & Sun & Bank holidays.

Juveniles: Welcome after 4.00pm with an adult.
Clubhouse Hours: 8.30am – 11.30pm.
Clubhouse Dress: Neat dress essential.
Clubhouse Facilities: Catering facilities available and bar open every day.
Open Competitions: Open Week – May.

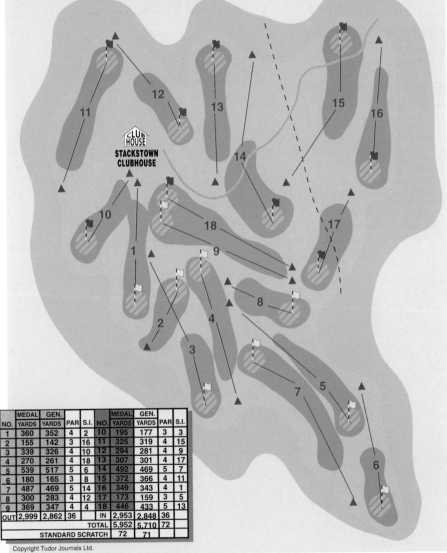

NO.	MEDAL YARDS	GEN. YARDS	PAR	S.I.	NO.	MEDAL YARDS	GEN. YARDS	PAR	S.I.
1	360	352	4	2	10	195	177	3	3
2	155	142	3	16	11	325	319	4	15
3	339	326	4	10	12	294	281	4	9
4	270	261	4	18	13	307	301	4	17
5	539	517	5	6	14	492	469	5	7
6	180	165	3	8	15	372	366	4	11
7	487	469	5	14	16	349	343	4	1
8	300	283	4	12	17	173	159	3	5
9	369	347	4	4	18	446	433	5	13
OUT	2,999	2,862	36		IN	2,953	2,848	36	
					TOTAL	5,952	5,710	72	
					STANDARD SCRATCH		72	71	

SUTTON

**Cush Point, Sutton,
Dublin 13.
Tel: (01) 8323013.**

LOCATION: Ten minutes from City
centre.
HONORARY SECRETARY: P. Bowen.
Tel: (01) 8322965.
PROFESSIONAL: N. Lynch.
Tel: (01) 8321703.
SECRETARY: Hugh O'Neill.

Links course with very narrow fairways and
one of the main features is that the course is
surrounded by water.

NO.	YARDS	PAR	S.I.	NO.	YARDS	PAR	S.I.
1	311	4	13	10	311	4	14
2	300	4	15	11	300	4	16
3	503	5	5	12	503	5	4
4	306	4	7	13	306	4	6
5	156	3	9	14	156	3	12
6	105	3	17	15	105	3	18
7	349	4	11	16	349	4	10
8	382	4	1	17	382	4	2
9	376	4	3	18	376	4	8
OUT	2,788	35		IN	2,788	35	
				TOTAL	67	70	
STANDARD SCRATCH							

COURSE INFORMATION

**Par 70; SSS 67; Length
5,718 yards.**
Visitors: Welcome.
Opening Hours: 9.00am – sunset.
Avoid: Tuesday and Saturday.
Green Fees: £20 Mon – Fri (£10
with member); £25 Sat, Sun & Bank
Hols (£10 with member).
Juveniles: Welcome no weekend
play. Lessons by prior arrangments.
Caddy cars available.
Clubhouse Hours:
9.00am onwards.
Clubhouse Dress: Casual, no
denims or trainers.
Clubhouse Facilities: Full
clubhouse facilities, by
arrangement.

N

CLUB
HOUSE
**SUTTON
CLUBHOUSE**

**Geraldine, Athy,
Co. Kildare.
Tel: (01507) 31729.**

LOCATION: Off the Kildare Road.
SECRETARY: Michael Hogan.
Tel: (0507) 31729.
PUBLIC RELATIONS OFFICE:
Kieran Breen.
Tel: (088) 589641.

Opened in 1993 among the features of this parkland course is a river which comes into play in four holes. All the new greens are totally sand based. Two of the par three's are over 200 yards long. The 16th hole has a deep "valley of sin" to the right and is 420 yards long. Heading for home the 17th is a unique dog-leg to the right down a hill to a two-tier elevated green.

COURSE INFORMATION

**Par 71; SSS 69;
Length 6,340 yards.
Visitors:** Welcome Mon – Fri.
Avoid: Weekends and Bank holidays.
Ladies: Thursday.

Green Fees: £13 Mon – Fri; £12 Sat (with member only); Sunday is member day.
Juveniles: Wed & Fri mornings during holiday periods.
Clubhouse Hours: Mon–Sun 10am–11pm.
Clubhouse Dress: Casual.
Clubhouse Facilities: By arrangement.
Open Competitions: Open Week – mid June; Husband and Wife – August.

NO.	CHAMP YARDS	MEDAL YARDS	PAR	S.I.	NO.	CHAMP YARDS	MEDAL YARDS	PAR	S.I.
1	354	349	4	6	10	402	384	4	3
2	176	162	3	14	11	336	329	4	15
3	301	291	4	18	12	203	188	3	9
4	369	356	4	8	13	487	478	5	13
5	154	147	3	10	14	217	203	3	7
6	421	411	4	2	15	365	356	4	11
7	373	364	4	4	16	423	413	4	1
8	503	499	5	16	17	387	374	4	5
9	362	354	4	12	18	507	501	5	17
OUT	3,013	2,933	35		IN	3,327	3,226	36	
						TOTAL	6,340	6,159	71
						STANDARD SCRATCH	70	69	

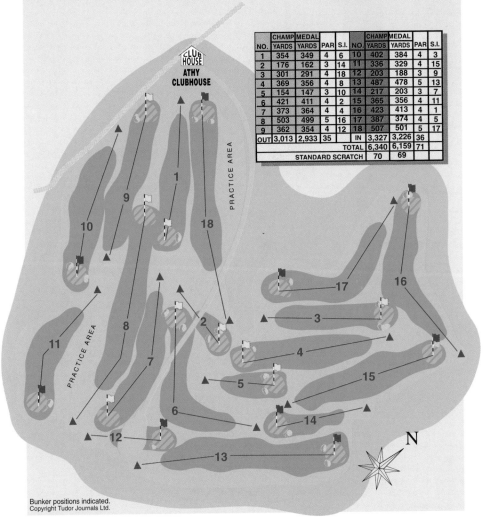

ATHY
CLUBHOUSE

N

Sallins, Co. Kildare.
Tel: (045) 897096.

LOCATION: Four miles outside Naas near Bodenstown graveyard.
SECRETARY: Bernadette Mather.
Tel: (045) 897096.

The Old Course in Bodenstown, with its ample fairways and large greens, some of which are raised, provides more than a fair test of golf. The

Ladyhill Course, also at Bodenstown, is a little shorter but still affords a fair challenge.

COURSE INFORMATION

Par 72; SSS 73; Length 6,321 yards (Old Course).
Visitors: Welcome.
Opening Hours: Sunrise – sunset.
Avoid: Main course at weekends. Ladyhill course available.

Ladies: Welcome Thursdays.
Green Fees: £12 Main Course; £10 Ladyhill Course.
Juveniles: Welcome.
Clubhouse Hours: 11.00am – 11.00pm. Full clubhouse facilities.
Clubhouse Dress: Informal.
Clubhouse Facilities: Full catering available.
Open Competitions: Open Week – June.

NO.	CHAMP YARDS	MEDAL YARDS	PAR	S.I.	NO.	CHAMP YARDS	MEDAL YARDS	PAR	S.I.
1	364	338	4	11	10	322	317	4	16
2	168	161	3	17	11	379	363	4	4
3	368	366	4	2	12	503	484	5	12
4	355	336	4	7	13	403	382	4	8
5	148	145	3	5	14	398	384	4	1
6	476	476	5	15	15	165	153	3	10
7	359	359	4	9	16	343	336	4	18
8	370	370	4	3	17	205	186	3	6
9	480	468	5	13	18	515	508	5	14
OUT	3,088	3,019	36		IN	3,233	3,113	36	
					TOTAL	6,321	6,132	72	
					STANDARD SCRATCH	73	71		

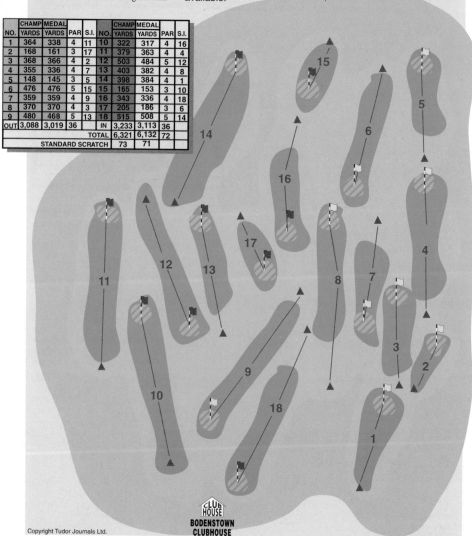

CLUB HOUSE
BODENSTOWN CLUBHOUSE

Castlewarden, Straffan, Co. Kildare.
Tel: Dublin (01) 4588218 (clubhouse).

LOCATION: Between Naas and Newlands Cross.
HON. SECRETARY: John Ferriter.
Tel: (01) 4589254 (office).
PROFESSIONAL: Gerry Egan.
Tel: (01) 4588219.

Throughout this relatively new course there are several scenic views of both the Dublin and Wicklow mountains.

The course features gently-contoured greens, with elevated tees and water hazards.

COURSE INFORMATION

Par 72; SSS 70; Length 6,624 yards.
Visitors: Welcome to play.
Opening Hours: Daylight to dusk.
Avoid: Saturdays and Sundays.
Ladies: Welcome.
Green Fees: Weekdays – £17 (£11 with a member – max. of 3 guests); weekend – £20 (£15 with a member). Lessons available by prior arrangement. Club Hire available also.

Clubhouse Hours:
1.00pm – 11.30pm (weekdays) & 11.00am – 11.30pm (weekends).
Clubhouse Dress: Neat.
Clubhouse Facilities: Available on request.

NO.	CHAMP YARDS	MEDAL YARDS	PAR	S.I.	NO.	CHAMP YARDS	MEDAL YARDS	PAR	S.I.
1	496	488	5	14	10	260	255	4	13
2	185	180	3	12	11	378	366	4	11
3	445	439	4	2	12	400	394	4	7
4	325	320	4	10	13	153	148	3	17
5	398	391	4	8	14	392	387	4	3
6	408	403	4	4	15	398	384	4	9
7	374	365	4	6	16	420	410	4	1
8	530	480	5	18	17	172	166	3	15
9	379	372	4	16	18	552	548	5	5
OUT	3,540	3,438	37		IN	3,125	3,064	35	
					TOTAL	6,665	6,502	72	
					STANDARD SCRATCH		70		

PUTTING GREEN

CLUB HOUSE

CASTLEWARDEN CLUBHOUSE

PRACTICE AREA

Bunker & Tree positions indicated.
Copyright Tudor Journals Ltd.

Little Curragh, Kildare, Co. Kildare.
Tel: (045) 521433/521295.

LOCATION: One mile west of Kildare town.
HON.SECRETARY: Paddy Flanagan.
PROFESSIONAL: Mark O'Boyle.
Tel: (045) 521295.

A course which is typical to many in the area with all the colour of the gorse and heather. Flat and relatively straight forward to play. A good choice for the middle and high handicappers.

COURSE INFORMATION

Par 71; SSS 70; Length 5,738 metres.
Visitors: Welcome.
Opening Hours: Sunrise – sunset.
Avoid: Wednesday, Sundays (Club Competitions).
Ladies: Welcome.

Ladies Day: Wednesday.
Green Fees: £10 Weekday; £12 Weekend; £7 with a member.
Juveniles: Welcome. Club Hire available; Handicap Certificate preferred; telephone appointment required.
Clubhouse Hours: 11.00am – 11.30pm.
Clubhouse Dress: Casual.
Clubhouse Facilities: 9.00am – 10.30pm daily (full facilities).

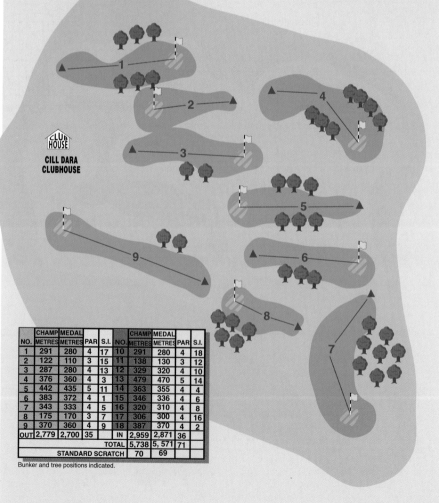

CILL DARA
CLUBHOUSE

NO.	CHAMP METRES	MEDAL METRES	PAR	S.I.	NO.	CHAMP METRES	MEDAL METRES	PAR	S.I.
1	291	280	4	17	10	291	280	4	18
2	122	110	3	15	11	138	130	3	12
3	287	280	4	13	12	329	320	4	10
4	376	360	4	3	13	479	470	5	14
5	442	435	5	11	14	363	355	4	4
6	383	372	4	1	15	346	336	4	6
7	343	333	4	5	16	320	310	4	8
8	175	170	3	7	17	306	300	4	16
9	370	360	4	9	18	387	370	4	2
OUT	2,779	2,700	35		IN	2,959	2,871	36	
					TOTAL	5,738	5,571	71	
					STANDARD SCRATCH	70	69		

Bunker and tree positions indicated.

**Craddockstown Golf Club,
Blessington Road,
Naas, Co. Kildare.
Tel: (045) 897610.**

LOCATION: 1 1/2 miles from Naas town.
SECRETARY: L.A. Watson.
Tel: (045) 897610.
ARCHITECT: A. Spring.

Testing, spacious course with young parkland trees, which when mature will increase accuracy needed. Greens well protected and some fairways include tricky water hazards.

COURSE INFORMATION

Par 71; SSS 70; Length 6,134 metres.
Visitors: Welcome any day.
Opening Hours:
8.30am onwards.
Avoid: Saturdays and Sundays until 3.00pm.
Ladies: Tuesdays, Saturdays* & Sundays* (*limited tee times).
Green Fees: Weekdays £14; weekends £18.
Juveniles: £5.
Clubhouse Hours:
9.30am – 11.30pm.

Clubhouse Dress:
Smart and neat, casual.
Clubhouse Facilities:
Changing rooms, showers, bar and catering by arrangement.
Open Competitions:
Semi-Opens Wednesdays; Open Week July.

NO.	METRES	PAR	S.I.	NO.	METRES	PAR	S.I.
1	385	4	6	10	412	4	15
2	371	4	8	11	297	4	7
3	181	3	18	12	208	3	17
4	391	4	4	13	329	4	1
5	462	5	14	14	366	4	11
6	397	4	10	15	517	5	5
7	326	4	2	16	360	4	9
8	183	3	16	17	191	3	3
9	319	4	12	18	439	5	13
OUT	3,015	35		IN	3,119	36	
				TOTAL	6,134	71	
				STANDARD SCRATCH	70		

CRADDOCKSTOWN
GOLF CLUB

Bunker & tree positions indicated.
Copyright Tudor Journals Ltd.

Curragh, Co. Kildare.
Tel: (045) 441714/441238.

LOCATION: Thirty two miles
south east of Dublin.
SECRETARY: Ann Culleton.
Tel: (045) 441714.
ARCHITECT: G.Burke.
Tel: (045) 441896.

A long testing course of over 6,000
meters. Hazards include tree lined
fairways, furze bushes and grazing
sheep. Every hole presents a separate

and distinctive challenge. A scenic
course with panoramic views of
Kildare and the Wicklow Mountains.

COURSE INFORMATION

Par 72; SSS 71; Length
6,001 metres.
Visitors: Welcome, advance
enquires are essential.
Opening Hours: Sunrise –
Sunset.
Avoid: Tuesdays, Sat & Sun.
Ladies: Tuesday.

Green Fees: £18 Mon – Fri;
£22 Sat & Sun & Bank
Holidays.
Juveniles: Welcome & must
be accompanied by an adult.
Leesons & club hire available
by prior arrangement with the
Club Professional; telephone
for appointment.
Clubhouse Hours: 10am –
10pm (all year).
Clubhouse Dress: Neat.
Club Competitions: June &
July.

NO.	CHAMP METRES	MEDAL METRES	PAR	S.I.	NO.	CHAMP METRES	MEDAL METRES	PAR	S.I.
1	450	436	5	15	10	170	158	3	10
2	335	324	4	5	11	400	392	4	2
3	272	266	4	13	12	391	360	4	6
4	180	174	3	7	13	285	273	4	16
5	322	315	4	11	14	460	449	5	14
6	120	334	4	3	15	459	449	5	12
7	483	473	5	9	16	124	105	3	18
8	166	157	3	17	17	412	403	4	4
9	407	403	4	1	18	344	337	4	8
OUT	2,956	2,882	36		IN	3,045	2,926	36	
					TOTAL	6,001	5,808	72	
					STANDARD SCRATCH	71	70		

Tree positions indicated.

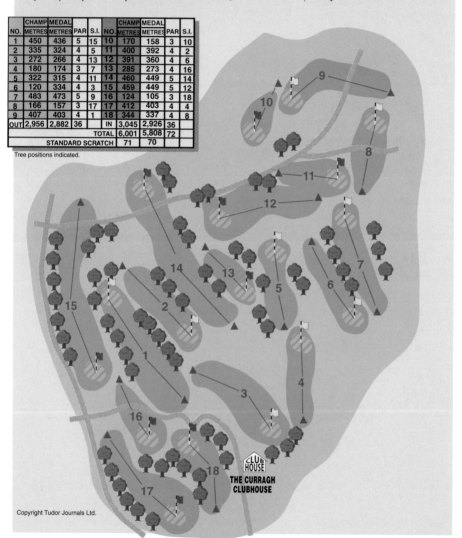

THE CURRAGH
CLUBHOUSE

Copyright Tudor Journals Ltd.

Highfield Golf Club,
Carbury, Co. Kildare.
Tel: (0405) 31021.

LOCATION: North Kildare. Within
one hour of Dublin, via M4
motorway.
SECRETARY: Margaret P Duggan.
Tel: (0405) 31021.
ARCHITECT: Alan Duggan.

Attractive 18 hole parkland course,
set in a quiet country area, featuring
leisurely fairways and mature
sycamore, beech & chestnut trees.

COURSE INFORMATION

Par 72; SSS 69; Length
6,277 yards.
Visitors: Welcome.
Opening Hours:
Sunrise – sunset.
Avoid: Early Saturday & Sunday.
Ladies: Welcome.
Green Fees: Mon – Fri £10 (£8
with member); Sat / Sun / Bank
Holidays £14 (£10 with member).
Juveniles: Must be accompanied
by an adult.

Clubhouse Hours:
8.30am – sunset.
Clubhouse Dress:
Smart / casual.
Clubhouse Facilities:
Available everyday – reception;
Restaurant.
Open Competitions:
Contact club for details.

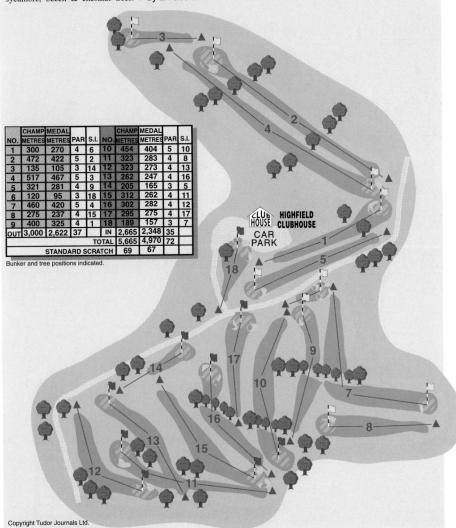

NO.	CHAMP METRES	MEDAL METRES	PAR	S.I.	NO.	CHAMP METRES	MEDAL METRES	PAR	S.I.
1	300	270	4	6	10	454	404	5	10
2	472	422	5	2	11	323	283	4	8
3	135	105	3	14	12	323	273	4	13
4	517	467	5	3	13	262	247	4	16
5	321	281	4	9	14	205	165	3	5
6	120	95	3	18	15	312	262	4	11
7	460	420	5	4	16	302	282	4	12
8	275	237	4	15	17	295	275	4	17
9	400	325	4	1	18	189	157	3	7
OUT	3,000	2,622	37		IN	2,665	2,348	35	
					TOTAL	5,665	4,970	72	
					STANDARD SCRATCH	69	67		

Bunker and tree positions indicated.

HIGHFIELD CLUBHOUSE

Kilkea Castle, Castledermot, Co. Kildare.
Tel: (0503) 45555.
Fax: (0503) 45505.

LOCATION: 40 miles from Dublin.
SECRETARY: Adeline Molloy.
Tel: (0503) 45555.
Fax: (0503) 45505.

A parkland course which surrounds the oldest inhabited castle in Ireland. The River Griese comes into play on ten of the holes.

COURSE INFORMATION

Par 70; SSS 71; Length 6,197 Metres.
Visitors: Welcome to play every day.
Opening Hours: Sunrise – Sunset.
Ladies: Welcome.
Green Fees: £25.
Hotel Residents: £20.

Juveniles: Welcome only when accompanied by adults.
Clubhouse Hours: 10.00am - 11.30pm.
Clubhouse Dress: Neat.
Clubhouse Facilities: Bar, restaurant, snooker room, pro-shop, putting green and pitching green. Conference facilities.

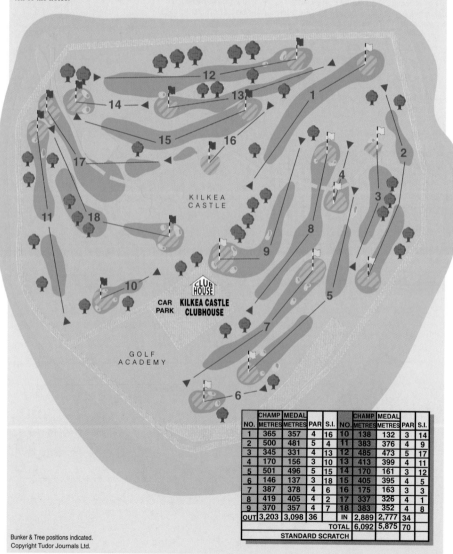

KILKEA CASTLE

CLUB HOUSE
CAR PARK **KILKEA CASTLE CLUBHOUSE**

GOLF ACADEMY

NO.	CHAMP METRES	MEDAL METRES	PAR	S.I.	NO.	CHAMP METRES	MEDAL METRES	PAR	S.I.
1	365	357	4	16	10	138	132	3	14
2	500	481	5	4	11	383	376	4	9
3	345	331	4	13	12	485	473	5	17
4	170	156	3	10	13	413	399	4	11
5	501	496	5	15	14	170	161	3	12
6	146	137	3	18	15	405	395	4	5
7	387	378	4	6	16	175	163	3	3
8	419	405	4	2	17	337	326	4	1
9	370	357	4	7	18	383	352	4	8
OUT	3,203	3,098	36		IN	2,889	2,777	34	
					TOTAL	6,092	5,875	70	
					STANDARD SCRATCH				

**Killeen Golf Club,
Kill, County Kildare,
Tel: (045) 866003.
Fax: (045) 875881.**

LOCATION: Two miles west of Kill village, off N7 Dublin – Cork Road.
SECRETARY / MANAGER: Peter Carey. Tel: (045) 866003.
ARCHITECT: Tom Craddock & Pat Ruddy.

1995 saw the introduction of six magnificent holes that feature all the elements associated with Craddock and Ruddy designs in recent years ... broad sweeping fairways, boldly shaped and placed fairways, water hazards that are very much in play and also perfectly conditioned greens

COURSE INFORMATION

Par 71; SSS 71; Length 5,815 metres.
Visitors: Welcome weekdays and at weekends.
Opening Hours: Summer 7.00am – 12.00pm; winter 8.00am – 6.00pm.
Avoid: Sat / Sun up to 4.00pm. At weekends telephone, appointments essential.
Ladies: Welcome Tuesday and Thursday.
Green Fees: £17 Mon – Fri; £20 Sat & Sun.
Caddy car & Club / Shoe hire available.
Clubhouse Hours: Summer 9.00am – 12 midnight; winter 9.00am – 6.00pm.
Clubhouse Dress: Neat.
Clubhouse Facilities: Pro shop open everyday. Licensed restaurant.

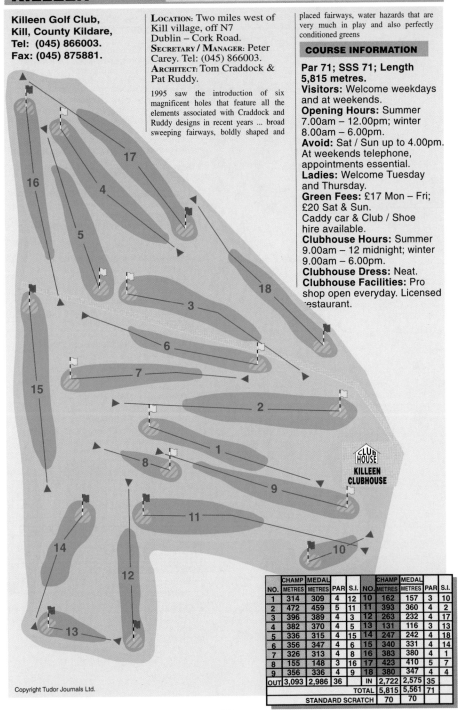

Copyright Tudor Journals Ltd.

NO.	CHAMP METRES	MEDAL METRES	PAR	S.I.	NO.	CHAMP METRES	MEDAL METRES	PAR	S.I.
1	314	309	4	12	10	162	157	3	10
2	472	459	5	11	11	393	360	4	2
3	396	389	4	3	12	263	232	4	17
4	382	370	4	5	13	131	116	3	13
5	336	315	4	15	14	247	242	4	18
6	356	347	4	6	15	340	331	4	14
7	326	313	4	8	16	383	380	4	1
8	155	148	3	16	17	423	410	5	7
9	356	336	4	9	18	380	347	4	4
OUT	3,093	2,986	36		IN	2,722	2,575	35	
					TOTAL	5,815	5,561	71	
					STANDARD SCRATCH	70	70		

77

Straffan, Co. Kildare.
Tel: (01) 6017300.

LOCATION: Co. Kildare.
GOLF DIRECTOR / MANAGER: Paul Crowe.
PROFESSIONAL: Ernie Jones.
ARCHITECT: Arnold Palmer.

A world class major championship designed golf course by Arnold Palmer. Eleven man made lakes, large sand bunkers, large mounds both sides of fairways. The River Liffey runs alongside four holes with the 7th green on the far side of the river. Large quantity of 300 year old trees.

COURSE INFORMATION

Par 72; SSS 74; Length 6,368 metres.
Visitors: Welcome.
Opening Hours: 8.00am (summer), 8.30am (winter).
Avoid: 1.30pm – 3.30pm. Prior arrangement required. Handicap certificate required.
Ladies: Welcome.
Green Fees: £120 (summer), £75 (winter). Lessons available by prior arrangement. Club Hire and Caddy service available. No Open Competitions.
Juveniles: Must be accompanied by an adult.
Clubhouse Dress: Jacket and tie after 7.00pm – otherwise casual but strictly no jeans.
Clubhouse Hours: 8.30am – 10pm (summer), 9pm (winter).
Clubhouse Facilities: Bar, snack bar, restaurant. Snack bar 9.00am – 9.00pm. Bar & Restaurant 11.00am – 9.00pm everyday.

PRACTICE AREA

NO.	MEDAL YARDS	GEN. YARDS	PAR	S.I.	NO.	MEDAL YARDS	GEN. YARDS	PAR	S.I.
1	529	512	5	5	10	364	364	4	6
2	373	351	4	9	11	361	361	4	12
3	160	148	3	17	12	132	132	3	18
4	368	351	4	7	13	497	497	5	10
5	196	177	3	15	14	358	358	4	2
6	406	376	4	11	15	376	376	4	4
7	553	543	5	3	16	339	339	4	8
8	341	306	4	13	17	160	140	3	16
9	395	392	4	1	18	460	460	5	14
OUT	3,321	3,156	36		IN	3,047	3,027	36	
					TOTAL	6,368	6,183	72	
					STANDARD SCRATCH	74	72		

KNOCKANALLY

Donadea, North Kildare.
Tel: (045) 869322.

LOCATION: North Kildare.
SECRETARY: Noel Lyons.
Tel: (045) 869322.
Fax: (045) 869322.
ARCHITECT: Noel Lyons.

A popular parkland course which is basically flat, and has several water hazards. Christy O'Connor Senior once described the first hole as "the most difficult opening hole in golf".

Home of the Irish International Professional Matchplay Championship. Palladian old world clubhouse is also an interesting feature.

COURSE INFORMATION

Par 72; SSS 72; Length 6,424 yards.
Visitors: Welcome. Telephone in advance.
Opening Hours: Sunrise – sunset.
Avoid: Saturday mornings.
Ladies: Welcome Tuesday and Thursday mornings.

Green Fees: Mon – Fri £18 (with member £10) Sat, Sun & Bank Hols £22 (with member £10).
Juveniles: Welcome. Lessons available by prior arrangement.
Clubhouse Hours: 8.30am – 12.00 midnight.
Clubhouse Dress: Smart / casual (no jeans).
Clubhouse Facilities: Available everyday. Members bar, restaurant, professional shop, offices, games rooms.

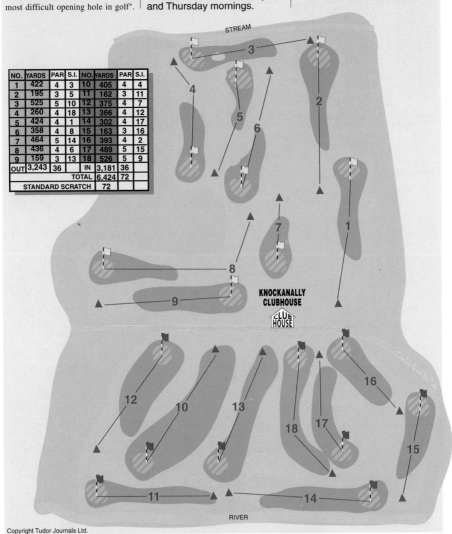

NO.	YARDS	PAR	S.I.	NO.	YARDS	PAR	S.I.
1	422	4	3	10	405	4	4
2	195	3	5	11	162	3	11
3	525	5	10	12	375	4	7
4	260	4	18	13	366	4	12
5	424	4	1	14	302	4	17
6	358	4	8	15	163	3	16
7	464	5	14	16	393	4	2
8	436	4	6	17	489	5	15
9	159	3	13	18	526	5	9
OUT	3,243	36		IN	3,181	36	
				TOTAL	6,424	72	
STANDARD SCRATCH			72				

KNOCKANALLY CLUBHOUSE

RIVER

Copyright Tudor Journals Ltd.

79

**Leixlip Golf Club,
Leixlip, Co. Kildare.
Tel: (01) 624 4978,
(01) 624 6185.**

LOCATION: From Dublin – turn
off M4 motorway at Leixlip.
SECRETARY: Edward McKone.
Tel: (01) 624 4978.
ARCHITECT: Eddie Hackett.

9 hole parkland course in a beautiful
setting. Wide fairways on all the
holes, but greens are well protected
by bunkers and trees.

COURSE INFORMATION

**Par 72; SSS 70; Length
6,068 yards.
Visitors:** Welcome.
Opening Hours: 7.30am.
Avoid: Saturday morning and
Wednesday evening.
Green Fees: Mon – Fri £13
(Juveniles £8); Sat & Sun £15
(Juveniles £12).

Juveniles: Welcome.
Clubhouse Dress:
Neat/Casual.
Clubhouse Facilities:
Coffee shop, on site restaurant
& bar.

NO.	YARDS	PAR	S.I.	NO.	YARDS	PAR	S.I.
1	460	4	1	10	460	4	2
2	509	5	9	11	509	5	10
3	373	4	5	12	373	4	6
4	347	4	3	13	347	4	4
5	111	3	15	14	111	3	16
6	311	4	13	15	311	4	14
7	262	4	17	16	262	4	18
8	171	3	7	17	171	3	8
9	490	5	11	18	490	5	12
OUT	3,034	36		IN	3,034	36	
				TOTAL	6,068	72	
	STANDARD SCRATCH				70		

Bunker and tree positions indicated.

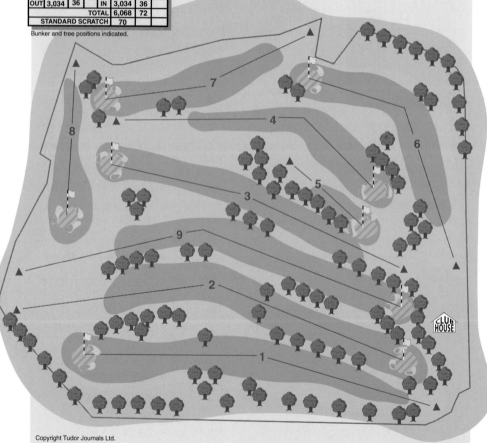

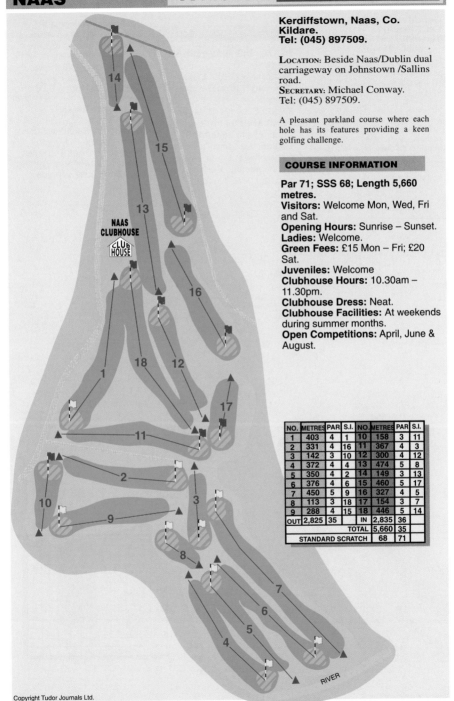

**Kerdiffstown, Naas, Co. Kildare.
Tel: (045) 897509.**

LOCATION: Beside Naas/Dublin dual carriageway on Johnstown /Sallins road.
SECRETARY: Michael Conway.
Tel: (045) 897509.

A pleasant parkland course where each hole has its features providing a keen golfing challenge.

COURSE INFORMATION

Par 71; SSS 68; Length 5,660 metres.
Visitors: Welcome Mon, Wed, Fri and Sat.
Opening Hours: Sunrise – Sunset.
Ladies: Welcome.
Green Fees: £15 Mon – Fri; £20 Sat.
Juveniles: Welcome
Clubhouse Hours: 10.30am – 11.30pm.
Clubhouse Dress: Neat.
Clubhouse Facilities: At weekends during summer months.
Open Competitions: April, June & August.

NO.	METRES	PAR	S.I.	NO.	METRES	PAR	S.I.
1	403	4	1	10	158	3	11
2	331	4	16	11	367	4	3
3	142	3	10	12	300	4	12
4	372	4	4	13	474	5	8
5	350	4	2	14	149	3	13
6	376	4	6	15	460	5	17
7	450	5	9	16	327	4	5
8	113	3	18	17	154	3	7
9	288	4	15	18	446	5	14
OUT	2,825	35		IN	2,835	36	
				TOTAL	5,660	35	
			STANDARD SCRATCH		68	71	

NAAS CLUBHOUSE

CALLAN

**Geraldine, Callan,
Co. Kilkenny.
Tel: (056) 25136
    (056) 25949.**

LOCATION: One mile from town of Callan on Knocktopher road.
HONORARY SECRETARY:
M. Duggan. Tel: (052) 54362.

Stream comes into play on six holes with the par 3 eighth requiring 155 yard carry over water to the green. In addition there are well placed spinneys to catch wayward drives. There is also a pond left of line of drive on the 6th. All greens are bunkered and well protected.

COURSE INFORMATION

Par 72; SSS 70; Length 6377 yards.
Visitors: Welcome to play.
Opening Hours: Daylight hours.
Avoid: Sundays all day and Saturdays after mid-day. Prior arrangement preferred.
Ladies: Welcome Tuesdays.
Green Fees: £11 all week; £6 with a member. Caddy service and Club Hire available.

Juveniles: Welcome if accompanied by an adult. Must be off the course by 6.00pm. Allocated days for juveniles only, telephone clubhouse for details.
Clubhouse Hours: 9.00am – 11.00pm.
Clubhouse Dress: Neat/Casual.
Clubhouse Facilities: Bar open 9.00am – 11.00pm. Catering facilities and times, anyday by prior arrangement. Golf Shop open everyday.

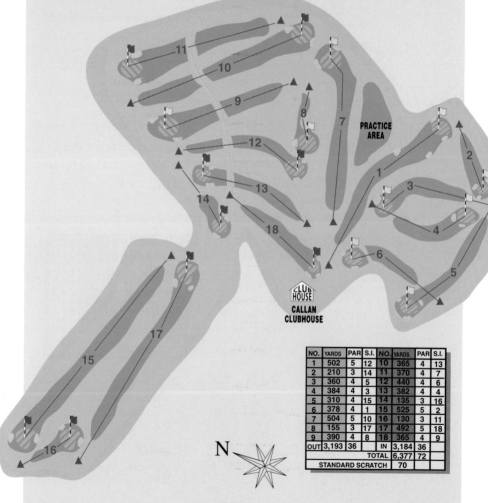

NO.	YARDS	PAR	S.I.	NO.	YARDS	PAR	S.I.
1	502	5	12	10	365	4	13
2	210	3	14	11	370	4	7
3	360	4	5	12	440	4	6
4	384	4	3	13	382	4	4
5	310	4	15	14	135	3	16
6	378	4	1	15	525	5	2
7	504	5	10	16	130	3	11
8	155	3	17	17	492	5	18
9	390	4	8	18	365	4	9
OUT	3,193	36		IN	3,184	36	
				TOTAL	6,377	72	
				STANDARD SCRATCH		70	

82

**Drumgoole, Castlecomer,
Co. Kilkenny.
Tel: (056) 41139.**

LOCATION: Edge of town on
Kilkenny road.
HONORARY SECRETARY:
Michael Doheny.
Tel: (056) 33333.
ARCHITECT: Pat Ruddy.

This course is in a sylvan setting bounded on
one side by the River Deen. A long course
considered a good test of golf, it is the third
longest nine hole course in Ireland.

COURSE INFORMATION

**Par 71; SSS 71; Length 5,547
metres.
Visitors:** Welcome.
Opening Hours: Sunrise – Sunset.
Avoid: All Sundays.
Ladies: Welcome.
Green Fees: £12 per day.
Juveniles: Welcome.
Clubhouse Hours: Sunrise –
Sunset.
Clubhouse Dress: Casual.
Clubhouse Facilities: Full
clubhouse facilities (by request for
groups).
Open Competitions: Open Week
July / Aug.

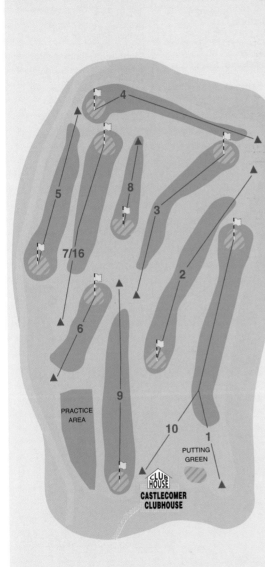

NO.	METRES	PAR	S.I.	NO.	METRES	PAR	S.I.
1	464	5	11	10	375	5	12
2	365	4	7	11	344	4	8
3	363	4	5	12	363	4	6
4	253	4	13	13	253	4	14
5	353	4	3	14	353	4	4
6	132	3	17	15	132	3	18
7	347	4	9	16	368	4	2
8	123	3	15	17	123	3	16
9	396	4	1	18	440	5	10
OUT	2,796	35		IN	2,751	36	
				TOTAL	5,547	71	
	STANDARD SCRATCH				71		

KILKENNY

Glendine, Kilkenny.
Tel: (056) 65400.
Members: (056) 22125.

LOCATION: One mile outside the city – off Castlecomer road.
SECRETARY: Mr Sean O'Neill.
Tel: (056) 65400.
PROFESSIONAL: Noel Leahy.
Tel: (056) 61730.
Parkland course with plenty of trees throughout the fairways which provide a good test of golf. GUI Irish finals are held here from time to time.

COURSE INFORMATION

Par 71; SSS 70; Length 5,859 metres.
Visitors: Welcome to play Mon – Fri, weekends by prior arrangement.
Opening Hours: Daylight hours.
Avoid: Saturday and Sunday – prior arrangement preferred.
Ladies: Welcome.
Green Fees: £20 week days

and £22 Weekends. Lessons available by prior arrangement. Club hire available. Caddy service available by prior arrangement.
Clubhouse Hours: As per licensing law.
Clubhouse Dress: Neat.
Clubhouse Facilities: Bar, food, snooker and pool.

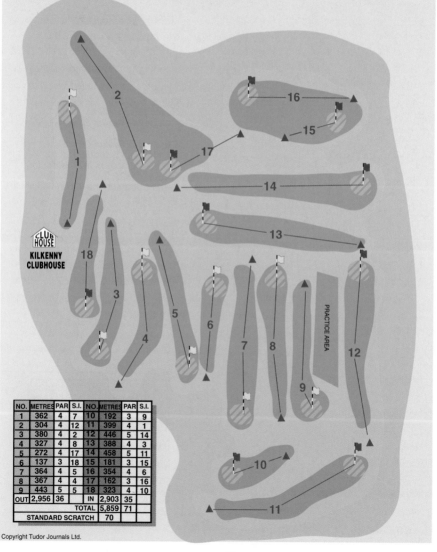

NO.	METRES	PAR	S.I.	NO.	METRES	PAR	S.I.
1	362	4	7	10	192	3	9
2	304	4	12	11	399	4	1
3	380	4	2	12	446	5	14
4	327	4	8	13	388	4	3
5	272	4	17	14	458	5	11
6	137	3	18	15	181	3	15
7	364	4	5	16	354	4	6
8	367	4	4	17	162	3	16
9	443	5	5	18	323	4	10
OUT	2,956	36		IN	2,903	35	
				TOTAL	5,859	71	
	STANDARD SCRATCH	70					

**Thomastown,
Co. Kilkenny.
Tel: (056) 24725
Fax: (056) 24828.**

LOCATION: Main Dublin – Waterford road, ten miles from Kilkenny.
SECRETARY: Tony Judge.
PROFESSIONAL: Mark Reid.
ARCHITECT: Jack Nicklaus.

The only Jack Nicklaus designed course in Ireland, it features old specimen trees, water hazards and bunkers. It is set in a beautiful old 1500 acre estate and appeals to all levels and standards of golfers. Accommodation is available in both Mount Juliet House and the clubhouse. New 18 hole putting course featuring par 2, 3 and 4.

COURSE INFORMATION

Par 72; SSS 72; Length 7112 yards.
Visitors: Welcome. Prior arrangement required. Handicap certificate required.
Opening Hours: Daily from 8.00am.
Avoid: No restrictions.
Ladies: Welcome.
Green Fees: Summer – Mon-Thur £70 & Fri-Sun £75. Winter – Mon-Thur £40 & Fri-Sun £50. Lessons available by prior arrangement. Club hire available. Caddy service available by prior arrangement.

available. 3 hole Teaching. Academy – lessons available with Mark Reid, the professional.
Juveniles: Welcome (no reduction in green fees).
Clubhouse Hours: 8.00am – 11.30pm.
Clubhouse Facilities: Changing rooms, Bar, Restuarant. 8.00am – 9.00pm (Must be booked in advance).

NO.	CHAMP YARDS	MEDAL YARDS	PAR	S.I.	NO.	CHAMP YARDS	MEDAL YARDS	PAR	S.I.
1	363	342	4	16	10	546	518	5	7
2	414	385	4	4	11	168	139	3	17
3	184	168	3	14	12	417	393	4	9
4	402	384	4	2	13	436	412	4	1
5	534	509	5	18	14	197	177	3	11
6	229	200	3	6	15	371	350	4	15
7	417	384	4	12	16	433	407	4	5
8	577	551	5	10	17	515	492	5	13
9	424	384	4	8	18	474	446	4	3
OUT	3,544	3,307	36		IN	3,557	3,334	36	
					TOTAL	7,101	6,641	72	
					STANDARD SCRATCH	74	72		

Tree positions indicated.

Newrath, Waterford.
Tel: (051) 876748.
Fax: (051) 853405.

LOCATION: Newrath.
SECRETARY: Joseph Condon.
Tel: (051) 876748.
ARCHITECT: James Braid.

A parkland course with good views of the countryside. The course character is as the undulating countryside around Newrath and will appeal to low and middle handicappers.

COURSE INFORMATION

Par 71; SSS 70; Length 5,722 metres.
Visitors: Welcome by prior arrangement.
Opening Hours: 8.00am – Sunset.
Avoid: Tue/Wed afternoons; all day Sunday.
Ladies: Welcome.
Ladies Day: Tuesday.
Green Fees: £20 Mon – Fri; £22 Sat/Sun/Bank Holidays.
Juveniles: Welcome.

Golf club just opened. Club Hire available; Caddy service also available during the summer months; Handicap certificate required for open competitions.
Clubhouse Hours: 8.00am – 12.00 midnight.
Clubhouse Dress: Casual.
Clubhouse Facilities: Bar and snacks; full catering from 4pm during the summer.
Open Competitions:
Waterford Crystal Open Week – July / Aug.

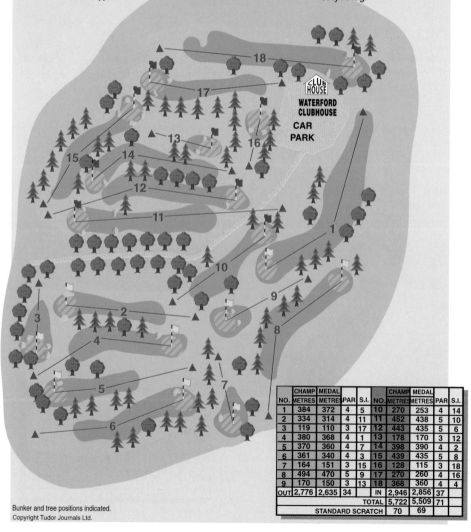

NO.	CHAMP METRES	MEDAL METRES	PAR	S.I.	NO.	CHAMP METRES	MEDAL METRES	PAR	S.I.
1	384	372	4	5	10	270	253	4	14
2	334	314	4	11	11	452	438	5	10
3	119	110	3	17	12	443	435	5	6
4	380	368	4	1	13	178	170	3	12
5	370	360	4	7	14	398	390	4	2
6	361	340	4	3	15	439	435	5	8
7	164	151	3	15	16	128	115	3	18
8	494	470	5	9	17	270	260	4	16
9	170	150	3	13	18	368	360	4	4
OUT	2,776	2,635	34		IN	2,946	2,856	37	
					TOTAL	5,722	5,509	71	
					STANDARD SCRATCH	70	69		

Bunker and tree positions indicated.

Rathmoyle, Abbeyleix, Portlaoise, Co Laois
Tel: (0502) 31450

LOCATION: Less than one mile north of the town on Stradbally road.
SECRETARY: Gerry O'Hara
Tel: (0502) 31138.

A parkland course which looks out over the picturesque Slieve Bloom Mountains. Mature trees and new spinneys increase the difficulty factor for most golfers.

COURSE INFORMATION

Par 70; SSS 68; Length 5,626 metres.
Visitors: Welcome to play on weekdays.
Opening Hours: Sunrise – Sunset.
Ladies: Welcome.
Green Fees: £8 Mon – Fri, £10 Sat/Sun, £6 with a member.
Juveniles: Only when accompanied by adults.

Clubhouse Hours: Fri, Sat, Sun in Winter. Most evenings in Summer..
Clubhouse Dress: Informal but respectable.
Clubhouse Facilities: General. Catering facilities and times; by prior arrangement.
Open Competitions: Open Week 2nd weekend & 3rd week of July; Open Hampers October and November.

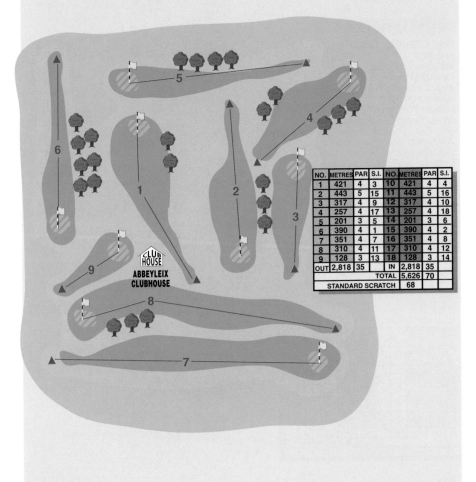

NO.	METRES	PAR	S.I.	NO.	METRES	PAR	S.I.
1	421	4	3	10	421	4	4
2	443	5	15	11	443	5	16
3	317	4	9	12	317	4	10
4	257	4	17	13	257	4	18
5	201	3	5	14	201	3	6
6	390	4	1	15	390	4	2
7	351	4	7	16	351	4	8
8	310	4	11	17	310	4	12
9	128	3	13	18	128	3	14
OUT	2,818	35		IN	2,818	35	
				TOTAL	5,626	70	
				STANDARD SCRATCH		68	

ABBEYLEIX CLUBHOUSE

Tree positions indicated.

**The Heath, Portlaoise, Co. Laois.
Tel: (0502) 46533.**

LOCATION: Three miles north east
Portlaoise town.
SECRETARY: Pat Carpendale.
Tel: (0502) 46622.
PROFESSIONAL: Eddie Doyle.
Tel: (0502) 46622.

This Par 71 course is playable all year round
and is exceptionally dry in wintertime. Set in
picturesque surroundings with views of the
rolling hills of Laois, the course incorporates
three natural lakes. Noted for its rough of
heather and gorse furze it is a challenge for
any golfer. The Heath Golf Club is the
seventh oldest Golf Club in Ireland, founded
in November 1889.

COURSE INFORMATION

**Par 72; SSS 70; Length 5,873
metres.**
Visitors: Welcome, please book.
Opening Hours: Sunrise – sunset.
Avoid: Weekends unless with
advance booking.
Ladies: Welcome.
Green Fees: £10 Mon – Fri; £17
Sat / Sun / Bank Holidays.
Juveniles: Welcome. Lessons
available by prior arrangement;
Club Hire available; Caddy service
available by prior arrangement;
telephone appointment required.
Clubhouse Hours: 10.30am –
11.30pm Mon – Sat; 10.30am –
11.00pm Sundays.
Clubhouse Dress: Casual (Neat).
Clubhouse Facilities:
Full catering facilities.
Open Competitions: Open Week
August. Other various days.

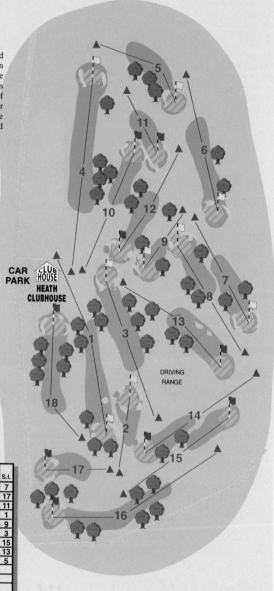

NO.	MEDAL METRES	GEN. METRES	PAR	S.I.	NO.	MEDAL METRES	GEN. METRES	PAR	S.I.
1	450	442	5	16	10	341	330	4	7
2	160	150	3	12	11	139	132	3	17
3	350	339	4	4	12	341	332	4	11
4	458	452	5	10	13	388	381	4	1
5	286	286	4	14	14	352	346	4	9
6	359	341	4	6	15	367	344	4	3
7	347	330	4	8	16	482	473	5	15
8	351	334	4	2	17	171	162	3	13
9	167	148	3	18	18	345	335	4	5
OUT	2,928	2,820	36		IN	2,926	2,835	35	
					TOTAL	5,854	5,655	71	
					STANDARD SCRATCH	70	69		

Tree positions indicated.

Knockinina, Mountrath, Co. Laois.
Tel: (0502) 32558.

LOCATION: Two miles Limerick side of Mountrath – just off the main Dublin/Limerick road.
SECRETARY: John Mulhare.

Extended to 18 holes in 1994, this is a pleasant course set on gently rolling land with the river Nore and an old Mill stream flowing through and coming into play on a number of holes. Lush fairways and good greens which are well bunkered make it an excellent test of golf.

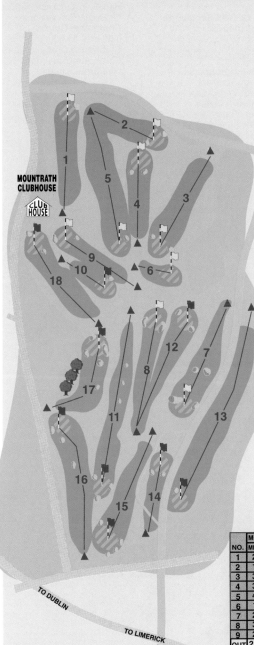

COURSE INFORMATION

Par 71; SSS 69; Length 5,493 metres.
Visitors: Welcome.
Ladies: Welcome Tuesdays.
Opening Hours: Sunrise – sunset.
Avoid: Saturday or Sunday mornings (check in clubhouse).
Green Fees: £10 per round Mon – Sun.
Clubhouse Hours: Evening service only, except for special occasions.
Clubhouse Dress: Casual.
Clubhouse Facilities: Catering facilities by prior arrangment.

NO.	MEDAL METRES	GEN. METRES	PAR	S.I.	NO.	MEDAL METRES	GEN. METRES	PAR	S.I.
1	288	374	4	3	10	127	117	3	17
2	154	142	3	12	11	445	430	5	11
3	352	298	4	1	12	373	350	4	2
4	347	329	4	6	13	463	440	5	8
5	440	418	5	13	14	177	140	3	5
6	111	105	3	16	15	290	268	4	9
7	270	250	4	18	16	378	360	4	4
8	337	320	4	7	17	269	248	4	15
9	287	283	4	10	18	285	265	4	14
OUT	2,686	2,519	35		IN	2,807	2,618	36	
					TOTAL	5,493	5,137	71	
					STANDARD SCRATCH	69	68		

PORTARLINGTON L E I N S T E R | LAOIS

Garryhinch, Portarlington, Co. Laois.
Tel: (0502) 23115.

LOCATION: Three miles from Portarlington.
HON. SECRETARY: Martin Turley
Tel: (0502) 23351.

The course has recently undergone extensive development from a nine hole course to an eighteen hole course. The new course was completed in November 1992 and provides a fresh test of skill and ability.

COURSE INFORMATION

Par 72; SSS 69; Length 5,628 metres.
Visitors: Welcome as members of societies and as individuals.
Opening Hours: 8.00am – sunset.
Avoid: Weekends.
Ladies: Tuesday.
Green Fees: Mon – Fri, £14 (+VAT); Saturday / Sunday / holidays £17 (+VAT) .

Juveniles: Welcome. Handicap Certificate required for Open Competitions.
Clubhouse Hours: 8.00am – 11.00pm.
Clubhouse Dress: Casual.
Clubhouse Facilities: By prior arrangement.

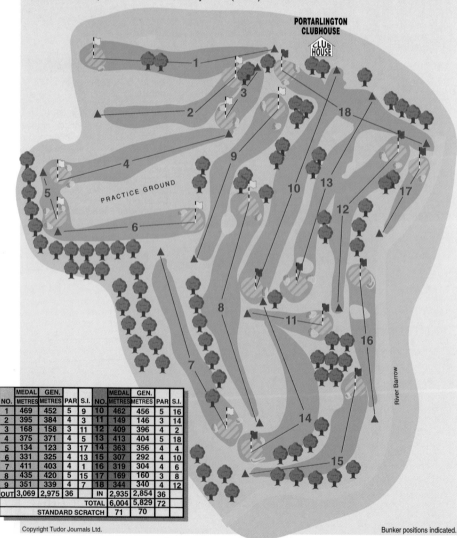

PORTARLINGTON CLUBHOUSE

River Barrow

NO.	MEDAL METRES	GEN. METRES	PAR	S.I.	NO.	MEDAL METRES	GEN. METRES	PAR	S.I.
1	469	452	5	9	10	462	456	5	16
2	395	384	4	3	11	149	146	3	14
3	168	158	3	11	12	409	396	4	2
4	375	371	4	5	13	413	404	5	18
5	134	123	3	17	14	363	356	4	4
6	331	325	4	13	15	307	292	4	10
7	411	403	4	1	16	319	304	4	6
8	435	420	5	15	17	169	160	3	8
9	351	339	4	7	18	344	340	4	12
OUT	3,069	2,975	36		IN	2,935	2,854	36	
					TOTAL	6,004	5,829	72	
	STANDARD SCRATCH		71	70					

Copyright Tudor Journals Ltd.

Bunker positions indicated.

90

Coulnaboul West,
Rathdowney,
Co. Laois.
Tel: (0505) 46170.

LOCATION: Less than one mile
east of Rathdowney.
SECRETARY: Sean Bolger.
Tel: (0505) 46233.

This inland course was redeveloped
to eighteen holes in 1997 and
provides the golfer with a varied
game, testing flexibility.

COURSE INFORMATION

**Par 70; SSS 69; Length
6,305 metres.**
Visitors: Welcome at all
times.
Opening Hours:
Sunrise – sunset.
Avoid: Bank Holidays,
Sundays, 1st week in July.
Ladies: Welcome.
Ladies Day: Wednesday.
Green Fees: £10 daily.

Juveniles: Welcome before
6.00pm.
Clubhouse Hours:
11.00am – 11.30pm.
Clubhouse Dress: Casual.
Clubhouse Facilities: Bar
open weekends and most
week nights; meals by prior
arrangement.
Open Competitions:
Intermediate Scratch Cup and
Open Week in July; Open
Hampers in November.

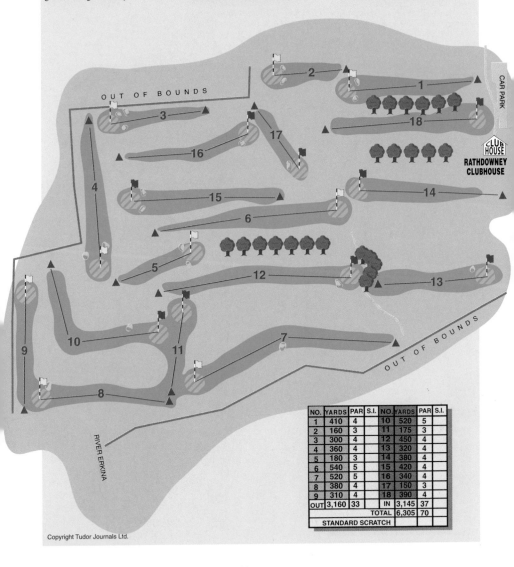

RATHDOWNEY
CLUBHOUSE

NO.	YARDS	PAR	S.I.	NO.	YARDS	PAR	S.I.
1	410	4		10	520	5	
2	160	3		11	175	3	
3	300	4		12	450	4	
4	360	4		13	320	4	
5	180	3		14	380	4	
6	540	5		15	420	4	
7	520	5		16	340	4	
8	380	4		17	150	3	
9	310	4		18	390	4	
OUT	3,160	33		IN	3,145	37	
				TOTAL	6,305	70	
STANDARD SCRATCH							

COUNTY LONGFORD L E I N S T E R LONGFORD

**Glack, Dublin Road,
Longford, Co. Longford**
Tel: (043) 46310.

LOCATION: Dublin Road,
Longford.
SECRETARY: Mark Connellan.
ARCHITECT: E. Hackett

An elevated parkland course,
overlooking Longford Town and
surrounding countryside.

COURSE INFORMATION

**Par 70; SSS 69; Length
6,044 yards.**
Visitors: Welcome.
Opening Hours: Sunrise –
Sunset (closed mon. in winter)
Avoid: Weekends and
Tuesdays.
Ladies: Welcome.
Ladies: Tuesday.
Green Fees: £10 Mon – Fri
(£8 with member); £12
Sat/Sun (£10 with member on
a one to one basis).

Juveniles: Welcome. Lessons
available; Club Hire and caddy
cars also available.
Clubhouse Hours: 12noon –
11pm.
Clubhouse Dress: Neat /
Casual.
Clubhouse Facilities: Meals
snacks and bar.
Open Competitions: Open
week July / August.

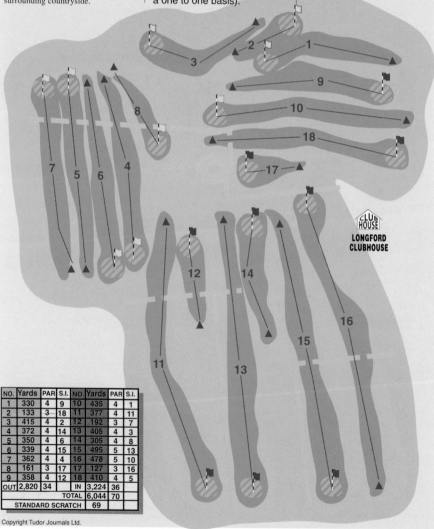

LONGFORD
CLUBHOUSE

NO.	Yards	PAR	S.I.	NO.	Yards	PAR	S.I.
1	330	4	9	10	435	4	1
2	133	3	18	11	377	4	11
3	415	4	2	12	192	3	7
4	372	4	14	13	405	4	3
5	350	4	6	14	305	4	8
6	339	4	15	15	495	5	13
7	362	4	4	16	478	5	10
8	161	3	17	17	127	3	16
9	358	4	12	18	410	4	5
OUT	2,820	34		IN	3,224	36	
				TOTAL	6,044	70	
	STANDARD SCRATCH				69		

Copyright Tudor Journals Ltd.

**Townparks, Ardee,
Co. Louth.
Tel: (041) 53227.**

LOCATION: Just north of Ardee town.
SECRETARY: Kevin McCarthy.
Tel: (041) 53227.
ARCHITECT: Mr Eddie Hackett.

A very fair test of golf and also a very pleasant walk with some beautiful old trees on this parkland course.

COURSE INFORMATION

**Par 69; SSS 69;
Length 6,046 yards.
Visitors:** Welcome.
Avoid: Sat & Sun mornings, Societies only.
Ladies: Welcome.
Green Fees: £17 Mon – Fri. No Green Fees Sat & Sun.
Juveniles: Welcome Mondays. Any other time adult company. Caddy Service

by prior arrangements.
Clubhouse Hours: 10.00am – 11.30pm.
Clubhouse Dress: Casual.
Clubhouse Facilities: Catering facilities available at all times.
Open Competitions: Several dates throughout year. Open Week – June.

NO.	CHAMP YARDS	MEDAL YARDS	PAR	S.I.	NO.	CHAMP YARDS	MEDAL YARDS	PAR	S.I.
1	354	349	4	6	10	402	384	4	3
2	176	162	3	14	11	336	329	4	15
3	301	291	4	18	12	203	188	3	9
4	369	356	4	8	13	487	478	5	13
5	154	147	3	10	14	217	203	3	7
6	421	411	4	2	15	365	356	4	11
7	373	364	4	4	16	423	413	4	1
8	503	499	5	16	17	387	374	4	5
9	362	354	4	12	18	507	501	5	17
OUT	3,013	2,933	35		IN	3,327	3,226	36	
					TOTAL	6,340	6,159	71	
					STANDARD SCRATCH	70	69		

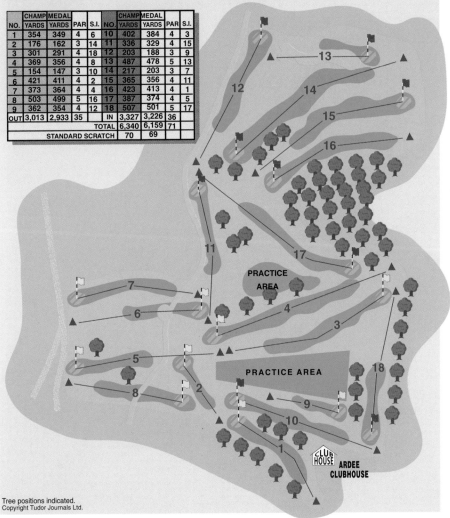

Tree positions indicated.
Copyright Tudor Journals Ltd.

Balltray, Co. Louth.
Tel: (041) 22329.

LOCATION: Five miles north east Drogheda.
SECRETARY: Michael Delany.
Tel: (041) 22329.
Professional: Paddy McGuirk.
Tel: (041) 22444.
ARCHITECT: Tom Simpson.

A championship links which can be enjoyed by every category of golfer which is not as well known as some of the other links courses. Balltray's demands are stern but its rewards are many, not least in the fun and enjoyment it evokes and the sense of freshness that prevails.

COURSE INFORMATION

Par 73; SSS 72; Length 6,783 metres.
Visitors: Welcome by prior arrangement.
Opening Hours: Winter 8.30am – Sunset; Summer 7.30am – Sunset.
Avoid: Weekends and Tuesdays.
Ladies: By prior arrangement.
Green Fees: £40 Mon – Fri; £50 Sat & Sun.
Juveniles: Restricted.

Lessons available by prior arrangement; Club Hire available; Caddy service available by prior arrangement; telephone appointment required.
Clubhouse Hours: 10.30am – 12.00 midnight.
Clubhouse Dress: Casual.
Clubhouse Facilities: 9.00am – 8.00pm (winter); 9.00am – 10.00pm (summer).

NO.	CHAMP METRES	MEDAL METRES	PAR	S.I.	NO.	CHAMP METRES	MEDAL METRES	PAR	S.I.
1	433	423	4	3	10	398	388	4	4
2	462	476	5	17	11	481	476	5	16
3	544	534	5	9	12	410	410	4	2
4	344	334	4	15	13	421	408	4	6
5	158	148	3	13	14	332	322	4	12
6	531	521	5	7	15	152	142	3	18
7	163	453	3	5	16	388	375	4	8
8	407	397	4	11	17	179	169	3	10
9	419	409	4	1	18	541	527	5	14
OUT	3,481	3,395	37		IN	3,302	3,302	36	
					TOTAL	6,783	6,783	73	
					STANDARD SCRATCH	72	72		

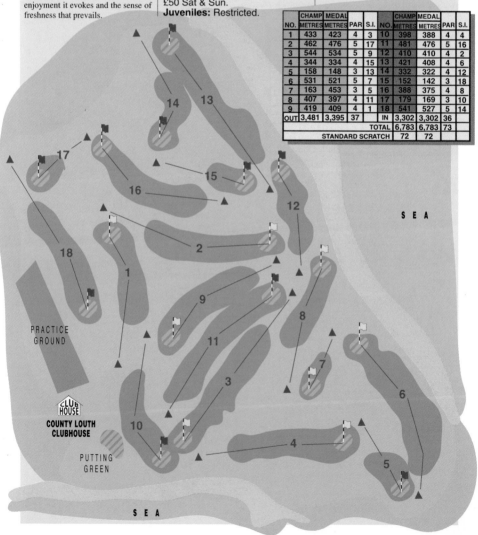

**Blackrock, Dundalk,
Co. Louth.
Tel: (042) 21731/22218.
Fax: (042) 22022.**

LOCATION: Three miles south of
Dundalk at Blackrock Village.
SECRETARY: Joe Carroll.
Tel: (042) 21731.
PROFESSIONAL: James Cassidy.
Tel: (042) 22102.
ARCHITECTS: Dave Thomas
& Peter Allis.

A difficult but fair course offering
panoramic views of Dundalk town
and Dundalk Bay with the backdrop
of the Cooley Mountains.

COURSE INFORMATION

**Par 72; SSS 72; Length
6,160 metres.
Visitors:** Welcome.
Opening Hours: Sunrise –
Sunset.
Avoid: Tuesdays and
Sundays. Prior appointment
preferable but not essential.
Ladies: Welcome except
Tuesdays and Sundays.
Green Fees: £16 Mon – Fri;
£20 Sat/Sun/Bank Holidays.
Juveniles: Before 6.00pm,
not Tuesdays or weekends.

Lessons available by prior
arrangement; Club hire
available; Caddy service
available by prior
arrangement.
Clubhouse Hours: Sunrise
to midnight.
Clubhouse Dress: Informal.
Clubhouse Facilities:
Snacks and full meals at
any time.
Open Competitions: May
& July.

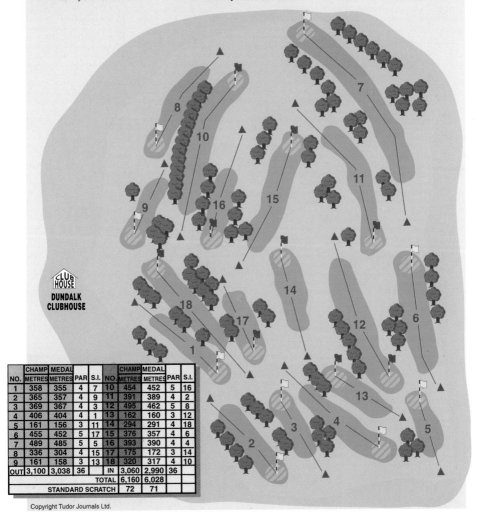

DUNDALK
CLUBHOUSE

NO.	CHAMP METRES	MEDAL METRES	PAR	S.I.	NO.	CHAMP METRES	MEDAL METRES	PAR	S.I.
1	358	355	4	7	10	454	452	5	16
2	365	357	4	9	11	391	389	4	2
3	369	367	4	3	12	495	462	5	8
4	406	404	4	1	13	162	160	3	12
5	161	156	3	11	14	294	291	4	18
6	455	452	5	17	15	376	357	4	6
7	489	485	5	5	16	393	390	4	4
8	336	304	4	15	17	175	172	3	14
9	161	158	3	13	18	320	317	4	10
OUT	3,100	3,038	36		IN	3,060	2,990	36	
					TOTAL	6,160	6,028		
	STANDARD SCRATCH					72	71		

Copyright Tudor Journals Ltd.

Greenore, Co. Louth.
Tel: (042) 73212.
Fax: (042) 73678.

LOCATION: Travelling form
Dublin – proceed through
Drogheda and Dundalk and take
the first turn right on the Newry
road out of Dundalk and proceed
to Greenore – fifteen minutes.
SECRETARY: Roisin Daly.
Tel: (042) 73212/73678.
ARCHITECT: Eddie Hackett.

An inland course with a links nature
on the shores of Carlingford Lough.
The course enjoys scenic views of
both the Lough and the Mountains of
Mourne. An unusual feature are the

tall pine trees, a rare sight on a
semi-links course, which come into
play on seven holes. The 14th or "pigs
back" is the most famous hole in
Greenore, a par 3 to an elevated
green.

COURSE INFORMATION

**Par 71; SSS 71; Length
6,514 yards.**
Visitors: Welcome to play
weekdays and weekends, but
appointment is recommended for
weekends.
Opening Hours: 8.00am (or
earlier by appointment) – Sunset.
Green Fees: £14 Mon – Fri

(£8 with a member); £20 Sat &
Sun & Ban Holidays (£12 with
a member). Students half
price.
Clubhouse Hours:
9am – 6pm (winter);
8am – 11.30pm (summer).
Clubhouse Dress: Informal.
Clubhouse Facilities: All days.
Open Competitions: Open
Week – 10th/19th July;
Carlingford Lough Classic –
August.

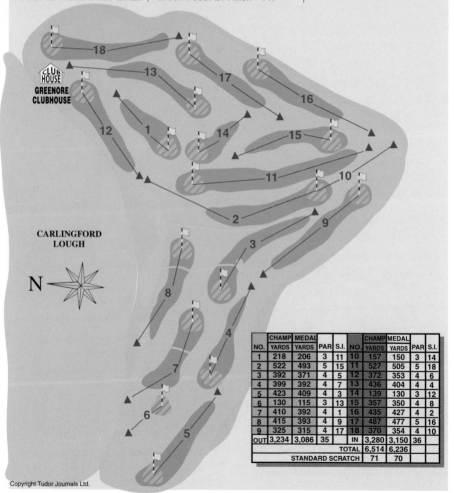

NO.	CHAMP YARDS	MEDAL YARDS	PAR	S.I.	NO.	CHAMP YARDS	MEDAL YARDS	PAR	S.I.
1	218	206	3	11	10	157	150	3	14
2	522	493	5	15	11	527	505	5	18
3	392	371	4	5	12	372	353	4	6
4	399	392	4	7	13	436	404	4	4
5	423	409	4	3	14	139	130	3	12
6	130	115	3	13	15	357	350	4	8
7	410	392	4	1	16	435	427	4	2
8	415	393	4	9	17	487	477	5	16
9	325	315	4	17	18	370	354	4	10
OUT	3,234	3,086	35		IN	3,280	3,150	36	
					TOTAL	6,514	6,236		
					STANDARD SCRATCH	71	70		

Killin Park Golf & Country Club, Killin, Dundalk, Co. Louth. Tel: (042) 39303.

LOCATION: Three miles from Dundalk town centre, off the Castleblayney road.
MANAGER: Noel Kilcoyne.
ARCHITECT: Eddie Hacket.

Killin Park is a privately owned course situated in rolling parkland with mature trees and scenic views of the Mourne Mountains. Bordered by Killin Wood and the Castletown River, this exceptionally free draining course has American style greens. Noted for its 9th hole which resmbles the 10th at the Belfry, this course offers a challenge even to the most experienced golfer.

COURSE INFORMATION

Par 69; SSS 65; Length 5,293 yards.
Visitors: Welcome all the time.
Ladies: Welcome Tuesdays.
Green Fees: £10 Mon – Fri; £14 weekends & public holidays.
Juveniles: Welcome. Under 13's must be accompanied by an adult.

Clubhouse Hours: Sunrise – sunset.
Clubhouse Dress: Neat dress.
Clubhouse Facilities: Bar snacks available everyday from 8.30am. Full catering facilities by prior arrangement. Club hire available.
Open Competitions: Various Open Days throughout the year, telephone Club for details.

NO.	CHAMP YARDS	MEDAL YARDS	PAR	S.I.	NO.	CHAMP YARDS	MEDAL YARDS	PAR	S.I.
1	114	109	3	16	10	280	277	4	17
2	360	351	4	3	11	161	161	3	4
3	196	177	3	5	12	177	160	3	6
4	358	354	4	1	13	476	473	5	8
5	310	305	4	14	14	396	382	4	2
6	312	307	4	9	15	310	310	4	11
7	492	487	5	10	16	291	291	4	7
8	280	268	4	18	17	160	160	3	15
9	261	244	4	13	18	359	342	4	12
OUT	2,683	2,602	35		IN	2,610	2,556	34	
					TOTAL	5,293	5,158	69	
					STANDARD SCRATCH	65	64		

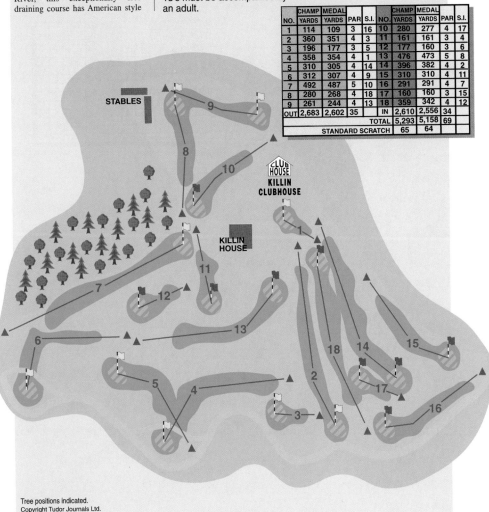

STABLES

CLUB HOUSE
KILLIN CLUBHOUSE

KILLIN HOUSE

Tree positions indicated.
Copyright Tudor Journals Ltd.

Ashbourne Golf Club,
Ashbourne, Co Meath.
Tel: (01) 835 2005.

LOCATION: One mile from
Ashbourne, 12 miles (20 mins
drive) from Dublin.
SECRETARY: Ronnie Sheehan.
Tel: (01) 835 2005.
ARCHITECT: Des Smyth.

Undulating parkland course with
great variety incorporated in design.
Water comes into play at eight holes
in the form of the Broadmeadow
River and a number

of lakes on the course. A fine blend of
established and younger trees contributes
to the players overall enjoyment of this
peaceful countryside course.

COURSE INFORMATION

Par 71; SSS 70; Length
6,420 yards.
Visitors: Welcome Mon – Fri and
Sat/Sun afternoons.
Opening Hours: 9.00am – dusk.
Ladies: No restrictions.
Green Fees: £17 (inc. VAT).

Juveniles: Must be
accompanied by an adult.
Clubhouse Hours:
Normal licensing hours.
Clubhouse Dress:
Neat casual dress required.
Clubhouse Facilities:
Lounge bar, bar food and full
restaurant.
Open Competitions:
Regularly during summer
months – Open Week mid
June.

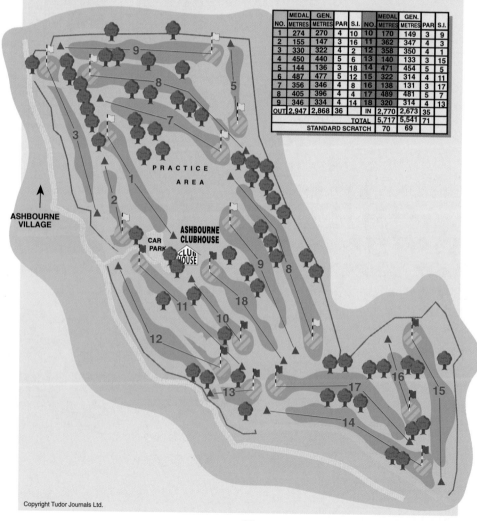

NO.	MEDAL METRES	GEN. METRES	PAR	S.I.	NO.	MEDAL METRES	GEN. METRES	PAR	S.I.
1	274	270	4	10	10	170	149	3	9
2	155	147	3	16	11	362	347	4	3
3	330	322	4	2	12	358	350	4	1
4	450	440	5	6	13	140	133	3	15
5	144	136	3	18	14	471	454	5	5
6	487	477	5	12	15	322	314	4	11
7	356	346	4	8	16	138	131	3	17
8	405	396	4	4	17	489	481	5	7
9	346	334	4	14	18	320	314	4	13
OUT	2,947	2,868	36		IN	2,770	2,673	35	
					TOTAL	5,717	5,541	71	
					STANDARD SCRATCH	70	69		

ASHBOURNE
VILLAGE

PRACTICE
AREA

ASHBOURNE
CLUBHOUSE
CAR
PARK

Thomastown, Dunshaughlin, Co. Meath.
Tel: (01) 8250021.
Fax (01) 8250400.

LOCATION: 1 mile from Dunshaughlin – off Ratoath road.
HON. SECRETARY: J. Rynd.
Tel: (01) 8250021.
ARCHITECT: R. J. Browne.
OFFICE MANAGER: David Dalton.

A new 27 hole course which opened in June 1990. It is situated in a beautiful parkland setting, with a memorable 1st hole playing over the lake. There is also a driving range available and a new nine hole course was opened in August 1992.

COURSE INFORMATION

27 Hole: Par 72; SSS 72;
Length 6,787 yards.

Visitors: Welcome any day.
Opening Hours: Sunrise – Sunset.
Avoid: Saturday and Sunday mornings (18 hole course only).
Ladies: Welcome.
Green Fees: £16 Mon – Fri; £22 Sat /Sun.
Juveniles: Must be accompanied by an adult. Telephone appointment required for weekend play.
Clubhouse Hours: 8.00am – midnight.
Clubhouse Dress: Casual daylight hours; No shorts or jeans.

Clubhouse Facilities: Dining room, snack bar and a la carte available all day. Pro Shop, Services professional, SOG practice balls, driving range & lessons Tel: 8259793
Open Competitions: Various open days in May, June and July; Open week – August.

COURSE A

NO.	CHAMP YARDS	MEDAL YARDS	PAR	S.I.	NO.	CHAMP YARDS	MEDAL YARDS	PAR	S.I.
1	558	464	5	9	10	503	470	5	18
2	170	153	3	7	11	397	383	4	12
3	580	536	5	5	12	394	383	4	8
4	158	133	3	15	13	164	153	3	16
5	416	383	4	1	14	432	416	4	4
6	383	366	4	11	15	400	388	4	2
7	421	410	4	3	16	186	175	3	10
8	361	328	4	13	17	378	361	4	14
9	462	443	5	17	18	567	525	5	6
OUT	3,509	3,216	37		IN	3,421	3,254	36	
					TOTAL	6,930	6,470	73	
					STANDARD SCRATCH	73	71		

COURSE B

NO.	CHAMP YARDS	MEDAL YARDS	PAR	S.I.	NO.	CHAMP YARDS	MEDAL YARDS	PAR	S.I.
1	503	470	5	18	10	353	332	4	13
2	397	383	4	12	11	184	170	3	7
3	394	383	4	8	12	522	509	5	11
4	164	153	3	16	13	377	344	4	9
5	432	416	4	4	14	437	421	4	1
6	400	388	4	2	15	345	331	4	15
7	186	175	3	10	16	140	132	3	17
8	387	361	4	14	17	394	383	4	3
9	567	525	5	6	18	386	364	4	5
OUT	3,421	3,254	36		IN	3,138	2,986	35	
					TOTAL	6,559	6,240	71	
					STANDARD SCRATCH	71	70		

COURSE C

NO.	CHAMP YARDS	MEDAL YARDS	PAR	S.I.	NO.	CHAMP YARDS	MEDAL YARDS	PAR	S.I.
1	353	332	4	14	10	558	464	4	18
2	184	170	3	8	11	170	153	4	12
3	522	509	5	12	12	580	536	3	8
4	377	344	4	10	13	158	133	5	14
5	437	421	4	2	14	416	383	4	4
6	345	331	4	16	15	383	366	4	10
7	140	132	3	18	16	421	410	3	6
8	394	383	4	4	17	361	328	5	16
9	386	364	4	6	18	462	443	4	2
OUT	3,138	2,986	35		IN	3,509	3,207	36	
					TOTAL	6,647	6,193	72	
					STANDARD SCRATCH	72	70		

COURSE A

BLACK BUSH CLUBHOUSE

CLUB HOUSE

COURSE A

COURSE C

COURSE B

BLACK BUSH CLUBHOUSE

CLUB HOUSE

HEADFORT

Kells, Co. Meath.
Tel: (046) 40146.
Fax: (046) 49282.

LOCATION: Kells/Navan road – within one mile of town.
HON. SECRETARY: Brendan McCabe.
Tel: (046) 40146.
PROFESSIONAL: Brendan McGovern.
Tel: (046) 40639.

Generally accepted as a first class parkland course, the Headfort Club is set in the rolling countryside of Kells.

COURSE INFORMATION

Par 72; SSS 71; Length 6,007 metres.
Visitors: Welcome.
Opening Hours: Sunrise – Sunset.
Avoid: Weekends and Tue.
Ladies: Welcome.
Green Fees: £18 Mon – Fri; £22 Sat/Sun/Bank Holidays.
Juveniles: Must be accompanied by an adult (adults with juveniles must give way). Lessons available by prior arrangement; Club hire available; Caddy service available by prior arrangments; Telephone appointment required.
Clubhouse Hours: 9.00am – 11.30pm.
Clubhouse Dress: Casual.
Clubhouse Facilities: Full facilities in new clubhouse.

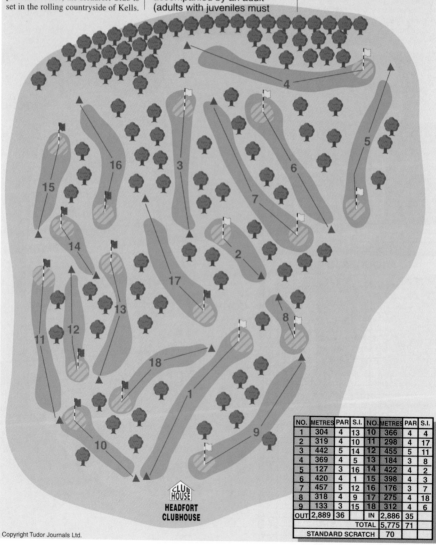

HEADFORT CLUBHOUSE

Copyright Tudor Journals Ltd.

NO.	METRES	PAR	S.I.	NO.	METRES	PAR	S.I.
1	304	4	13	10	366	4	4
2	319	4	10	11	298	4	17
3	442	5	14	12	455	5	11
4	369	4	5	13	184	3	8
5	127	3	16	14	422	4	2
6	420	4	1	15	398	4	3
7	457	5	12	16	176	3	7
8	318	4	9	17	275	4	18
9	133	3	15	18	312	4	6
OUT	2,889	36		IN	2,886	35	
				TOTAL	5,775	71	
				STANDARD SCRATCH	70		

**Gallow, Kilcock,
Co. Meath.
Tel: (01) 6287592/6287283.**

LOCATION: South Meath.
SECRETARY: Sean Dowling.
Tel: (01) 6242439/6244242.
PROFESSIONAL: Gerard Canning.
Tel: (01) 6287283.
ARCHITECT: Eddie Hackett.

A relatively easy course for experienced players. Large greens and tees. Generally flat but slopes into a centre stream that features in the course. The club has 400 members and all visitors are welcome. An extra

nine holes, recently constructed to the west of the 6th green, create more of a challenge now. What is shown as the 7th, 8th, and 9th, are now the 16th, 17th, and 18th. The new nine holes (not shown in the diagram below) are similar to the original nine holes and include two par 5's.

COURSE INFORMATION

Par 71; SSS 70; Length 5,775 metres.
Visitors: Welcome except Sunday morning. Saturday by prior arrangement.
Opening Hours: Sunrise – sunset.

Ladies: Welcome except Sunday morning and Saturday afternoon.
Green Fees: £9 Mon – Fri; £10 Sat / Sun; £4 Juveniles.
Juveniles: Welcome except Sunday morning (must be accompanied by an adult).
Clubhouse Dress: Neat.
Clubhouse Facilities: Bar open everyday. Catering by prior arrangement.
Open Competitions: Open Week – July. Various other Open Days throughout the summer.

NO.	YARDS	PAR	S.I.	NO.	YARDS	PAR	S.I.
1	288	4	10	10	304	4	9
2	285	4	13	11	285	4	14
3	442	5	11	12	385	4	2
4	369	4	5	13	369	4	6
5	127	3	15	14	127	3	16
6	413	4	1	15	444	5	12
7	176	3	7	16	176	3	8
8	275	4	17	17	275	4	18
9	312	4	3	18	312	4	4
OUT	2,687	35		IN	2,677	36	
				TOTAL	5,364	71	
	STANDARD SCRATCH			68			

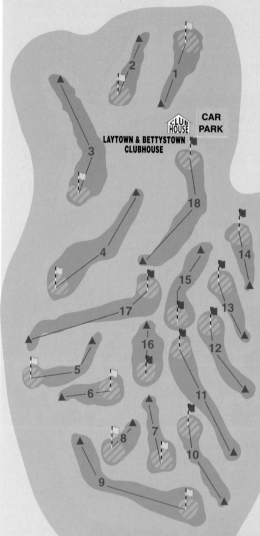

Bettystown, Co. Meath.
Tel: (041) 27170/27534/27563.

LOCATION: Thirty miles north of Dublin.
SECRETARY: Stella Garvey-Hoey.
Tel: (041) 27170.
PROFESSIONAL: Robert J Browne.
Tel: (041) 28793.

This is a traditional links course with the reputation of a tough par of 70. It has produced many fine players, the best known of whom is Des Smyth.

COURSE INFORMATION

Par 70; SSS 69; Length 5,652 metres.
Visitors: Welcome Mon – Fri.
Opening Hours: 8.30am – Sunset.
Avoid: Weekends.
Ladies: Welcome.
Ladies Days: Mon. and Thurs.
Green Fees: £21 Mon – Fri; £26 Sat/Sun.
Juveniles: Welcome – must be accompanied by an adult before 6pm. Lessons available by prior arrangement; Club Hire available.
Clubhouse Hours: 10.30am – licencing hours.
Clubhouse Dress: Neat Dress.
Clubhouse Facilities: Full bar and catering facilities available everyday.
Open Competitions: Open weeks June, July & August. Booking through office only – Tel: (041) 27170.

NO.	MEDAL METRES	GEN. METRES	PAR	S.I.	NO.	MEDAL METRES	GEN. METRES	PAR	S.I.
1	292	272	4	13	10	347	343	4	5
2	310	306	4	10	11	420	420	4	1
3	373	337	4	3	12	357	348	4	4
4	440	433	5	14	13	313	310	4	16
5	335	329	4	8	14	150	143	3	17
6	169	167	3	15	15	359	353	4	7
7	363	363	4	6	16	174	174	3	9
8	164	159	3	11	17	278	274	4	18
9	372	322	4	2	18	436	429	5	12
OUT	2,818	2,688	35		IN	2,834	2,794	35	
					TOTAL	5,652	5,482	70	
					STANDARD SCRATCH	69			

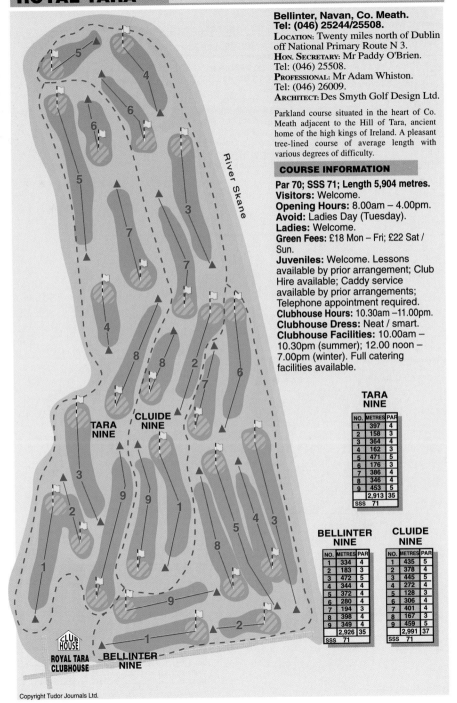

Bellinter, Navan, Co. Meath.
Tel: (046) 25244/25508.
LOCATION: Twenty miles north of Dublin
off National Primary Route N 3.
HON. SECRETARY: Mr Paddy O'Brien.
Tel: (046) 25508.
PROFESSIONAL: Mr Adam Whiston.
Tel: (046) 26009.
ARCHITECT: Des Smyth Golf Design Ltd.

Parkland course situated in the heart of Co.
Meath adjacent to the Hill of Tara, ancient
home of the high kings of Ireland. A pleasant
tree-lined course of average length with
various degrees of difficulty.

COURSE INFORMATION

Par 70; SSS 71; Length 5,904 metres.
Visitors: Welcome.
Opening Hours: 8.00am – 4.00pm.
Avoid: Ladies Day (Tuesday).
Ladies: Welcome.
Green Fees: £18 Mon – Fri; £22 Sat /
Sun.
Juveniles: Welcome. Lessons
available by prior arrangement; Club
Hire available; Caddy service
available by prior arrangements;
Telephone appointment required.
Clubhouse Hours: 10.30am –11.00pm.
Clubhouse Dress: Neat / smart.
Clubhouse Facilities: 10.00am –
10.30pm (summer); 12.00 noon –
7.00pm (winter). Full catering
facilities available.

TARA NINE

NO.	METRES	PAR
1	397	4
2	158	3
3	364	4
4	162	3
5	471	5
6	176	3
7	386	4
8	346	4
9	453	5
	2,913	35
SSS	71	

BELLINTER NINE

NO.	METRES	PAR
1	334	4
2	183	3
3	472	5
4	344	4
5	372	4
6	280	4
7	194	3
8	398	4
9	349	4
	2,926	35
SSS	71	

CLUIDE NINE

NO.	METRES	PAR
1	435	5
2	378	4
3	445	5
4	272	4
5	128	3
6	306	4
7	401	4
8	167	3
9	459	5
	2,991	37
SSS	71	

TRIM

Newtownmoynagh, Trim, Co. Meath.
Tel: (046) 31463.

LOCATION: Three miles from Trim on Longwood road
SECRETARY: Mr John Ennis.
Tel: (046) 31463 / 31825.
ARCHITECT: E. Hackett.

Originally a pleasing nine hole course which has been recently developed into eighteen holes. Work was completed on the course in 1990.

COURSE INFORMATION

Par 73; SSS 72; Length 6,720 yards.
Visitors: Welcome.
Opening Hours: 8.00am – Sunset.
Avoid: Thursday.
Ladies: Welcome.
Ladies Day: Thursday.
Green Fees: £15 Mon – Fri; £18 Sat/Sun/Bank Holidays.
Societies; Mon – Fri £14; Sat/Sun/Bank Holidays £17.

Juveniles: Welcome.
Clubhouse Hours: 10.30am – 11.30pm.
Clubhouse Dress: Casual.
Clubhouse Facilities: Full catering facilities.

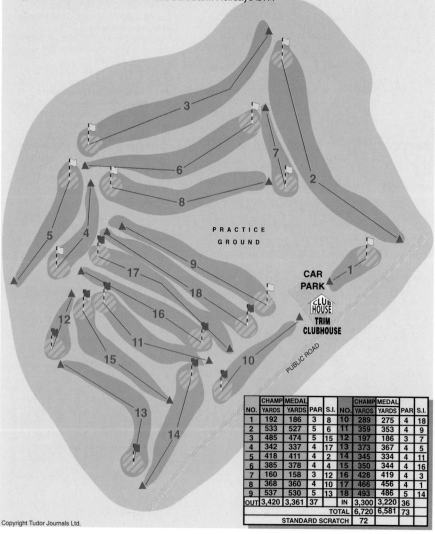

NO.	CHAMP YARDS	MEDAL YARDS	PAR	S.I.	NO.	CHAMP YARDS	MEDAL YARDS	PAR	S.I.
1	192	186	3	8	10	289	275	4	18
2	533	527	5	6	11	359	353	4	9
3	485	474	5	15	12	197	186	3	7
4	342	337	4	17	13	373	367	4	5
5	418	411	4	2	14	345	334	4	11
6	385	378	4	4	15	350	344	4	16
7	160	158	3	12	16	428	419	4	3
8	368	360	4	10	17	466	456	4	1
9	537	530	5	13	18	493	486	5	14
OUT	3,420	3,361	37		IN	3,300	3,220	36	
					TOTAL	6,720	6,581	73	
					STANDARD SCRATCH	72			

The Glenns, Birr, Co. Offaly.
Tel: (0509) 20082.

LOCATION: Two miles west
of Birr.
SECRETARY: Mr. Jim McMenamin.

Undulating parkland course with
sandy sub-soil, the greatest
difficulties being "blind" shots and
the strategic placing of pines.

COURSE INFORMATION

**Par 70; SSS 70; Length
5,727 metres.**
Visitors: Welcome, limited
to 11.00am – 12.00 noon on
Sundays.
Opening Hours: Sunrise –
sunset.
Avoid: Weekends if possible.
Ladies: Welcome.

Green Fees: £12 Mon – Fri;
£14 per round Sat / Sun /
Bank Holidays.
Juveniles: Welcome.
Clubhouse Hours:
10.00am – 12.00 midnight.
Clubhouse Dress: Casual.
Clubhouse Facilities: By
prior arrangement.

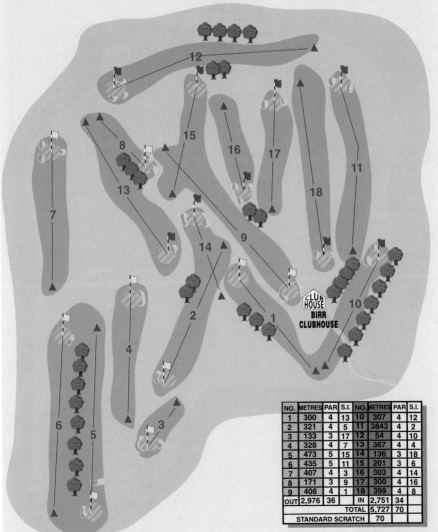

NO.	METRES	PAR	S.I.	NO.	METRES	PAR	S.I.
1	300	4	13	10	307	4	12
2	321	4	5	11	3843	4	2
3	133	3	17	12	54	4	10
4	328	4	7	13	367	4	4
5	473	5	15	14	136	3	18
6	435	5	11	15	201	3	6
7	407	4	3	16	303	4	14
8	171	3	9	17	300	4	16
9	408	4	1	18	399	4	8
OUT	2,976	36		IN	2,751	34	
				TOTAL	5,727	70	
				STANDARD SCRATCH	70		

Copyright Tudor Journals Ltd.

Castle Barna Golf Club,
Daingean, Co. Offaly.
Tel: (0506) 53384.

LOCATION: 8 miles south of main Dublin to Galway road (N6). One hour from Dublin.
SECRETARY: Evelyn Mangan.
Tel: (0506) 53384.
ARCHITECT: Alan Duggan.

18 hole parkland course, with rolling parkland and natural water hazards making it an interesting course to play. The 9th hole (par 3) set alongside the Grand Canal is a real challenge.

COURSE INFORMATION

Par 72; SSS 69; Length 6,200 yards.
Visitors: Welcome.
Opening Hours: Sunrise – sunset.
Ladies: Welcome every day.
Green Fees: Weekdays £7; weekends £10.
Juveniles: Weekdays £3; weekends £4.
Clubhouse Hours: 8.00am – sunset.

Clubhouse Dress: Neat.
Clubhouse Facilities: Coffee shop, golf clubs for hire, golf shop, bar.
Open Competitions: June, July and August.

NO.	MEDAL METRES	FWARD METRES	PAR	S.I.	NO.	MEDAL METRES	FWARD METRES	PAR	S.I.
1	326	310	4	6	10	425	405	5	15
2	277	275	4	14	11	170	146	3	13
3	163	153	3	8	12	296	290	4	9
4	268	255	4	12	13	270	245	4	17
5	158	155	3	4	14	325	305	4	7
6	478	458	5	10	15	365	345	4	1
7	402	390	5	16	16	456	435	5	11
8	375	365	4	2	17	384	374	4	3
9	119	114	3	18	18	393	373	4	5
OUT	2,566	2,475	35		IN	3,084	2,918	37	
					TOTAL	5,650	5,393	72	
					STANDARD SCRATCH	69	68		

CASTLE BARNA CLUBHOUSE

GRAND CANAL

Bunker and tree positions indicated.
Copyright Tudor Journals Ltd.

Kishawanny, Edenderry,
Co. Offaly.
Tel: (0405) 31072.

LOCATION: Just under a mile from the town centre.
SECRETARY: Niall Dempsey.
Tel: (0405) 31575.
ARCHITECT: Havers (original nine hole). E. Hackett (new nine holes).

Unique in so much that it is built almost entirely on fen peat. An attractive 18 hole course, the par 3's in particular being challenging. Trees and traps are ideally located.

COURSE INFORMATION

Par 72; SSS 72; Length 6,029 metres.
Visitors: Welcome (Weekends Limited).
Opening Hours: 8.30am – Sunset.
Avoid: Thursdays (Ladies Comp. Day).
Ladies: Welcome.
Green Fees: Weekend £14 (£12 with member) Weekday £12 (£10 with member). Reductions for groups and societies.

Juveniles: Must be accompanied by an adult.
Clubhouse Hours: 11.00am – 11.00pm March – October.
Clubhouse Dress: Casual.
Clubhouse Facilities: Full bar & catering facilities.
Open Competitions: First week in August & most Bank Holidays.

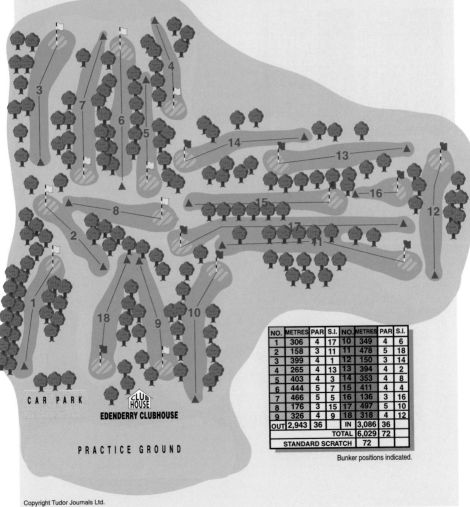

CAR PARK

EDENDERRY CLUBHOUSE

PRACTICE GROUND

NO.	METRES	PAR	S.I.	NO.	METRES	PAR	S.I.
1	306	4	17	10	349	4	6
2	158	3	11	11	478	5	18
3	399	4	1	12	150	3	14
4	265	4	13	13	394	4	2
5	403	4	3	14	353	4	8
6	444	5	7	15	411	4	4
7	466	5	5	16	136	3	16
8	176	3	15	17	497	5	10
9	326	4	9	18	318	4	12
OUT	2,943	36		IN	3,086	36	
				TOTAL	6,029	72	
				STANDARD SCRATCH		72	

Bunker positions indicated.

Esker Hills Golf & Country Club, Ballykilmurray, Tullamore, Co. Offaly.
Tel: (0506) 55999.
Fax: (0506) 55989.

LOCATION: Three miles from Tullamore town, off the main Tullamore – Clara road.
DIRECTOR: Donal Molloy.
Tel: (0506) 55999/(088) 677567.
ARCHITECT: C. O'Connor Jnr.

The course has a series of valleys and plateaux, part of the Esker Riada which together with the natural lakes and woodlands makes for an amazing variety of challenging golf holes. "A great test of golf to all who care to challenge it."

COURSE INFORMATION

Par 71; SSS 71; Length 6,669 yards.
Visitors: Welcome every day.
Avoid: Saturdays & Sundays as time sheet is used.
Opening Hours:
Summer: 8am – sunset.
Winter: 9am – 5pm.

Green Fees: £15 weekdays; £20 weekends.
Juveniles: £8 per round. Must be accompanied by an adult. After 2.00pm only during weekends.
Clubhouse Dress: Smart / Casual.
Additional Facilities: Canal cruising and fishing, Clay pigeon shooting and Equestrian centre.

NO.	MEDAL METRES	GEN. METRES	PAR	S.I.	NO.	MEDAL METRES	GEN. METRES	PAR	S.I.
1	493	475	5	17	10	307	299	4	18
2	355	337	4	11	11	390	371	4	4
3	490	459	4	1	12	396	349	4	6
4	393	358	4	5	13	201	166	3	16
5	171	161	3	15	14	360	344	4	10
6	535	511	5	9	15	191	176	3	8
7	428	395	4	3	16	580	540	5	14
8	355	333	4	13	17	450	427	4	2
9	181	163	3	7	18	393	376	4	12
OUT	3,401	3,192	36		IN	3,268	3,048	35	
					TOTAL	6,669	6,240	71	
					STANDARD SCRATCH	71	71		

Bunker and tree positions indicated.

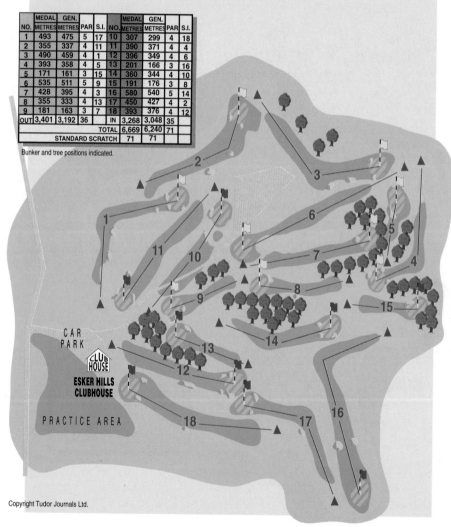

CAR PARK

CLUB HOUSE

ESKER HILLS CLUBHOUSE

PRACTICE AREA

TULLAMORE

Brookfield, Tullamore, Co. Offaly.
Tel: (0506) 21439.
Fax: (0506) 51757.

LOCATION: Three miles south of Tullamore town.
SECRETARY: Pat Burns.
Tel: (0506) 51240.
PROFESSIONAL: Donagh MacArdle.
Tel: (0506) 51757.
ARCHITECT: James Braid, Paddy Merrigan.

Parkland course situated in a very attractive tree lined setting on the outskirts of Tullamore.

COURSE INFORMATION

Par 71; SSS 70; Length 6,457 yards.

Visitors: Welcome. Tel Professional for tee-times. Societies contact Hon. Secretary well in advance.
Opening Hours: Sunrise – sunset.
Avoid: Tuesday.
Ladies: Tuesday. Lessons available, Club hire & Caddy service available, telephone appointment required for groups only. (Advised for other days).
Green Fees: Mon - Fri £16; weekends £20.

Clubhouse Hours: 8.30am – 11.30pm.
Clubhouse Dress: Neat dress.
Clubhouse Facilities: Full bar and catering facilities.
Open Competitions: Open Charity Fourball - March/August; Open Week - June; Mixed - July; Intermediate Scratch Cup – September; Mixed Hamper – October; Men's Foursomes Hamper – November.

NO.	YARDS	PAR	S.I.	NO.	YARDS	PAR	S.I.
1	359	4	17	10	382	4	2
2	177	3	5	11	325	4	8
3	429	4	7	12	197	3	14
4	492	5	13	13	387	4	18
5	439	4	1	14	480	5	6
6	212	3	9	15	548	5	16
7	489	5	15	16	419	4	12
8	338	4	3	17	184	3	4
9	148	3	11	18	452	4	10
OUT	3,083	35		IN	3,374	36	
				TOTAL	6,457	71	
				STANDARD SCRATCH	70		

OUT OF BOUNDS

CLUB HOUSE
TULLAMORE CLUBHOUSE

Glasson Golf and Country Club, Glasson, Athlone, Co. Westmeath.
Tel: (0902) 85120. (Office)
Tel: (0902) 85470. (Clubhouse)
Fax: (0902) 85444.

LOCATION: 6 miles north of Athlone Town.
SECRETARY: Fidelma Reid.
Tel: (0902) 85120.
ARCHITECT: Christy O'Connor Jnr.

A Christy O'Connor Jnr. design that has golfers talking. Every hole is fascinating and measuring over 7000 yds from the championship tees it is a true test for all golfing standards.

COURSE INFORMATION

Par 72; SSS 74; Length 7,120 Yards.
Visitors: Welcome anyday.
Opening Hours: Sunrise – Sunset.

Green Fees: £25 Mon – Thur, £28 Fri & Sun, £30 Sat.
Caddies available on request.
Clubhouse Facilities: Catering facilities available at all times.
Open Competitions: Easter weekend, August bank holiday weekend.

NO.	CHAMP YARDS	MEDAL YARDS	PAR	S.I.	NO.	CHAMP YARDS	MEDAL YARDS	PAR	S.I.
1	396	373	4	15	10	513	476	5	18
2	552	536	5	7	11	183	165	3	14
3	219	190	3	5	12	406	380	4	16
4	406	384	4	9	13	397	369	4	6
5	199	177	3	17	14	566	521	5	12
6	559	535	5	13	15	185	170	3	8
7	410	386	4	1	16	452	417	4	4
8	432	404	4	11	17	450	432	4	2
9	412	377	4	3	18	383	361	4	10
OUT	3,585	3,362	36		IN	3,535	3,291	36	
					TOTAL	7,120	6,653	72	
					STANDARD SCRATCH	74	72		

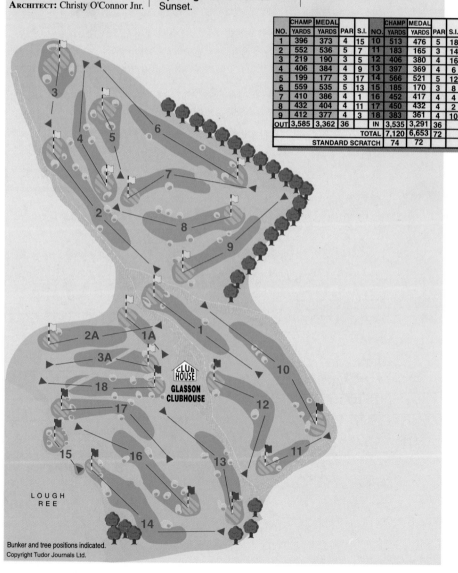

GLASSON CLUBHOUSE

LOUGH REE

Bunker and tree positions indicated.
Copyright Tudor Journals Ltd.

**Ballinagarby, Moate,
Co. Westmeath.
Tel: (0902) 81271.**

LOCATION: Less than one mile north of Moate on Mount Temple road.
HON SECRETARY: Joe Creggy.
Tel: (0902) 81270.
PRESIDENT: Michael Glennon.
CAPTAIN: Liam Galvin.

A narrow course which adds to the degree of difficulty. A nine hole parkland course with eighteen tees. It enjoys good drainage which means it is not affected by heavy rainfall and is playable throughout the winter.

COURSE INFORMATION

Par 72; SSS 70; Length 6,287 yards.
Visitors: Welcome.
Opening Hours: Sunrise – sunset.
Avoid: Sunday.
Ladies: Welcome. Letter of introduction / handicap certificate for Open Competitions.
Green Fees: Mon – Fri £10 (with member £6); Sat, Sun & Bank Hols £13 (with member £6).
Juveniles: Welcome.
Caddy service available by prior arrangement; handicap certificate required for open competitions; telephone appointment required.
Clubhouse Hours: 10.00am – 11.00 pm.
Clubhouse Dress: Casual.
Clubhouse Facilities: New clubhouse with full catering and bar facilities at all times (official opening Sep '97).
Open Competitions: Inter Scratch Cup; Junior Scratch Cup May 4th & 5th; Open Week July 5th – 13th; Open Mixed Hamper18th & 19th October; Open Weekend September 12th & 14th.

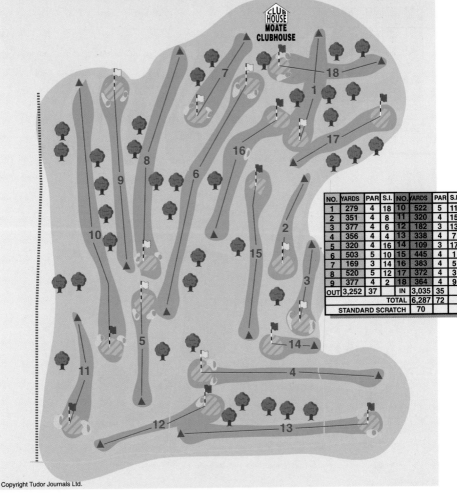

NO.	YARDS	PAR	S.I.	NO.	YARDS	PAR	S.I.
1	279	4	18	10	522	5	11
2	351	4	8	11	320	4	15
3	377	4	6	12	182	3	13
4	356	4	4	13	338	4	7
5	320	4	16	14	109	3	17
6	503	5	10	15	445	4	1
7	169	3	14	16	383	4	5
8	520	5	12	17	372	4	3
9	377	4	2	18	364	4	9
OUT	3,252	37		IN	3,035	35	
				TOTAL	6,287	72	
				STANDARD SCRATCH	70		

MULLINGAR

**Belvedere, Mullingar,
Co. Westmeath.
Tel: (044) 48629/48366.**

LOCATION: Three miles south
of Mullingar.
HON. SECRETARY: John Wims.
Tel: (044) 42753 (H).
SECRETARY / MANAGER:
Brian Kiely. Tel: (044) 48366.
Fax: (044) 41499.
PROFESSIONAL: John Burns.
Tel: (044) 40085.

This parkland golf at its most
sublime. Generous, rolling fairways
wind their paths through mature

timbers. It hosts an important
amateur events in Britain and
Ireland annually in the shape of the
Mullingar Scratch Cup.

COURSE INFORMATION

**Par 72; SSS 71; Length
6,198 metres.
Visitors:** Welcome. Prior
arrangement required for
weekends.
Opening Hours:
8.00am – sunset.
Avoid: Wednesday and
weekends.

Green Fees: Winter – £15
Mon – Fri; £20 weekends.
Summer – £20 Mon – Fri;
£25 weekends.
Ladies: Welcome.
Juveniles: Welcome.
Clubhouse Hours:
10.00am – 11.30pm.
Clubhouse Dress:
Casual, no shorts.
Clubhouse Facilities:
Bar food.

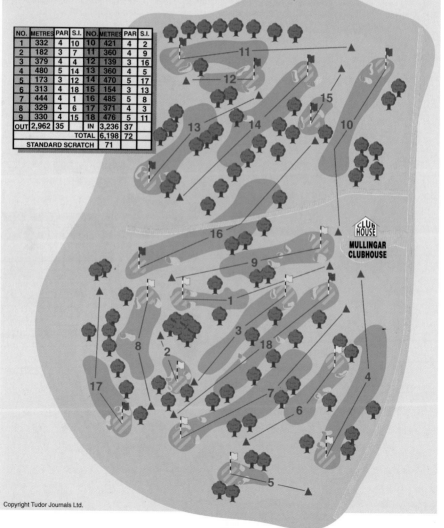

NO.	METRES	PAR	S.I.	NO.	METRES	PAR	S.I.
1	332	4	10	10	421	4	2
2	182	3	7	11	360	4	9
3	379	4	4	12	139	3	16
4	480	5	14	13	360	4	5
5	173	3	12	14	470	5	17
6	313	4	18	15	154	3	13
7	444	4	1	16	485	5	8
8	329	4	6	17	371	4	3
9	330	4	15	18	476	5	11
OUT	2,962	35		IN	3,236	37	
				TOTAL	6,198	72	
STANDARD SCRATCH		71					

**Mount Temple Golf Club,
Mount Temple Village,
Moate, Co. Westmeath.
Tel: (0902) 81841/81545.
Fax: (0902) 81957.**

LOCATION: 4½ miles west of Moate
and 5 miles east of Glasson.
SECRETARY: Michelle Allen.
Tel: (0902) 81841 clubhouse, (0902)
81545 office,
Internet: Mzzemple@iol.ie.
PROFESSIONAL: Paul Power.
ARCHITECT: Michael Dolan.

Inland parkland course with links
qualities brought together in this 18
hole championship status course.

Natural water hazards come into play
on five holes. Panoramic views of the
Midlands and playable all year.

COURSE INFORMATION

**Par 71; SSS 71; Length
5,872 metres.
Visitors:** Welcome.
Opening Hours:
Sunrise – sunset.
Avoid: Playable all week,
but check weekends.
Ladies: Welcome.
Green Fees: £14
weekdays; £16 weekends
and public holidays.

Juveniles: Welcome.
Lessons and caddy service
available by prior
arrangement.
Clubhouse Hours:
8.30am – 11.30pm.
Clubhouse Dress:
Neat and casual.
Clubhouse Facilities:
Farmhouse cuisine.
Open Competitions:
Open monthly sponsored.
Competitions included on
green fee.

NO.	METRES	MEDAL METRES	PAR	S.I.	NO.	METRES	MEDAL METRES	PAR	S.I.
1	125	161	3	17	10	260	397	4	1
2	300	326	4	12	11	458	458	5	15
3	320	348	4	4	12	310	372	4	5
4	415	435	5	14	13	320	398	4	10
5	320	364	4	6	14	300	363	4	7
6	320	320	4	13	15	118	118	3	18
7	300	350	4	3	16	435	453	5	9
8	183	183	3	8	17	120	143	3	11
9	230	288	4	16	18	370	395	4	2
OUT	2513	2775	35		IN	2691	3097	36	
					TOTAL	5204	5872	71	
					STANDARD SCRATCH		71		

Bunker and tree positions indicated.

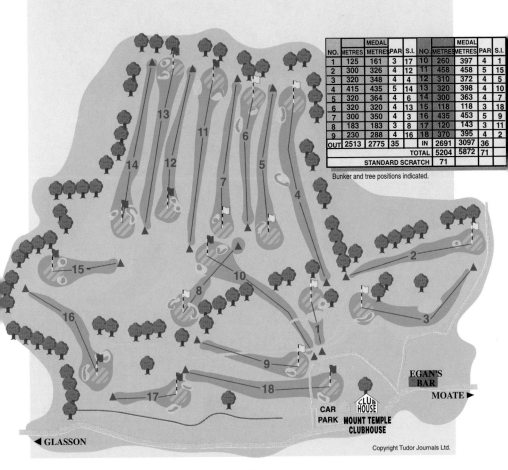

113

**Kiltennel, Gorey,
Co. Wexford
Tel: (055) 25166.
Fax: (055) 25553.**

LOCATION: 3 miles from Gorey.
SECRETARY/ MANAGER: David Cleere.
Tel: (055) 25166.
PROFESSIONAL: John Coone.
Tel: (055) 25558 / 25166.

This is a heavily wooded parkland
course. Features are the 4 par 3's,
particularly the nerve wracking 18th.
Top class bar and catering facilities
complement this excellent course.

The newly refurbished clubhouse has
panoramic views across the course
and the Irish Sea.

COURSE INFORMATION

**Par 71; SSS 71; Length
5,898 metres.
Visitors:** Welcome except on
major competition days and
Tuesdays.
Opening Hours:
Sunrise – sunset.
Ladies: Welcome. Lessons
available; Club Hire available;
Caddy cars available.

Green Fees: Winter – £14
weekdays, £18 weekends &
Bank Hols, Summer – £18
weekdays, £23 weekends &
Bank Hols.
Clubhouse Hours:
10.30am – 11.30pm.
Clubhouse Dress:
Casual/Neat.
Clubhouse Facilities:
April – October full catering
available.
Open Competitions: Open
Week June.

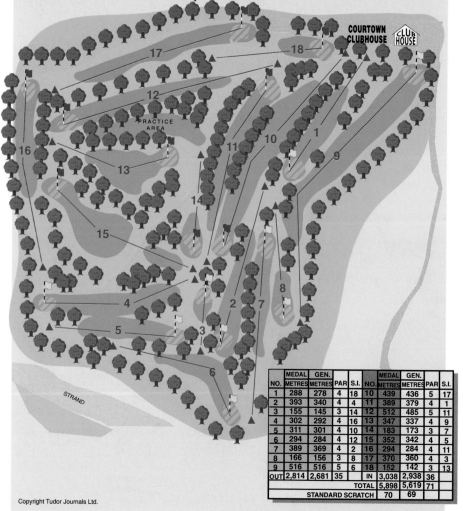

NO.	MEDAL METRES	GEN. METRES	PAR	S.I.	NO.	MEDAL METRES	GEN. METRES	PAR	S.I.
1	288	278	4	18	10	439	436	5	17
2	393	340	4	4	11	389	379	4	1
3	155	145	3	14	12	512	485	5	11
4	302	292	4	16	13	347	337	4	9
5	311	301	4	10	14	183	173	3	7
6	294	284	4	12	15	352	342	4	5
7	389	369	4	2	16	294	284	4	11
8	166	156	3	8	17	370	360	4	3
9	516	516	5	6	18	152	142	3	13
OUT	2,814	2,681	35		IN	3,038	2,938	36	
					TOTAL	5,898	5,619	71	
					STANDARD SCRATCH		70	69	

**Knockmarshall, Enniscorthy,
Co. Wexford.
Tel: (054) 33191.**

LOCATION: 2 miles from Enniscorthy
post office off main New Ross Road.
SECRETARY / MANAGER: Ann Byrne.
Tel: (054) 33191.
PROFESSIONAL: Martin Sludds.
ARCHITECT: E. Hackett.

Reasonably straight forward course that
will provide little trouble for either the
low or high handicap golfer.

COURSE INFORMATION

**Par 72; SSS 70; Length 5,808
metres.
Visitors:** Welcome.
Opening Hours: Sunrise –
Sunset.
Avoid: Sundays (telephone first).
Ladies: Welcome.
Juveniles: Welcome. Telephone
appointment required for open
competitions.
Green Fees: £14 Mon – Fri;
£16 Sat / Sun / Bank Holidays.
Clubhouse Hours: 11.00am –
11.00pm; Full clubhouse facilities;
Catering facilities up to
9.00pm daily.
Clubhouse Dress: Casual.

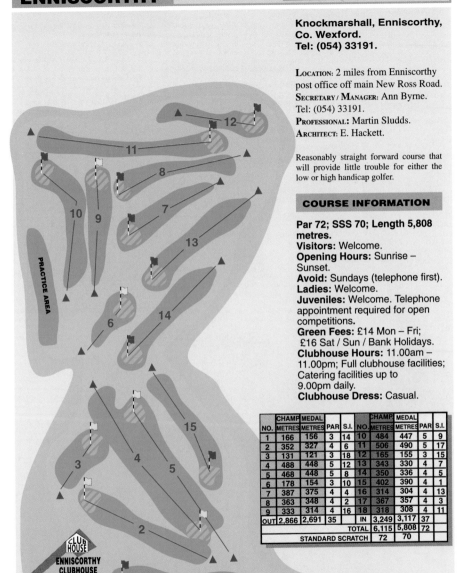

NO.	CHAMP METRES	MEDAL METRES	PAR	S.I.	NO.	CHAMP METRES	MEDAL METRES	PAR	S.I.
1	166	156	3	14	10	484	447	5	9
2	352	327	4	6	11	506	490	5	17
3	131	121	3	18	12	165	155	3	15
4	488	448	5	12	13	343	330	4	7
5	468	448	5	8	14	350	336	4	5
6	178	154	3	10	15	402	390	4	1
7	387	375	4	4	16	314	304	4	13
8	363	348	4	2	17	367	357	4	3
9	333	314	4	16	18	318	308	4	11
OUT	2,866	2,691	35		IN	3,249	3,117	37	
					TOTAL	6,115	5,808	72	
					STANDARD SCRATCH	72	70		

ENNISCORTHY
CLUBHOUSE

Tinneranny, New Ross, Co. Wexford.

LOCATION: Tinneranny.
HONORARY SECRETARY: Edward Conway.
SECRETARY / MANAGER: Kathleen Daly.
Tel: (051) 21433.

Pleasant, well kept 18 hole golf course. Straight hitting and careful placing of shots is very important as the fairways are tight and allow little room for errors.

COURSE INFORMATION

Par 71; SSS 70; Length 5,751 metres.
Visitors: Welcome weekdays and Saturdays.
Avoid: Sundays.
Ladies: Welcome. Ladies day Wednesday.
Juveniles: Welcome –

mornings only.
Green Fees: £14 Mon – Fri; £16 Sat / Sun.
Clubhouse Hours: 8am – 11.30pm (summer); 9am – 10.30pm (winter).
Clubhouse Dress: Neat / Casual.
Clubhouse Facilities: Full catering by arrangement and bar every day.
Open competitions: Open Week – 20th to 28th June, Open Team Event, 22nd/23rd Aug.

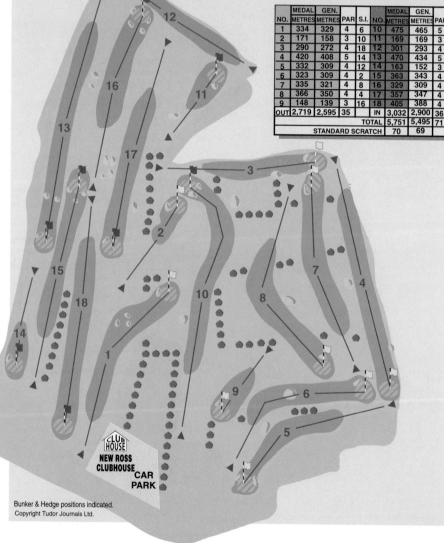

NO.	MEDAL METRES	GEN. METRES	PAR	S.I.	NO.	MEDAL METRES	GEN. METRES	PAR	S.I.
1	334	329	4	6	10	475	465	5	5
2	171	158	3	10	11	169	169	3	9
3	290	272	4	18	12	301	293	4	17
4	420	408	5	14	13	470	434	5	15
5	332	309	4	12	14	163	152	3	11
6	323	309	4	2	15	363	343	4	1
7	335	321	4	8	16	329	309	4	13
8	366	350	4	4	17	357	347	4	7
9	148	139	3	16	18	405	388	4	3
OUT	2,719	2,595	35		IN	3,032	2,900	36	
					TOTAL	5,751	5,495	71	
					STANDARD SCRATCH	70	69		

NEW ROSS CLUBHOUSE
CLUB HOUSE
CAR PARK

Bunker & Hedge positions indicated.

Rosslare, Co. Wexford.
Tel: (053) 32113.
Fax: (053) 32203.

Location: In the village of Rosslare.
Secretary: Emily Ward
Manager: James F. Hall.
Professional: Austin Skerritt.
Tel: (053) 32238.

Pleasant links which provides a good test of golf. An enjoyable course for both the good and not so good golfer.

COURSE INFORMATION

Par 72; SSS 72;
Length 6,577 yards.
Visitors: Welcome.
Opening Hours:
Sunrise – Sunset.
Avoid: No particular day.
Telephone first to avoid disappointment.
Ladies: Welcome.
Ladies Day Tuesday.
Juveniles: Welcome.
Lessons available by prior arrangment; Club Hire available; Caddy service available by prior arrangment;

must be accompanied by an adult.
Green Fees: £22 Mon – Fri;
£30 Sat / Sun.
Clubhouse Hours: 9.00am – 11.30pm. Full clubhouse facilities;
Full catering facilities.
Clubhouse Dress: Casual / neat.
Open Competitions: Most Sundays.
In high season open to visitor paying green fees.

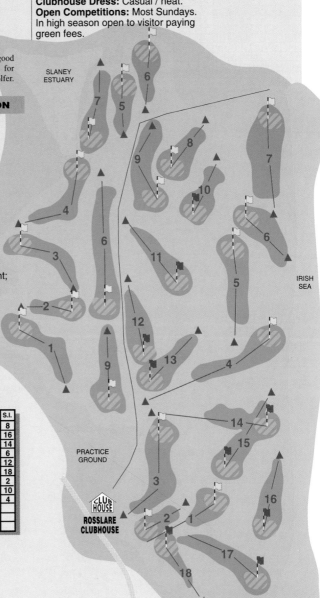

NO.	YARDS	PAR	S.I.	NO.	YARDS	PAR	S.I.
1	356	4	12	10	164	4	8
2	172	3	11	11	469	3	16
3	518	5	9	12	472	4	14
4	373	4	6	13	282	4	6
5	443	4	2	14	160	4	12
6	335	4	18	15	403	3	18
7	554	5	7	16	365	4	2
8	177	3	13	17	418	5	10
9	399	4	4	18	482	4	4
OUT	3,327	36		IN	3,215	35	
				TOTAL	6,554	72	
	STANDARD SCRATCH			72			

117

NO.	CHAMP METRES	MEDAL METRES	PAR	S.I.	NO.	CHAMP METRES	MEDAL METRES	PAR	S.I.
1	410	399	5	17	10	488	463	5	4
2	379	367	4	6	11	175	164	3	12
3	192	183	3	10	12	406	386	4	1
4	288	280	4	18	13	419	405	4	5
5	305	298	4	8	14	299	290	4	14
6	308	296	4	16	15	567	482	5	9
7	165	159	3	13	16	368	360	4	11
8	412	400	4	2	17	192	186	3	3
9	478	461	5	7	18	240	234	4	15
OUT	2,937	2,843	36		IN	3,154	2,970	36	
					TOTAL	6,091	5,813	72	
					STANDARD SCRATCH	72	71		

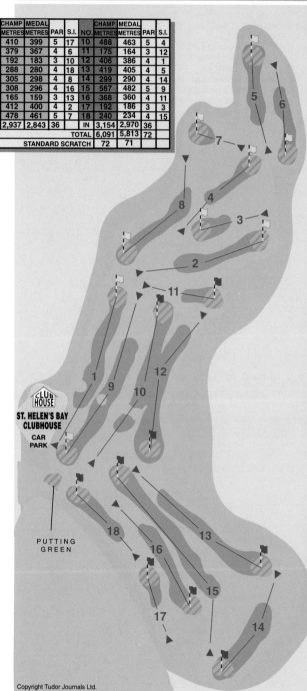

St. Helen's, Kilrane,
Rosslare Harbour,
Co. Wexford.
Tel: (053) 33234/33669.
Fax: (053) 33803.

LOCATION: 2 miles from
Rosslare Port; 10 miles from
Wexford; 90 miles from Dublin.
SECRETARY: Larry Byrne.
Tel: (053) 33234/33669.
Public Tel: (053) 33806.
Fax: (053) 33803.
COURSE DESIGN / ARCHITECT:
Philip Walton.

Set in the beautiful location beside
St. Helen's Bay, 14 holes of the
course overlook the coast and
Tuskar Lighthouse. It is a design,
by Philip Walton, which takes full
advantage of the onshore winds and
gently sloping rural land, totally at
one with nature. There are nine
water features and 5,000 trees, as
well as strategically lined bunkers.

COURSE INFORMATION

**Par 72; SSS 72; Length
6,091 Metres.**
Type: Parkland / Links course.
Opening Hours: Daylight
Hours
Avoid: None.
Green Fees: £16 Mon – Fri.
£20 Sat /Sun. £22 (High
Season), £18 (Low Season).
Club hire available, Caddie
Service available.
Clubhouse Hours: Licencing
Hours.
Clubhouse Dress: Neat,
casual dress.
Clubhouse Facilities: Full
catering and clubhouse
facilities available. Telephone
Caterer: Ext. 21.
Accomodation available on
site.
Open Competitions: Various
Open Days throughout the
year and three Open Weeks.

ST. HELEN'S BAY
CLUBHOUSE
CAR
PARK

CLUB
HOUSE

PUTTING
GREEN

Mulgannon, Co. Wexford.
Tel: (053) 42238.

LOCATION: Wexford Town.
HON. SECRETARY: Pat Daly.
ARCHITECT: H. Stutt & Co.

Parkland course with many mature trees. The location has beautiful views of County Wexford, including the Saltee Islands, Bletchin Mountains and Wexford Harbour.

COURSE INFORMATION

Par 72; SSS 71; Length 6,306 yards, 5,734 metres.
Visitors: Welcome (except on Sundays). Should book in advance.
Opening Hours: Sunrise – sunset.
Avoid: Sunday.
Ladies Day: Thursday.
Juveniles: Lessons available by prior arrangments; Club Hire available; Caddy service available by prior arrangments; Telephone appointment required.
Green Fees: Weekdays £17 (summer) £15 (winter); Sat, Sun & Bank Hols £18 (all year round).
Clubhouse Hours: 8am – 11.30pm (summer).
Clubhouse Dress: Casual.
Clubhouse Facilities: Bar snacks available all day every day. Full catering available by arrangement.

WEXFORD CLUBHOUSE

NO.	YARDS	PAR	S.I.	NO.	YARDS	PAR	S.I.
1	190	3	6	10	340	4	9
2	317	4	14	11	505	5	11
3	395	4	7	12	166	3	12
4	348	4	13	13	491	5	16
5	386	4	4	14	451	4	3
6	151	3	8	15	134	3	17
7	263	4	18	16	399	4	1
8	540	5	10	17	462	5	15
9	433	4	2	18	335	4	5
OUT	3,023	35		IN	3,283	37	
				TOTAL	6,306	72	
	STANDARD SCRATCH		70				

Abbeylands, Arklow, Co Wicklow.
Tel: (0402) 32492.

LOCATION: Just south of the town centre.

SECRETARY / MANAGER: Brendan Timmons.
Tel: (0402) 32971 (home).

ARCHITECT: Haughtry and Taylor.

A typical links course with majestic scenery and the opportunity to play throughout the year. Sited just outside the townland of Arklow.

COURSE INFORMATION

Par 68; SSS 67; Length 5,404 metres.
Visitors: Welcome.
Opening Hours: 9am – 6pm in Winter, 8am – Sunset in Summer.
Avoid: Weekends.
Ladies: Welcome Mondays.

Juveniles: Must by accompanied by an adult. Handicap Certificate required for Open Competitions.
Green Fees: £18 seven days a week.
Clubhouse Hours: Winter: 9am – 6pm. Summer: 8am – Sunset.
Clubhouse Dress: Casual.
Clubhouse Facilities: By prior arrangments.
Open Competitions: Open Week July / August.

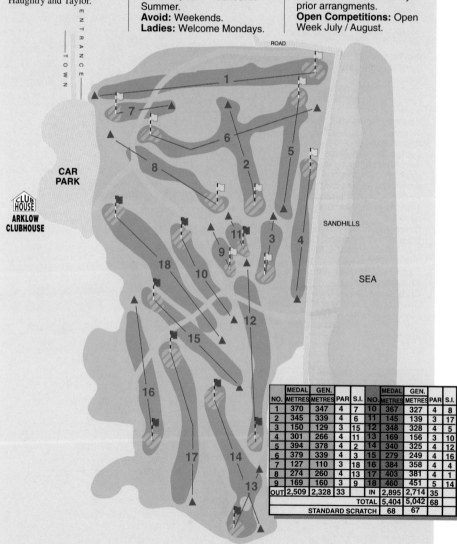

CAR PARK

ARKLOW CLUBHOUSE

ROAD

SANDHILLS

SEA

NO.	MEDAL METRES	GEN. METRES	PAR	S.I.	NO.	MEDAL METRES	GEN. METRES	PAR	S.I.
1	370	347	4	7	10	367	327	4	8
2	345	339	4	6	11	145	139	3	17
3	150	129	3	15	12	348	328	4	5
4	301	266	4	11	13	169	156	3	10
5	394	378	4	2	14	340	325	4	12
6	379	339	4	3	15	279	249	4	16
7	127	110	3	18	16	384	358	4	4
8	274	260	4	13	17	403	381	4	1
9	169	160	3	9	18	460	451	5	14
OUT	2,509	2,328	33		IN	2,895	2,714	35	
					TOTAL	5,404	5,042	68	
					STANDARD SCRATCH	68	67		

Baltinglass
Co. Wicklow.
Tel: (0508) 81350.

Location: Baltinglass.
Secretary: Fintan Doyle.
Tel: (0508) 81609.
Architect: Michael Murphy.

Nine hole course with alternate tees for each nine. A scenic situation compliments what is a difficult rating for a nine hole course – par 34.

NO.	YARDS	PAR	S.I.	NO.	YARDS	PAR	S.I.
1	367	4	3	10	356	4	4
2	325	4	13	11	309	4	11
3	137	3	17	12	133	3	18
4	395	4	5	13	391	4	6
5	368	4	7	14	366	4	8
6	148	4	1	15	409	4	2
7	339	3	16	16	143	3	15
8	314	4	9	17	332	4	10
9	314	4	14	18	301	4	12
OUT	2,809	34		IN	2,740	34	
				TOTAL	5,439	68	
				STANDARD SCRATCH	69		

Bunker and tree positions indicated.

COURSE INFORMATION

Par 68; SSS 69; Length 6,072 yards, 5,549 metres.
Visitors: Welcome.
Opening Hours: 9.00am – Sunset. Closed in Winter months.
Avoid: Competition dates, weekends and Thursdays.
Ladies: Welcome. Ladies Day Thursday.
Green Fees: Mon – Fri £10 (£6 with a member); Sat/Sun/Bank Holidays £12 (£8 with a member).
Juveniles: Welcome. Caddy service available by prior arrangement, telephone appointment required.
Clubhouse Dress: Casual.
Clubhouse Facilities: Catering prior arrangements except weekends.
Clubhouse Facilities: 9.00am – 6.00pm (winter) 9.00am – 11.00pm (summer).
Open Competiions: Open Week June/July.

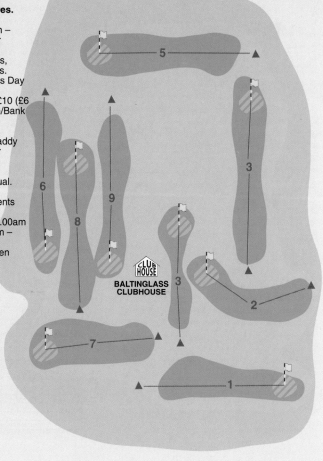

BALTINGLASS
CLUBHOUSE

Blainroe, Co Wicklow.
Tel: (0404) 68168.
Fax: (0404) 69369.

LOCATION: 4 miles south of Wicklow
Town; 35 miles south of Dublin.
SECRETARY / MANAGER: W. O'Sullivan.
Tel: (0404) 68168.
PROFESSIONAL: J. McDonald.
Tel: (0404) 68168.
ARCHITECT: Charles Hawtree.

This is a parkland course overlooking the
sea. Two holes worth noting are the 14th,
which is played from the cliff peninsula,
and the par 3 15th hole over the lake.
There is a total of 58 sand bunkers which
makes it a very challenging test to all
golfers.

COURSE INFORMATION

Par 72; SSS 72;
Length 6,171 metres.
Visitors: Welcome.
Opening Hours: Sunrise –
Sunset.
Avoid: Weekends.
Ladies: Welcome.
Juveniles: Welcome. Lessons
available by prior arrangements;
Club Hire available; Caddy cars
available by prior arrangements.
Green Fees: £25 Mon – Fri;
£35 Sat/Sun/Bank Holidays.
Clubhouse Hours: 11.00am –
11.00pm. Full Clubhouse facilities.
Clubhouse Dress: Neat dress
essential.
Clubhouse Facilities: Available
in season and weekends.

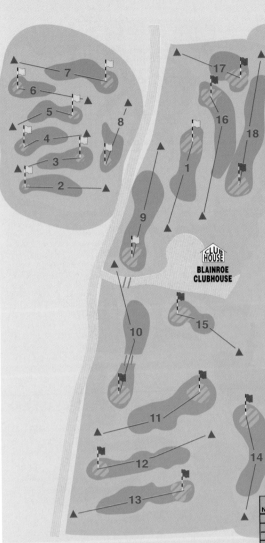

BLAINROE
CLUBHOUSE

NO.	MEDAL METRES	GEN. METRES	PAR	S.I.	NO.	MEDAL METRES	GEN. METRES	PAR	S.I.
1	330	326	4	15	10	344	336	4	6
2	394	389	4	2	11	356	351	4	12
3	384	378	4	5	12	390	386	4	4
4	480	475	5	13	13	363	357	4	10
5	445	441	5	9	14	303	287	4	17
6	332	328	4	3	15	208	198	3	8
7	338	333	4	11	16	417	408	4	1
8	193	187	3	7	17	112	109	3	18
9	335	329	4	14	18	445	440	5	16
OUT	3,231	3,186	37		IN	2,940	2,800	35	
					TOTAL	6,171	5,986	72	
					STANDARD SCRATCH	72	71		

**Ravenswell Road, Bray,
Co Wicklow.
Tel: 2862092.**

LOCATION: Bray Town.
SECRETARY / MANAGER: T. Brennan.
Tel: 2862484.
PROFESSIONAL: Michael Walby.
Tel: 2760057.

Relatively short nine holes with separate tees for 1st and 2nd nine. A mostly flat inland course, but still a reasonable test of golf.

COURSE INFORMATION

Par 70; SSS 69; Length 5,784 metres.
Visitors: Welcome.
Opening Hours: 8.am – Sunset.
Avoid: Weekends and Mondays.
Ladies: Monday. Lessons available by prior arrangment.
Green Fees: £17.
Clubhouse Hours: 8.30am – Sunset.
Clubhouse Dress: No Jeans (Course or Clubhouse); proper golf attire on course.
Clubhouse Facilities: By arrangement.

BRAY CLUBHOUSE

Tree positions indicated.
Copyright Tudor Journals Ltd.

NO.	MEDAL METRES	GEN. METRES	PAR	S.I.	NO.	MEDAL METRES	GEN. METRES	PAR	S.I.
1	335	327	4	5	10	357	344	4	3
2	477	453	5	13	11	424	378	4	1
3	339	326	4	6	12	334	311	4	9
4	148	138	3	14	13	138	132	3	17
5	374	351	4	4	14	354	327	4	7
6	155	142	3	11	15	172	162	3	10
7	334	321	4	15	16	312	300	4	16
8	420	392	4	2	17	445	397	5/4	18
9	324	311	4	12	18	340	317	4	8
OUT	2,908	2,761	35		IN	2,876	2,668	35	
					TOTAL	5,784	5,429	70/69	
					STANDARD SCRATCH	70	68		

CHARLESLAND L E I N S T E R ■ WICKLOW

Greystones, Co Wicklow.
Tel: (01) 2874350.
Fax: (01) 2874360.

LOCATION: 18 Miles south of
Dublin.
GOLF ADMINISTRATION: Geoff Bell /
Robert Calder.
PROFESSIONAL: Paul Heany /
Gillian Burell.
ARCHITECT: Eddie Hackett.

Parkland course in a superb setting on
a delightfully rolling terrain, sweeping
towards the Irish Sea. Well bunkered,

with water hazards on seven of the
holes. An all weather course playable
twelve months of the year.

COURSE INFORMATION

**Par 72; SSS 72; Length
6,159 metres.**
Visitors: Welcome.
Opening Hours: Sunrise –
Sunset.
Juveniles: Welcome with
adult or handicap certificate.
Lessons available by prior
arrangement.

Green Fees: Mon – Fri £25;
Sat / Sun / Bank Holidays
£32.
Clubhouse Dress: Neat
dress essential.
Clubhouse Facilities: Full
facilities available. Bar food
menu and Dining room
available every day. Also 12
en-suite bedrooms.
Competitions:
Open Week – May,
Golf Festival – August.

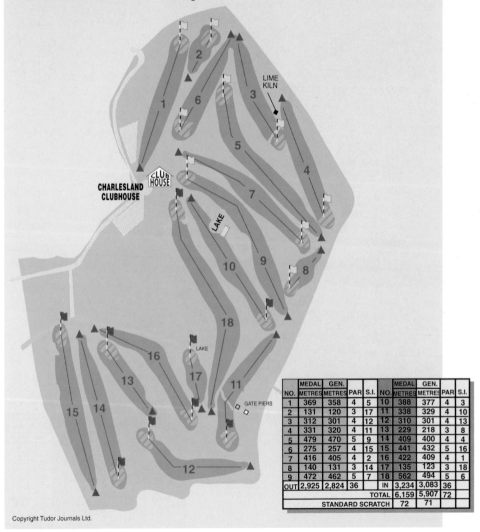

NO.	MEDAL METRES	GEN. METRES	PAR	S.I.	NO.	MEDAL METRES	GEN. METRES	PAR	S.I.
1	369	358	4	5	10	388	377	4	3
2	131	120	3	17	11	338	329	4	10
3	312	301	4	12	12	310	301	4	13
4	331	320	4	11	13	229	218	3	8
5	479	470	5	9	14	409	400	4	4
6	275	257	4	15	15	441	432	5	16
7	416	405	4	2	16	422	409	4	1
8	140	131	3	14	17	135	123	3	18
9	472	462	5	7	18	562	494	5	6
OUT	2,925	2,824	36		IN	3,234	3,083	36	
					TOTAL	6,159	5,907	72	
					STANDARD SCRATCH	72	71		

Copyright Tudor Journals Ltd.

124

COOLLATTIN

LEINSTER **WICKLOW**

Shillelagh, Co. Wicklow.
Tel: (055) 29125.

LOCATION: South Wicklow.
HON. SECRETARY: Patrick Cleere.
Tel: (055) 26345.
ARCHITECT: Peter McAvoy.

A picturesque parkland course with excellent fairways and greens. The large number of trees of different varieties add greatly to the character of the course. Part of the Old Fitzwilliam Solate, set in a lovely countryside. New 18 hole course opened in March 1998, built to U.S.G.A. standards.

COURSE INFORMATION

Par 70; SSS 69; Length 6,221 yards, 5,688 metres.
Visitors: Welcome.
Opening Hours: Sunrise – Sunset.
Avoid: Weekends.
Juveniles: Welcome, up to 4.00pm Mon – Fri.
Green Fees: £15 Mon – Fri; £20 weekends.
Clubhouse Hours: 12.00pm – close. All day Sat / Sun.
Clubhouse Dress: Casual.

Clubhouse Facilities: Full clubhouse facilities.
Open Competitions: Open Week July.

NO.	METRES	PAR	S.I.	NO.	METRES	PAR	S.I.
1	287	4	18	10	147	3	9
2	172	3	6	11	458	5	12
3	346	4	7	12	117	3	17
4	395	4	4	13	498	5	14
5	177	3	10	14	380	4	2
6	561	5	11	15	376	4	5
7	390	4	8	16	246	4	16
8	314	4	13	17	459	4	1
9	358	4	3	18	150	3	15
OUT	3,000	35		IN	2,831	35	
				TOTAL	5,831	70	
	STANDARD SCRATCH			68			

COOLLATTIN CLUBHOUSE

PRACTICE GROUND

Bunker positions indicated.
Copyright Tudor Journals Ltd.

125

Delgany, Co Wicklow.
Tel: (01) 2874536.

Location: Delgany Village.
Secretary / Manager:
R.J. Kelly.
Tel: (01) 2874536.
Professional: Gavin
Kavanagh.
Tel: (01) 2874697.

Slightly hilly parkland course with beautiful scenery and views, situated in the attractive village of Delgany.

COURSE INFORMATION

Par 69; SSS 68; Length 5,474 metres.
Visitors: Welcome Monday, Thursday and Friday. Weekends by arrangment only.
Opening Hours: 8.00am – Sunset.
Avoid: Tuesday and Wednesday afternoon.
Ladies: Welcome.
Juveniles: Welcome.
Lessons available by prior

arrangements; Club hire available; Caddy service available prior arrangements; Telephone appointment required.
Green Fees: £23 Mon – Fri; £27 Sat/Sun.
Clubhouse Hours: 8.30am – close.
Clubhouse Dress: Neat/casual.
Clubhouse Facilities: Snacks & bar food from 11am. Dining room from 1pm.

NO.	Metres	PAR	S.I.	NO.	Metres	PAR	S.I.
1	367	4	4	10	437	5/4	9
2	276	4	12	11	159	3	7
3	344	4	2	12	395	4	1
4	352	4	16	13	294	4	15
5	178	3	6	14	163	3	11
6	359	4	8	15	346	4	13
7	302	4	10	16	153	3	17
8	126	3	18	17	367	4	3
9	368	4	14	18	488	5	5
OUT	2,672	34		IN	2,802	35	
				TOTAL	5,474	69	
				STANDARD SCRATCH		69	

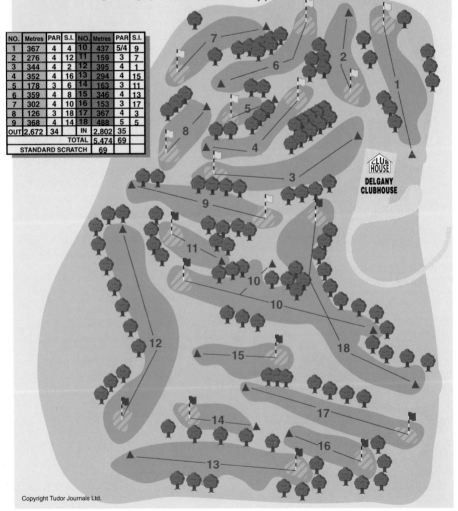

DELGANY
CLUBHOUSE

Djouce Mountain, Roundwood, Co. Wicklow.
Tel: (01) 2818585.

LOCATION: 30 mins from Dublin city. Turn right at Kilmacanogue.
SECRETARY: Ed Melbourne.
Tel: (01) 2821313.
ARCHITECT: Eddie Hackett.

Very level with testing tight fairways. Panoramic views with the course surrounded by the Dublin and Wicklow Mountains.

COURSE INFORMATION

Par 71; SSS 69; Length 6,167 yards.
Visitors: Welcome.
Opening Hours: 8.00am onwards.
Ladies: Welcome.
Green Fees: Weekdays £8 (9 holes) / £10 (18 holes); weekends / Bank Holidays £10.
Juveniles: Welcome.
Clubhouse Hours: 9.00am – closing.
Clubhouse Dress: Smart / casual.
Clubhouse Facilities: Restaurant and coffee shop (up to 100 people).
Open Competitons: Ladies Open Day 13th June.

DJOUCE MOUNTAIN GOLF CLUB

NO.	METRES	YARDS	PAR	S.I.	NO.	METRES	YARDS	PAR	S.I.
1	124	135	3	17	10	124	135	3	18
2	362	395	4	8	11	354	386	4	10
3	283	308	4	4	12	285	311	4	1
4	270	294	4	5	13	270	294	4	6
5	288	314	4	12	14	280	305	4	11
6	171	186	3	3	15	148	161	3	13
7	279	304	4	15	16	298	325	4	14
8	342	373	4	9	17	389	424	4	16
9	478	521	5	7	18	476	519	5	2
OUT	2,597	2,830	35		IN	2,624	2,860	36	
					TOTAL	5,221	5,690		
	STANDARD SCRATCH					69	69		

127

DRUIDS GLEN

L E I N S T E R   **WICKLOW**

Newtownmountkennedy,
Co. Wicklow.
Tel: (01) 2873600.
Fax: (01) 2873699.

LOCATION: Twenty-three miles
south of Dublin City. Two miles
east of Newtownmountkennedy
off the N11.
GOLF DIRECTOR: Eddie Dunne.
Tel: (01) 2873600
PROFESSIONAL: Eamonn Darcy.
COURSE DESIGNERS: Pat Ruddy &
Tom Craddock.

Druids Glen situated on the ancestral
estate of Sir Thomas Wentworth is
already an acknowledged masterpiece
and had the honour of hosting the
1996 and now the 1997 Murphy's Irish
Open Championship.

COURSE INFORMATION

Par 72; Length 7,058 yards.
Visitors: Welcome – tee times
by arrangement.
Opening Hours: 8.00am –
Sunset.

Green Fees: Mon – Sun £55
before 9.00am; £75.00 after
9.00am (including trolley).
Clubhouse Hours: 8.00am –
onwards.
Clubhouse Dress: Neat
Casual.
Clubhouse Facilities:
Snacks, Lunch, Dinner and
conference facilities available.
Caddies also available by prior
arrangement.

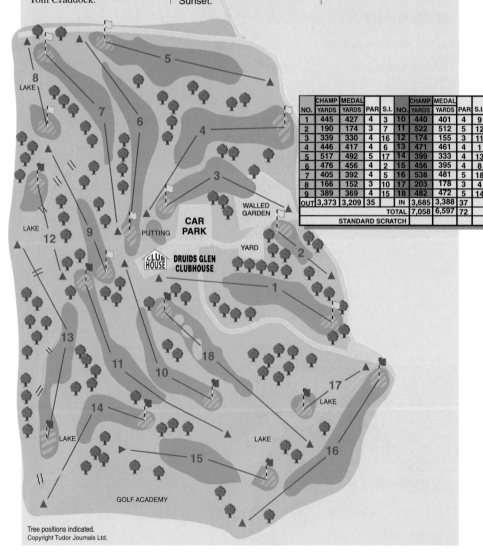

NO.	CHAMP YARDS	MEDAL YARDS	PAR	S.I.	NO.	CHAMP YARDS	MEDAL YARDS	PAR	S.I.
1	445	427	4	3	10	440	401	4	9
2	190	174	3	7	11	522	512	5	12
3	339	330	4	16	12	174	155	3	11
4	446	417	4	6	13	471	461	4	1
5	517	492	5	17	14	399	333	4	13
6	476	456	4	2	15	456	395	4	8
7	405	392	4	5	16	538	481	5	18
8	166	152	3	10	17	203	178	3	4
9	389	369	4	15	18	482	472	5	14
OUT	3,373	3,209	35		IN	3,685	3,388	37	
					TOTAL	7,058	6,597	72	
					STANDARD SCRATCH				

Tree positions indicated.
Copyright Tudor Journals Ltd.

128

Brittas Bay, Wicklow.
Tel: (0404) 47415.
Fax: (0404) 47449.

LOCATION: 45 minutes from city centre via the Bray – Shankill Bypass.
SECRETARY / MANAGER: Pat & Sidon Ruddy.
ARCHITECT: Mr. Pat Ruddy.

The links offers a rare variety of golf challenges and awesome scenery as the holes plunge into deep valleys in the sand dunes, run on a sand spit through age old marshlands and along and up into the rugged cliffs of Mizen Head. The Irish sea can be seen from every hole on the links and the Wickow Hills complete the scenic cocktail inland.

COURSE INFORMATION

Par 71; SSS 72; Length 6,860 yards.
Visitors: Welcome.
Opening Hours: Summer: 8am – 5pm; Winter: 8.30am – 12.30pm (tee times).
Ladies: Welcome.

Juveniles: Must be accompanied by an adult and have playing skills.
Green Fees: £35 per round (any day) — £55 per day.
Clubhouse Hours: Open 8.00am until licensing hours.
Clubhouse Dress: Smart / casual.
Clubhouse Facilities: Full clubhouse and catering facilities. Caddy car hire available.

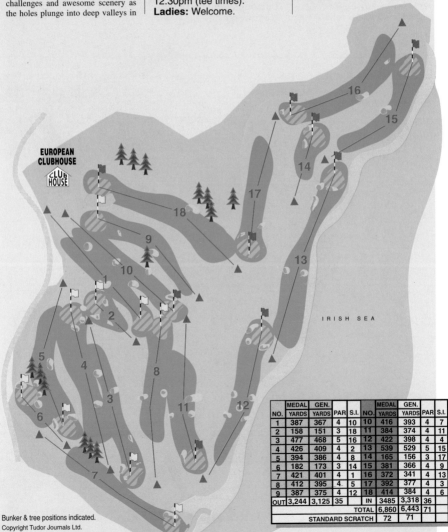

NO.	MEDAL YARDS	GEN. YARDS	PAR	S.I.	NO.	MEDAL YARDS	GEN. YARDS	PAR	S.I.
1	387	367	4	10	10	416	393	4	7
2	158	151	3	18	11	384	374	4	11
3	477	468	5	16	12	422	398	4	4
4	426	409	4	2	13	539	529	5	15
5	394	386	4	8	14	165	156	3	17
6	182	173	3	14	15	381	366	4	9
7	421	401	4	1	16	372	341	4	13
8	412	395	4	5	17	392	377	4	3
9	387	375	4	12	18	414	384	4	6
OUT	3,244	3,125	35		IN	3485	3,318	36	
					TOTAL	6,860	6,443	71	
					STANDARD SCRATCH	72	71		

Bunker & tree positions indicated.
Copyright Tudor Journals Ltd.

**Glenmalure Golf Club,
Greenane, Rathdrum,
Co. Wicklow.
Tel: (0404) 46679.**

LOCATION: Greenane, Glenmalure, 2 1/2 miles west of Rathdrum (35 miles south of Dublin via N11).
SECRETARY: Chris Morris.
Tel: (0404) 46679.
ARCHITECT: P.Suttle & Sporting Concepts Ltd.

Set in a beautiful location overlooking the Glenmalure & Vale of Avoca in the Wicklow Hills. A delightful course with inclines, a plateau and downhill.

COURSE INFORMATION

Par 77; SSS 66 (under revision); Length 5,364 yards.
Visitors: Welcome.
Opening Hours:
8.00am – dusk.
Ladies: Welcome.
Green Fees: £12 weekdays; £17 weekends & Bank Holidays.
Juveniles: £5.
Clubhouse Hours: Normal licencing hours.

Clubhouse Dress: No special requirements.
Clubhouse Facilities: Full bar and catering available.
Open Competitions: Contact Club for details.

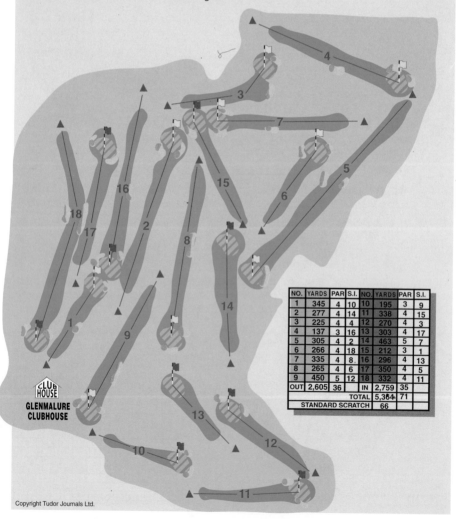

GLENMALURE
CLUBHOUSE

NO.	YARDS	PAR	S.I.	NO.	YARDS	PAR	S.I.
1	345	4	10	10	195	3	9
2	277	4	14	11	338	4	15
3	225	4	4	12	270	4	3
4	137	3	16	13	303	4	17
5	305	4	2	14	463	5	7
6	266	4	18	15	212	3	1
7	335	4	8.	16	296	4	13
8	265	4	6	17	350	4	5
9	450	5	12	18	332	4	11
OUT	2,605	36		IN	2,759	35	
				TOTAL	5,364	71	
				STANDARD SCRATCH		66	

NO.	MEDAL METRES	GEN. METRES	PAR	S.I.	NO.	MEDAL METRES	GEN. METRES	PAR	S.I.
1	177	168	3	10	10	400	393	4	1
2	286	284	4	16	11	160	151	3	9
3	377	356	4	4	12	374	360	4	3
4	339	334	4	6	13	321	315	4	7
5	202	194	3	12	14	148	128	3	15
6	284	276	4	2	15	449	437	5	13
7	334	329	4	14	16	127	125	3	17
8	277	254	4	18	17	364	362	4	5
9	455	446	5	8	18	327	263	4	11
OUT	2,731	2,641	35		IN	2,670	2,534	34	
					TOTAL	5,401	5,175	69	
					STANDARD SCRATCH	68	67		

Greystones, Co Wicklow.
Tel: (01) 2876624.

LOCATION: 20 miles south of Dublin.
SECRETARY / MANAGER: Oliver Walsh.
Tel: (01) 2874136.
PROFESSIONAL: Kevin Daly.
Tel: (01) 2875308.

A parkland course with considerable contrasts. The first two holes and the final six are hilly and provide good views which is in stark contrast to the others which are on more level terrain. Since the building of a new clubhouse the club has been experimenting with the course layout which may be altered since our publication date.

COURSE INFORMATION

Par 69; SSS 68; Length 5,401 metres.
Visitors: Welcome Mon, Tues and Frid mornings.
Opening Hours: 9.00am – Sunset.
Avoid: Wed, Thurs and Weekends.
Ladies: Welcome.
Juveniles: Welcome. Lessons available by prior arrangment; Club hire available; Caddy cars available.
Green Fees: £12 weekdays; £20 weekend.
Clubhouse Hours: 9.00am – 12.00 midnight.
Clubhouse Dress: Casual. No jeans or sneakers.
Clubhouse Facilities: By prior arrangment.
Open Competitions: Open Week July; Intermediate Scratch Cup July.

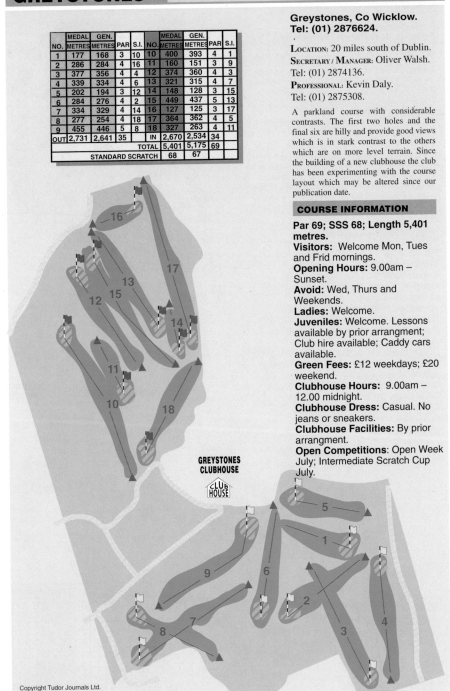

GREYSTONES
CLUBHOUSE

131

**Powerscourt Golf Club PLC,
Powerscourt Estate, Enniskerry,
Co. Wicklow.
Tel: (01) 2046033. Fax: (01) 2761303.**

LOCATION: Set in Powerscourt Estate with
its world famous Gardens, 4 miles west of
Bray. Powerscourt is 25 minutes from
Dublin City Centre adjacent to
Enniskerry village.
SECRETARY / MANAGER: Bernard Gibbons.
Tel: (01) 2046033.
PROFESSIONAL: Paul Thompson.

Powerscourt is a free draining course with links
characteristics. Built to championship standard, with
top quality tees and exceptional tiered greens, it is
set in some of Ireland's most beautiful parkland. The
course has an abundance of mature trees and natural
features, with stunning views to the sea and Sugar
Loaf Mountain.

COURSE INFORMATION

Par 72; SSS 74; Length 6,410 metres.
Visitors: Welcome.
Avoid: Saturday / Sunday mornings.
Opening Hours: 8.00am – sunset.
Ladies: Welcome.
Juveniles: With handicap welcome,
Caddies, club and trolley hire available,
practice range and short game practice
area also available.
Green Fees: £50 weekdays; £60 weekends;
£40 per round for groups of 30 or more
people, corporate days (weekdays only).
Clubhouse Hours: 8.00am – 12.00pm.
Clubhouse Dress: Casual. No jeans.
Clubhouse Facilities: Golf shop,
restaurant and full bar facilities.

Bunkers and trees positions indicated.
Copyright Tudor Journals Ltd.

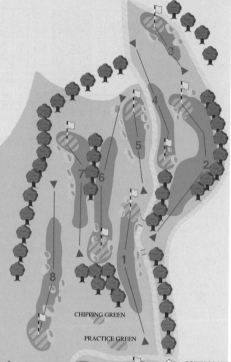

CHIPPING GREEN

PRACTICE GREEN

CLUB HOUSE **POWERSCOURT CLUBHOUSE**

PRACTICE GROUND

NO.	CHAMP METRES	MEDAL METRES	PAR	S.I.	NO.	CHAMP METRES	MEDAL METRES	PAR	S.I.
1	401	384	4	12	10	387	351	4	3
2	461	434	5	8	11	382	354	4	11
3	154	131	3	14	12	498	485	5	15
4	332	295	4	6	13	156	136	3	9
5	216	191	3	10	14	350	299	4	17
6	484	461	5	16	15	357	333	4	7
7	383	336	4	4	16	145	126	3	5
8	422	401	4	2	17	544	488	5	1
9	348	306	4	18	18	390	347	4	13
OUT	3,201	2,939	36		IN	3,209	2,919	36	
					TOTAL	6,410	5,858	72	
					STANDARD SCRATCH	74	71		

NO.	MEDAL YARDS	GEN. YARDS	PAR	S.I.	NO.	MEDAL YARDS	GEN. YARDS	PAR	S.I.
1	571	506	5	10	10	465	438	4	1
2	454	436	4	4	11	515	505	5	7
3	398	364	4	14	12	385	355	4	11
4	170	154	3	16	13	153	134	3	17
5	396	373	4	6	14	350	332	4	13
6	502	490	5	8	15	382	369	4	9
7	176	177	3	18	16	536	516	5	5
8	382	351	4	12	17	173	170	3	15
9	462	406	4	2	18	450	426	4	3
OUT	3,511	3,257	36		IN	3,409	3,245	36	
					TOTAL	6,920	6,502	72	

STANDARD SCRATCH

Dunlavin, Co. Wicklow.
Tel: 045 403316.
Fax: 045 403295.

LOCATION: 15 miles southeast of Naas.
DIRECTOR OF GOLF: Michael Bermingham.
ARCHITECT: Peter McEvoy/Christy O'Connor Jnr.

Parkland layout on 252 acres with thousands of mature trees, water and spectacular U.S.G.A. specification greens.

COURSE INFORMATION

Par 72; Length 6,920 yards.
Visitors: Welcome (best on week days).
Opening Hours: 8am – Sunset.
Avoid: 9am–11am at weekends.
Ladies: No restrictions.
Green Fees: £25 Mon; Tues – Thur £30; £40 weekends (Fri, Sat & Sun & Bank Hols.).
Juveniles: Restricted.
Clubhouse Dress: Smart/Casual.
Clubhouse Facilities: Full restaurant / bar facilities and golf shop.

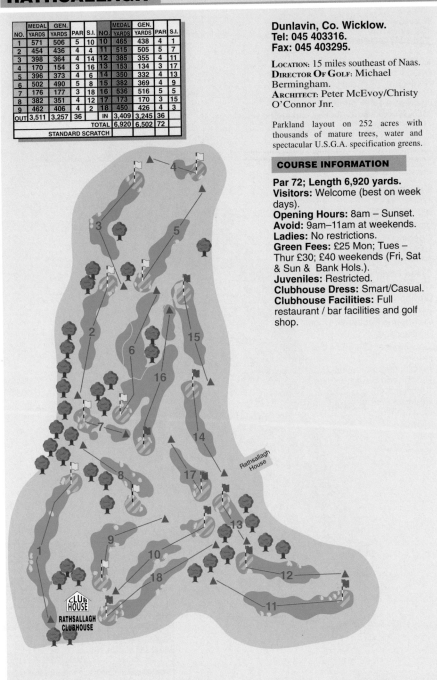

Bunker and tree positions indicated.

Newtownmountkennedy,
Co. Wicklow.
Tel: (01) 2818488.

LOCATION: Accessible from the M11
Dublin to Arklow road.
SECRETARY: Mr Michael McGuirk.
Tel: (01) 2818488.
ARCHITECT: Dr G. Smillie,
Dr A. Morgan & Mr M. Mc Guirk.

All sand greens built to U.S.P.G.A.
standards. Water hazards and forestry.
Heathland/parkland plays like links.
Magnificent views of coast, mountains and
Roundwood lakes.

COURSE INFORMATION

Par 72; Length 6,685 yards.
Visitors: Welcome.
Opening Hours: 7am – 8pm.
Ladies: Welcome.
Juveniles: Restricted.
Green Fees: £20 weekdays;
£25 weekends & holidays.
Clubhouse Dress:
Smart / Casual.
Clubhouse Facilities: Under
Construction.

NO.	MEDAL YARDS	GEN. YARDS	PAR	S.I.	NO.	MEDAL YARDS	GEN. YARDS	PAR	S.I.
1	413	379	4	12	10	182	172	3	7
2	176	166	3	10	11	397	382	4	9
3	480	470	5	16	12	435	420	4	3
4	427	383	4	2	13	184	146	3	13
5	556	541	5	8	14	320	300	4	17
6	347	337	4	6	15	501	481	5	5
7	125	119	3	18	16	446	360	4	1
8	381	371	4	4	17	211	183	3	15
9	515	505	5	14	18	589	579	5	11
OUT	3,420	3,271	37		IN	3,265	3,023	35	
					TOTAL	6,685	6,294	72	
					STANDARD SCRATCH				

Bunker and tree positions indicated.

Blessington, Co Wicklow.
Tel: (045) 864574.

LOCATION: 5 Miles from Blessington.
SECRETARY / MANAGER: Mr Adrian Williams.
Tel: (045) 864574.
ARCHITECT: Eddie Hackett.

A very interesting course with the added attraction of mature trees, good views of the Blessington Lakes and Wicklow Mountains, with the 9th hole being the toughest on the course. The course will become an 18 hole course in 1998.

COURSE INFORMATION

Par 72; SSS 69; Length 5,612 metres.
Visitors: Welcome Mon - Fri. Weekends by arrangements. '
Opening Hours: 7.00am – 10.00pm.
Ladies: Welcome.
Juveniles: Welcome. Lessons available by prior arrangment; Club hire available; Caddy service available by prior arrangement; Telephone appointment required. Under 16s not allowed on the course.
Green Fees: £11 Mon – Fri; £14 Sat / Sun / Bank Holidays; Juveniles £4.50 Mon – Fri; £5.50 Sat / Sun / Bank Holidays.
Clubhouse Hours: 10.00am - 11.00pm; Extensive Clubhouse facilities.
Clubhouse Dress: Neat dress essential.
Clubhouse Facilities: Courtyard Bar Snacks 12.30pm – 10.00pm; Courtyard Restaurant 7.00pm – 9.30pm.

NO.	METRES	PAR	S.I.	NO.	METRES	PAR	S.I.
1	149	3	15	10	149	3	16
2	424	5	9	11	424	5	10
3	362	4	3	12	362	4	4
4	340	4	5	13	340	4	6
5	156	3	13	14	156	3	14
6	415	5	11	15	415	5	12
7	327	4	7	16	327	4	8
8	249	4	17	17	249	4	18
9	384	4	1	18	384	4	2
OUT	2,806	36		IN	2,806	36	
				TOTAL	5,612	72	
		STANDARD SCRATCH		69			

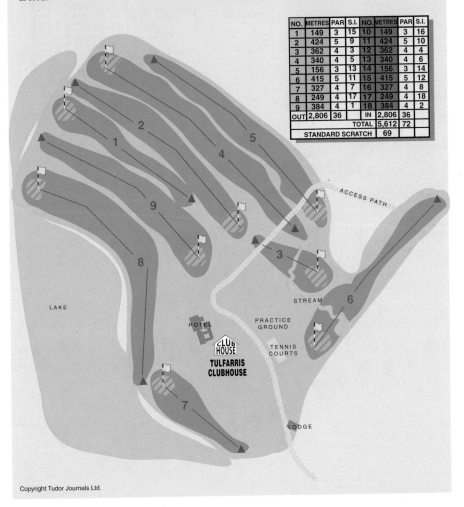

**Vartry Lakes Golf Course,
Roundwood, Co. Wicklow.
Tel: (01) 2818115.**

LOCATION: 24 miles south
of Dublin.
SECRETARY: Anne McDonald.
Tel: (01) 2818115.

This course in the Wicklow
Mountains is situated alongside the
beautiful Vartry Lakes and has
spectacular scenic views off every
hole. A well designed course it has
proved a tough test for all golfers.

COURSE INFORMATION

**Par 70; SSS 70; Length
5,246 metres.
Visitors:** Welcome.
Opening Hours:
7.00am – sunset.
Avoid: Weekends and
Tuesday (Ladies day).
Juveniles: Welcome with an
adult.

Green Fees: £10 Mon – Fri.
£12 Weekends.
Clubhouse Hours:
7.00am – sunset.
Clubhouse Dress:
Neat dress.
Clubhouse Facilities:
All day.

NO.	METRES	PAR	S.I.	NO.	METRES	PAR	S.I.
1	144	3	11	10	144	3	12
2	369	4	3	11	369	4	4
3	377	4	1	12	377	4	2
4	146	3	15	13	146	3	16
5	446	5	7	14	446	5	8
6	282	4	5	15	282	4	6
7	294	4	9	16	294	4	10
8	282	4	17	17	282	4	18
9	283	4	13	18	283	4	14
OUT	2,623	35		IN	2,623	35	
				TOTAL	5,246	70	
				STANDARD SCRATCH		70	

VARTRY LAKES
CLUBHOUSE

Dunbur Road, Wicklow.
Tel: (0404) 67379

LOCATION: Wicklow town; 30 miles south of Dublin city.
HONORARY SECRETARY: J Kelly.
Tel: (0404) 67361.
PROFESSIONAL: David Daly.

The course makes full use of the natural contours and features of the terrain, creating a challenging and spectacular test of golf.

COURSE INFORMATION

Par 71; SSS 70; Length 5,695 metres.
Visitors: Welcome.
Opening Hours: Sunrise – Sunset.
Avoid: Wednesday and Sunday.
Ladies: Ladies Day Wednesday.
Juveniles: Must be accompanied by an adult.

Green Fees: £20.
Clubhouse Hours: 9.00am Normal Licensing hours.
Clubhouse Dress: Neat, no jeans after 7pm.
Clubhouse Facilities: By prior arrangement. Full facilities every day except Tuesday.
Open Competitions: Regularly throughout the season. Visitors welcome with prior arrangement.

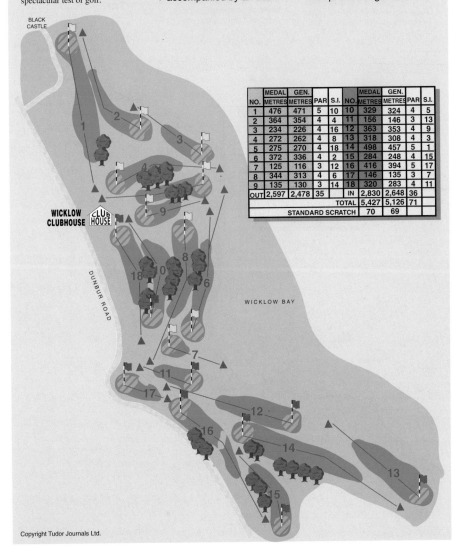

NO.	MEDAL METRES	GEN. METRES	PAR	S.I.	NO.	MEDAL METRES	GEN. METRES	PAR	S.I.
1	476	471	5	10	10	329	324	4	5
2	364	354	4	4	11	156	146	3	13
3	234	226	4	16	12	363	353	4	9
4	272	262	4	8	13	318	308	4	3
5	275	270	4	18	14	498	457	5	1
6	372	336	4	2	15	284	248	4	15
7	125	116	3	12	16	416	394	5	17
8	344	313	4	6	17	146	135	3	7
9	135	130	3	14	18	320	283	4	11
OUT	2,597	2,478	35		IN	2,830	2,648	36	
					TOTAL	5,427	5,126	71	
					STANDARD SCRATCH	70	69		

BLACK CASTLE

WICKLOW CLUBHOUSE   CLUB HOUSE

DUNBUR ROAD

WICKLOW BAY

**Woodenbridge, Arklow,
Co Wicklow.
Tel: (0402) 35202.**

LOCATION: 4 miles west of
Arklow town.
SECRETARY / MANAGER:
Henry Crummy.
HON. SECRETARY:
Diarmuid Healy.
Tel: (0402) 32116 / 31571.

An 18 hole level parkland course,
renowned for the quality of its greens.
Carefully appointed trees and bunkers
demand accurate shots. Sitting
scenically in the beautiful Vale of
Avoca, crouched under hills of

magnificent forests and encircled by
the meandering Rivers Avoca &
Aughrim, it posses a charm and
character very special to
Woodenbridge.

COURSE INFORMATION

**Par 71; SSS 71; Length
6,344 yards.
Visitors:** Welcome all week
except Thursday and
Saturday.
Opening Hours:
Sunrise – sunset.
Avoid: Thursdays and
Saturdays.

Ladies: Thursdays.
Juveniles: Welcome.
Green Fees: £27 mid week,
£35 Sundays.
Clubhouse Hours:
9.00am – 11.00pm.
Clubhouse Dress:
Informal – neat and tidy.
Clubhouse Facilities:
Full clubhouse facilities.
Mid-day – 9.00pm. Dinner
menu and a la carte. Prior
telephone call for special
service.

NO.	YARDS	PAR	S.I.	NO.	YARDS	PAR	S.I.
1	362	4	11	10	455	4	2
2	419	4	5	11	194	3	4
3	346	4	13	12	353	4	16
4	183	3	7	13	361	4	10
5	415	4	3	14	293	4	18
6	437	4	1	15	500	5	12
7	324	4	15	16	357	4	14
8	123	3	17	17	167	3	6
9	502	5	9	18	553	5	8
OUT	3,111	35		IN	3,233	36	
				TOTAL	6,344	71	
	STANDARD SCRATCH				71		

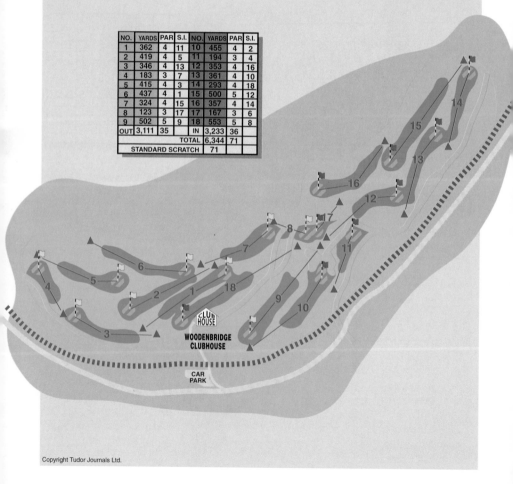

WOODENBRIDGE
CLUBHOUSE

CAR
PARK

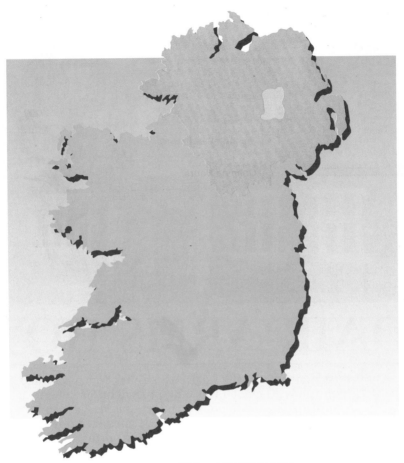

ULSTER

BY JACK MAGOWAN

Peter Dobereiner never tried to keep it a secret. His love affair with Irish golf, and the Royal Co Down links in particular, never waned one iota in all of his years as Europe's most erudite and best read writer on the game.

It was this Wartime fighter pilot turned law student golf scribe who first announced that Royal Co. Down was the best course in the world outside America, and nobody in the Press tent had more front door keys to more top clubs in the Emerald Isle.

For me, Dobereiner's death left a void that may never be filled. Ireland was where there were six days in the week, plus one for Guinness and golf. "It's informal and welcoming", he

ADAIR ARMS HOTEL

A warm welcome awaits you at the Adair Arms Hotel, which is owned and run by the McLarnon family. The hotel was built in 1846 by Sir Robert Adair and designed by the famous architect Charles Lanyon.
Situated in the heart of Ballymena, it is ideally located for touring the romantic Glens of Antrim, Slemish Mountain and the north Antrim coast.
The hotel has recently been refurbished. It has a relaxing lounge area, bar and two restaurants, including our new Brasserie.

GOLFING FACILITIES

LOCAL GOLF COURSES
- Galgorm Castle
- Moyola
- Ballymena
- Royal Portursh

OTHER GOLF COURSES
- Royal Co. Down
- Portstewart
- Castlerock
- Ballycastle

ACCOMMODATION FACILITIES
· B&B from £38.50 · Open All Year
All Major Credit Cards

Prop/Manager: G. McLarnon.

Ballymoney Road, Ballymena, Co. Antrim, BT43 585.

Malone golf course in County Down – one of the most
attractive and popular of the inland courses.

would say. "And the welcome is genuine because clubs there actually like visitors".

Peter must have told the story a thousand times, yet I, for one, never tire of hearing it.... of how the former U.S. Ryder Cup ace, Mike Souchak, lost all awareness of time and place on a visit to Killarney some years ago.

For business reasons, Souchak had to be back in New York as quickly as possible after filming ended in one of Shell's 'Wonderful World' matches.

Mike was still in spiked shoes as he set off by taxi for a speedy ride to Shannon Airport. Aer Lingus was alerted and the ground-staff briefed to expect a last-minute VIP. Infact, they even agreed to hold the flight for Mike.

Alas, it was three days later when the burly American checked in. If Dobers says he was singing a song about Rafferty's pig as he boarded the aircraft, you had better believe it.

Nobody ever got to hear exactly what happened to Souchak, but you can be sure that the taxi driver had a hand in it somehow. He could have had a cousin who lived close to Shannon and made only the best poteen in his own private

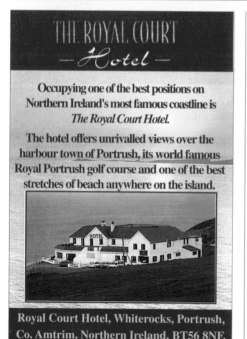

still. Would Mike like to sample a quick toot? "Sure now, we've plenty of time to spare, and this is a grand car, to be sure."

Life had nothing richer to offer, so Souchak unwittingly said 'yes', a decision he never regretted.

They say the gifts of the Irish have enriched other nations more than their own, but in golf it's different. Here the game so many of us get a kick out of playing badly has everything going for it, a wide and exciting choice of courses, close to 30 on Dublin's doorstep alone; weather conditions that can be uncharitable but never hazardous, and the kind of friendship and hospitality

The wooded fairways of Royal Belfast.

143

A round of sandwedges and some afternoon tee

Come golfing in the Antrim Coast & Glens and you'll find more than just culinary delights! Play one of our stunning links courses and take in magnificent views of Scotland and Rathlin Island. Challenge your handicap on some of the best parkland courses on this island, including the new 'pay & play' clubs at Galgorm and Gracehill. And to make it even easier, we've a handy pocket guide with all the information you'll need on the 16 great golf courses in this beautiful and historic region of Northern Ireland.

To obtain your FREE Antrim Coast & Glens Golfing guide and for full information on places to stay and visit call:
ANTRIM COAST & GLENS
Larne Tourist Information Centre
Narrow Gauge Road,
Larne, Co. Antrim BT40 1XB
Tel / Fax 01574 260088

One of the top courses in the world — Royal County Down.

Souchak and a multitude of others have found so hard to resist.

It was in August 1981 that Royal Belfast celebrated its centenary as Ireland's oldest club. Rasputin was a thorn in the flesh of the Czar and a gallon of whiskey cost 24 shillings (£1.20) when the game perfected by Scots was played for the first time over a course at Carnalea.

No competition could begin until the 11 o'clock train arrived from Belfast. The ladies of the club had their own wooden clubhouse built and furnished for less than £100, but without the modern-day luxury of a warm shower. There were rocks nearby, so

quite a few of the pretty young set would go bathing to cool off after their round. Subject to one condition, that is.

"Would ladies kindly refrain from passing the main clubhouse window in swim attire while the men are at lunch", said a notice bolted to the wooden fence.

It was in the mid-20's that Royal Belfast moved to Craigavad, £6,000 – that's how much they paid for the handsome Victorian manor and 140-acre estate which is now home to one of the most celebrated clubs in the game.

First Royal Belfast. Then Royal Dublin, Royal Curragh, Mullingar, Royal Portrush, Aughnacloy and Royal Co Down. By the time the Golfing

Union was born in 1891, there were twenty-one golf clubs in Ireland, half of them Ulster clubs. In fact, the GUI is the grandfather of all national golf Unions, older than the United States Golf Association by three years and the Welsh Union by four.

Remarkably, the Scottish Union wasn't formed until 1920, probably because of the Royal and Ancient Club's influence there, and it was four years after that again before England had a ruling body.

What a virtuoso role Royal Portrush has played in the game. Hosts to more major championships and tournaments than they can count, the club's roll-call is dotted with players of distinction, names like Fred Daly, Joe Carr, Catherine Lacoste, Max Faulkner, Darren Clarke and Garth McGimpsey, not forgetting such legends of the past as Hughie McNeill, Anthony

Babington, Rhona Adair, Zara Bolton and the Hezlet sisters.

Like Sir Anthony, P. G. Stevenson was a pillar of this great club for over half-a-century. And a fine teacher, clubmaker and storyteller, too. Nobody could remember Faulkner's historic Open victory better than Stevie, or when Sunday golf there was outlawed as a sin, and the par for Dunluce was 81, repeat 81!. A milestone, surely, in the chequered history of Ulster golf.

A recent poll of Ireland's top 30 courses listed six in the North with probably only two notable omissions, Clandeboye and Belvoir Park. Portstewart and Malone were there (naturally!), and Slieve Russell, and Donegal as well.

Malone came in for a shower of kudos from Gary Player even before his victory in the Irish Seniors' championship of '93, and like good

Scenic nine hole seaside course of Helen's Bay.

Photo: Esler Crawford Photography.

wine, he seems to improve with age.

Nobody attracted a bigger gallery in the British Seniors' Open at Dunluce than South Africa's knight in black, winner in 1997.

After the K-Club, Mount Juliet and Druid's Glen, Malone could be the pick of Ireland's best inland courses, and some of them are very good indeed.

It was an American writer of hard-boiled detective stories who compared golf in Ireland to playing poker with nothing wild. "It's the real thing," declared Larry Ferguson after a month-

147

Photo: Esler Crawford Photography.

Golf on a grand scale at Royal Portrush – to get a perspective
on size, the dots on the beach are people.

long safari here. "Irish golf is not for players who like to be petted and protected. It's for pulling on a sweater, feeling the spray in your face, then boring long irons under winds that may keep the Coast Guard in port!"

Is it possible that globe-trotter Ferguson may have played Portrush or Newcastle on a bad day in March? It's not that Irish weather can't be trusted. There's just so much of it, that's all!

There are some places you have to come back to in order to discover them for the first time, wrote Tom Callahan, in *Golf Digest* after a visit to Ulster, and we know he'll be back to the course he rates the best in Ireland.

" Tom Watson cleaves to Ballybunion," says Callahan. "He agrees the front nine at Newcastle is close to perfection, but suggests that the closing couple of holes are not up to the rest of the course's extreme standard." A view shared by most critics, perhaps, not all of them Americans.

To the west in Donegal superb scenery goes in harmony with some great golf, especially on the Inishowen as well as Fanad Peninsulas. And what they say of the natives there is true. They are the salt of the earth.

148

Bird's-eye view of Royal Portrush with the town of Portrush in the distance.

ALLEN PARK

**Allen Park Golf Centre, 45
Castle Road (Randalstown
Rd), Antrim, BT41 4NA.
Tel: (01849) 429001.**

LOCATION: 2½ miles from Antrim
town centre on the road from
Antrim to Randalstown.
MANAGER: Marie Agnew.
ARCHITECT: Mr T. McAuley.

The course opened in the Spring 1996.
This gently undulating parkland course
will test the skill and ability of even the
more experienced golfer. The shortest
hole is 196 yards with the longest being
559 yards. Three lakes provide
interesting features in the back nine
holes.

COURSE INFORMATION

**Par 72; SSS 72;
Length 6,683 yards.**

Visitors: Welcome.
Opening Hours: Dawn–Dusk.
Ladies: Welcome.
Green Fees: *Mon/Fri* – £10:
Adults, £5: Senior Citizen (Over
60), £5:Junior (Under 18).
Weekends & Holidays – £12:
Adults, £6: Senior Citizen (Over
60), £6: Junior (under 18).
Juveniles: Welcome.
Clubhouse Dress: Casual.
Clubhouse Facilities: Locker
rooms, Snooker table and
catering facilities.

NO.	MEDAL YARDS	GEN YARDS	PAR	S.I.	NO.	MEDAL YARDS	GEN YARDS	PAR	S.I.
1	419	347	4	5	10	427	360	4	3
2	197	175	3	7	11	290	252	4	16
3	396	322	4	9	12	319	277	4	13
4	477	407	5	18	13	306	259	4	15
5	559	479	5	14	14	503	452	5	17
6	196	175	3	6	15	555	463	5	12
7	364	320	4	11	16	203	181	3	8
8	201	179	3	4	17	445	365	4	1
9	388	332	4	10	18	438	373	4	2
OUT	3,197	2,736	35		IN	3,486	2,982	37	
					TOTAL	6,683	5,718	72	
					STANDARD SCRATCH	72			

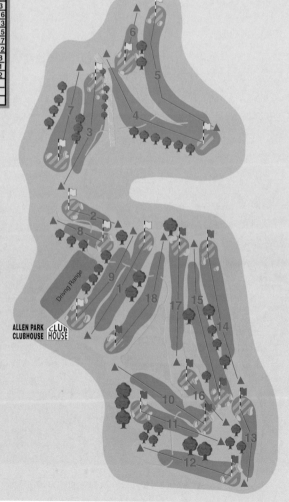

ALLEN PARK
CLUBHOUSE CLUB HOUSE

Bunker and tree positions indicated.
Copyright Tudor Journals Ltd.

**Cushendall Road,
Ballycastle, Co. Antrim
BT54 6QP.
Tel: (012657) 62536.**

LOCATION: On the north coast of Antrim at the eastern end of the Causeway Coast — adjacent to the Glens of Antrim.
SECRETARY: Mr. H.A. Fraser. Tel: (012657) 63857.
PROFESSIONAL: Ian McLaughlin. Tel: (012657) 62506.

The opening five holes are parkland bordered by the Margy and Carey Rivers and played around the ruins of a 13th Century Friary. The Warren area of four holes is true links and the final nine are played in an adjacent upland, giving panoramic views including Mull of Kintyre, Rathlin Island and Ballycastle Bay. Accurate iron play is essential for good scoring.

COURSE INFORMATION

Par 71; SSS 68; Length 5,629 yards.
Visitors: Welcome.
Opening Hours: Summer 9.00am – 6.00pm; Winter 9.00am – 3.00pm.
Avoid: Sat morning and Sun morning.
Ladies: Friday Ladies day.
Green Fees: £18 (£10 with member) Mon – Fri; £25 (£13 with member) Sat / Sun and public holidays. Juveniles under 18 years – 1/2 rates.
Juveniles: Welcome before 6.00pm in July and August. Lessons by prior arrangement; Club hire available; Caddy service available by prior arrangement.
Clubhouse Hours: 11.30am – 11.00pm (July & August); Restricted in winter.
Clubhouse Dress: Casual dress acceptable.
Clubhouse Facilities: Bar snacks and meals throughout the day. Evening meals by prior arrangement.
Open Competitions: Open Week – July; other competitions throughout the season.

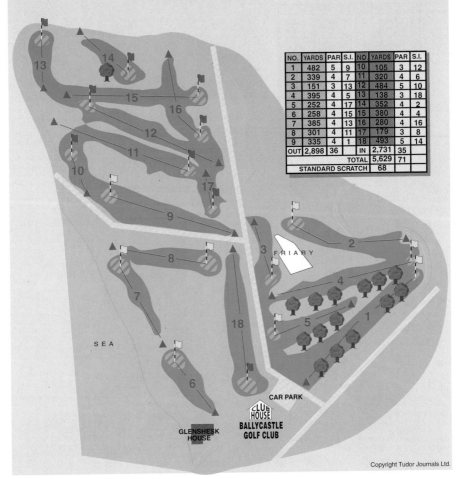

NO.	YARDS	PAR	S.I.	NO.	YARDS	PAR	S.I.
1	482	5	9	10	105	3	12
2	339	4	7	11	320	4	6
3	151	3	13	12	484	5	10
4	395	4	5	13	138	3	18
5	252	4	17	14	352	4	2
6	258	4	15	15	380	4	4
7	385	4	13	16	280	4	16
8	301	4	11	17	179	3	8
9	335	4	1	18	493	5	14
OUT	2,898	36		IN	2,731	35	
				TOTAL	5,629	71	
				STANDARD SCRATCH	68		

**25 Springvale Road,
Ballyclare, Co. Antrim.
Tel: (01960) 322696.**

LOCATION: Two miles north of
Ballyclare.
SECRETARY: H. McConnell.
Tel: (01960) 322696.
ARCHITECT: T. McCauley.

Parkland course which makes good use of
the local river and streams. The fairways
are tree-lined and as expected, accurate
driving is required for a good score.

COURSE INFORMATION

**Par 72; SSS 71; Length 5,745
metres.
Visitors:** Welcome Mon, Tues,
Wed, Fri, & Sun.
Opening Hours: Dawn–Dusk.
Avoid: Sunday mornings,
Thursdays from 1.30pm and
Saturdays.
Ladies: Welcome.
Green Fees: £16 Mon – Fri;
£22 Sunday/Bank Holidays.
Juveniles: Mon – Fri before

4.30pm; Sat/Sun after
4.30pm.
Clubhouse Hours: 12.30 –
11.30pm.
Clubhouse Dress: Jacket
and tie after 7.00pm.
Clubhouse Facilities: Meals
from 12.30pm unless by prior
arrangement.

NO.	METRES	PAR	S.I.	NO.	METRES	PAR	S.I.
1	293	4	13	10	331	4	10
2	458	5	17	11	151	3	8
3	392	4	1	12	435	5	18
4	333	4	5	13	399	4	4
5	345	4	3	14	368	4	12
6	144	3	9	15	117	3	16
7	343	4	7	16	382	4	2
8	322	4	15	17	441	5	14
9	151	3	11	18	340	4	6
OUT	2,781	35		IN	2,964	36	
				TOTAL	5,745	72	
				STANDARD SCRATCH	71		

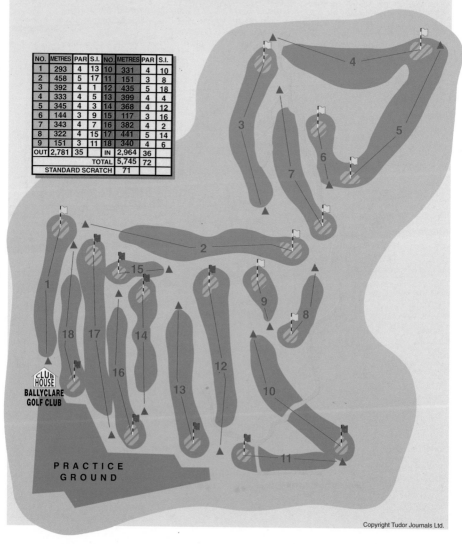

CLUB
HOUSE
BALLYCLARE
GOLF CLUB

PRACTICE
GROUND

NO.	MEDAL METRES	GEN. METRES	PAR	S.I.	NO.	MEDAL METRES	GEN. METRES	PAR	S.I.
1	323	315	4	9	10	187	177	3	12
2	167	158	3	7	11	404	393	4	2
3	449	441	5	11	12	375	348	4	6
4	130	118	3	15	13	268	258	4	18
5	362	350	4	5	14	197	188	3	10
6	351	320	4	1	15	357	318	4	4
7	104	93	3	17	16	192	184	3	8
8	340	332	4	3	17	326	316	4	14
9	439	427	5	13	18	295	285	4	16
OUT	2,665	2,554	35		IN	2,601	2,467	33	
					TOTAL	5,266	5,021	68	
					STANDARD SCRATCH	68	68		

128 Raceview Road, Ballymena.
Tel: (01266) 861487.

LOCATION: Three miles east of Ballymena.
SECRETARY: Carl McAuley.
Tel: (01266) 861487.
PROFESSIONAL: Ken Revie.

A flat course comprised mainly of heathland with numerous bunkers. The Glens of Antrim lie to the northeast and Slemish Mountain is clearly visible to the east.

COURSE INFORMATION

Par 68; SSS 68; Length 5,299 Metres.
Visitors: Welcome.
Men's Competitions – Saturdays.
Ladies: Tuesdays.
Green Fees: Adults: £15 Mon – Fri; £20 Sat /Sun. Societies 10% discount for parties of 20 or more.
Juveniles: Weekdays before 6.00pm; Sat after 6.00pm; Sunday all day. Lessons by prior arrangement. Club Hire available. Caddy Cars available.
Clubhouse Dress: Casual except function nights.
Clubhouse Facilities: Catering facilities: bar snacks; restaurant 11.30am – 9.00pm everyday except Mon in winter.
Open competions: Open Week 24th – 30th May. Open Day 20th Sept. Open charity mixed foursommes Sunday 2nd August.

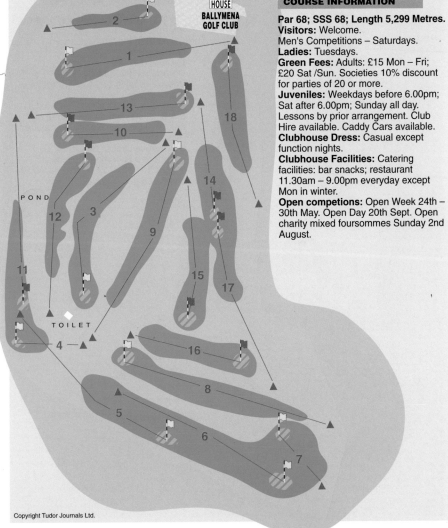

BALLYMENA
GOLF CLUB

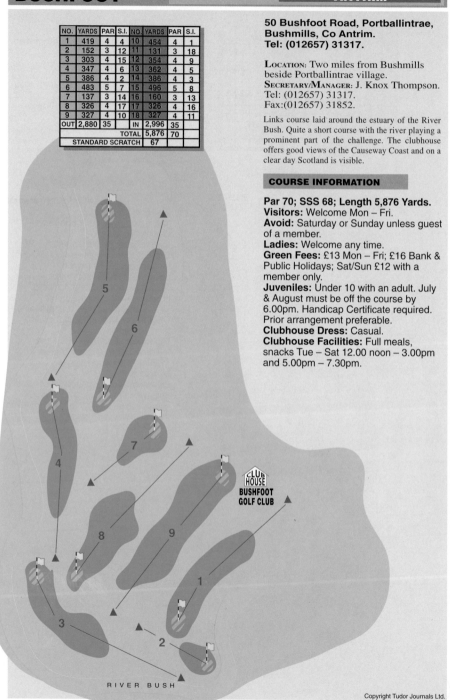

NO.	YARDS	PAR	S.I.	NO.	YARDS	PAR	S.I.
1	419	4	4	10	454	4	1
2	152	3	12	11	131	3	18
3	303	4	15	12	354	4	9
4	347	4	6	13	362	4	5
5	386	4	2	14	386	4	3
6	483	5	7	15	496	5	8
7	137	3	14	16	160	3	13
8	326	4	17	17	326	4	16
9	327	4	10	18	327	4	11
OUT	2,880	35		IN	2,996	35	
				TOTAL	5,876	70	
				STANDARD SCRATCH		67	

50 Bushfoot Road, Portballintrae, Bushmills, Co Antrim.
Tel: (012657) 31317.

LOCATION: Two miles from Bushmills beside Portballintrae village.
SECRETARY/MANAGER: J. Knox Thompson.
Tel: (012657) 31317.
Fax:(012657) 31852.

Links course laid around the estuary of the River Bush. Quite a short course with the river playing a prominent part of the challenge. The clubhouse offers good views of the Causeway Coast and on a clear day Scotland is visible.

COURSE INFORMATION

Par 70; SSS 68; Length 5,876 Yards.
Visitors: Welcome Mon – Fri.
Avoid: Saturday or Sunday unless guest of a member.
Ladies: Welcome any time.
Green Fees: £13 Mon – Fri; £16 Bank & Public Holidays; Sat/Sun £12 with a member only.
Juveniles: Under 10 with an adult. July & August must be off the course by 6.00pm. Handicap Certificate required. Prior arrangement preferable.
Clubhouse Dress: Casual.
Clubhouse Facilities: Full meals, snacks Tue – Sat 12.00 noon – 3.00pm and 5.00pm – 7.30pm.

**192 Coast Road,
Ballygally, Larne.
Tel: (01574) 583324.**

LOCATION: Four miles north of Larne.

SECRETARY/MANAGER:
Nat Moore
Tel: (01574) 583324.
PROFESSIONAL: Mr R. Walker.
Tel: (01574) 583417.

Parkland course built on the face of a hill known as Ballygally Head. One of the more scenic courses in Ireland, views to Scotland, down the coast to Carnlough and Antrim Hills. From the third tee which is 200ft above sea level beware of the hazardous valley on the right hand side and the rocks in front. Your drive has to carry 175 yards to the fairway — apart from the level of difficulty this is one of the most scenic holes.

COURSE INFORMATION

Par 70; SSS 69; Length 5,611 metres.
Visitors: Welcome any day except Saturday.
Opening Hours: From 9.00am.
Green Fees: £15 Mon – Thur; £20 Fri; £24 Sat / Sun. Ladies half price.
Ladies: Mon – Fri £10. Sun £15.
Juveniles: 9.00am – 6.00pm Monday – Friday; Saturday after 7.00pm; Sunday after 6.00pm. Club Hire available.
Clubhouse Hours: 8.00am – 11.00pm.
Clubhouse Dress: No Denims or tracksuits. Collar and tie.
Clubhouse Facilities: Catering facilities: bar and restaurant 5.00pm – 11.00pm. Outside these hours, by prior arrangement.
Open Competitions: Open Week – July.

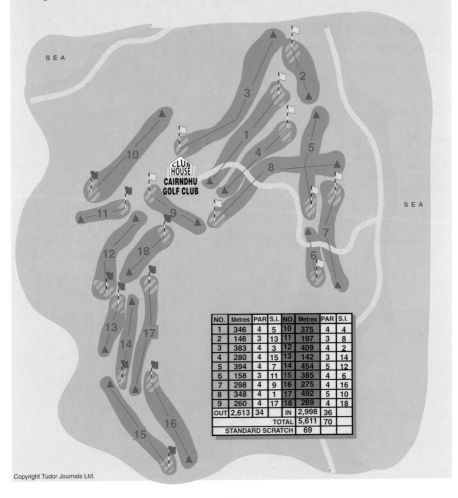

NO.	Metres	PAR	S.I.	NO.	Metres	PAR	S.I.
1	346	4	5	10	375	4	4
2	146	3	13	11	197	3	8
3	383	4	3	12	409	4	2
4	280	4	15	13	142	3	14
5	394	4	7	14	454	5	12
6	158	3	11	15	385	4	6
7	298	4	9	16	275	4	16
8	348	4	1	17	492	5	10
9	260	4	17	18	269	4	18
OUT	2,613	34		IN	2,998	36	
				TOTAL	5,611	70	
				STANDARD SCRATCH	69		

35 North Road, Carrickfergus, BT38 8LP.
Tel: (019603) 63713.

Location: On outskirts of town.
Secretary / Manager: R. J. Campbell.
Tel: (019603) 63713.
Professional: Ray Stevenson.
Tel: (019603) 51803.

A parkland course with a spectacular first hole. The first drive, from an elevated tee is over the infamous dam which is full of water and quite intimidating! Although a reasonably flat course there are several demanding holes to be tackled. The Par 4, 6th hole is a dog-leg left playing to a hidden green beside the dam. The course is well maintained throughout the year and there are some very pleasant views across the Belfast Lough to Co. Down.

COURSE INFORMATION

Par 68; SSS 68; Length 5,752 Yards.
Visitors: Welcome any day during the week. Sunday after 11.30am..
Avoid: Tuesday, Saturday and Sunday.
Ladies: Tuesdays.
Green Fees: £14 Mon – Fri; £20 Sat / Sun.
Juveniles: Up to 4.00pm – restricted times at weekends. Lessons by prior arrangement.
Clubhouse Dress: Jacket and tie in Dinning Room after 7.00pm – otherwise neat / casual.
Clubhouse Facilities: Catering facilities: bar snacks, meals 12.00 noon – 9.00pm everyday.
Open Competitons: Open Week – July / Aug.

NO.	MEDAL YARDS	GEN. YARDS	PAR	S.I.	NO.	MEDAL YARDS	GEN. YARDS	PAR	S.I.
1	418	416	4	8	10	444	439	4	1
2	107	104	3	16	11	409	405	4	7
3	384	376	4	4	12	164	154	3	17
4	122	118	3	18	13	436	426	4	3
5	322	312	4	10	14	197	186	3	13
6	426	421	4	2	15	355	353	4	5
7	126	124	3	14	16	301	300	4	15
8	283	273	4	12	17	490	488	5	9
9	440	400	4	6	18	328	320	4	11
OUT	2,628	2,544	33		IN	3,124	3,071	35	
					TOTAL	5,752	5,615	68	
	STANDARD SCRATCH		68						

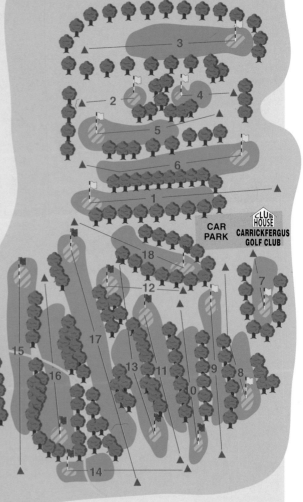

CLUB HOUSE
CAR PARK
CARRICKFERGUS GOLF CLUB

21 Shore Road, Cushendall, Co. Antrim.
Tel: (012667) 71318.

LOCATION: In Cushendall village on road to beach.
SECRETARY: Shaun McLaughlin.
Tel: (012667) 58366.
ARCHITECT: Dan Delargy.

Beautifully situated course where the River Dall winds through the fairways in seven of the nine holes. Cushendall is quite a short course, it has three par 3's and no par 5's, but it requires great accuracy as it is possible to go out of bounds at every hole.

COURSE INFORMATION

Par 66; SSS 63; Length 4,386 metres.
Visitors: Check with club in advance.
Avoid: Sundays anytime (time sheet).
Ladies: Any time but not Sunday before 1.00pm. Priority on Thursdays.
Green Fees: £13 Mon – Fri; £18 Sat / Sun / Bank Holidays.
Juveniles: Weekdays up to 5.00pm. Must be off course

by 1.00pm Sat and no play on Sun. Lessons can be arranged.
Clubhouse Dress: Casual.
Clubhouse Facilities: Full bar and Catering available at all times during summer.
Open Competitions: Glens of Antrim mixed foursomes – May / June. Most weekends. Handicap Certificate required for Open Competitions.

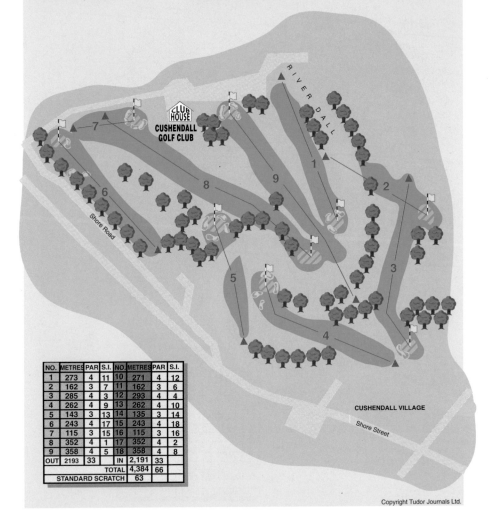

NO.	METRES	PAR	S.I.	NO.	METRES	PAR	S.I.
1	273	4	11	10	271	4	12
2	162	3	7	11	162	3	6
3	285	4	3	12	293	4	4
4	262	4	9	13	262	4	10
5	143	3	13	14	135	3	14
6	243	4	17	15	243	4	18
7	115	3	15	16	115	3	16
8	352	4	1	17	352	4	2
9	358	4	5	18	358	4	8
OUT	2193	33		IN	2,191	33	
				TOTAL	4,384	66	
	STANDARD SCRATCH			63			

CUSHENDALL VILLAGE

Shore Street

DOWN ROYAL

**Dunygarton Road, Maze,
Lisburn, BT27 5RT.
Tel: (01846) 621339.**

LOCATION: Within the Maze
racecourse.
SECRETARY / MANAGER:
Mr. J. Tinnion.
Tel: (01846) 621339.
ARCHITECT: Golf Design
Associates.

Situated in the Lagan Valley amid
pleasant rural surroundings the course
is conveniently situated to many of

the major provincial towns. Set in 150
acres of rolling heathland with gorse
lined fairways within the Down Royal
(Maze) Racecourse. The nature of the
soil being sandy loam ensures the
course is playable all year round. The
course is in two loops of nine and a
classical Par 72, with four Par 5's,
four Par 3's and ten Par 4's.

COURSE INFORMATION

**Par 72; SSS 72; Length
6,824 Yards.**

Visitors: Welcome.
Ladies: Welcome.
Green Fees: £14 Mon – Fri; £15
Sat; £17 Sun / Bank Holidays.
Juveniles: Must be accompanied
by an adult.
Clubhouse Dress: Smart – collar
and tie after 7.00pm.
Clubhouse Facilities: Licensed
restaurant nearby – open
everyday.

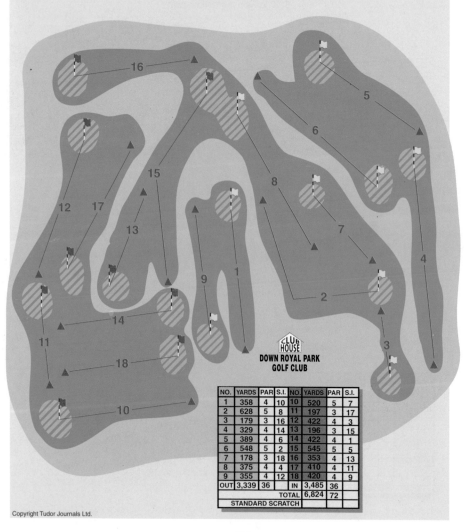

DOWN ROYAL PARK
GOLF CLUB

NO.	YARDS	PAR	S.I.	NO.	YARDS	PAR	S.I.
1	358	4	10	10	520	5	7
2	628	5	8	11	197	3	17
3	179	3	16	12	422	4	3
4	329	4	14	13	196	3	15
5	389	4	6	14	422	4	1
6	548	5	2	15	545	5	5
7	178	3	18	16	353	4	13
8	375	4	4	17	410	4	11
9	355	4	12	18	420	4	9
OUT	3,339	36		IN	3,485	36	
				TOTAL	6,824	72	
				STANDARD SCRATCH			

**Galgorm Castle Golf Club,
Galgorm Castle,
Galgorm Road,
Ballymena, BT42 1HL.
Tel: (01226) 46161.**

LOCATION: Galgorm, Ballymena.
SECRETARY: Susan Headley.
Tel: (01226) 46161.
ARCHITECT: Simon Gidman.

18 hole championship course set in
220 acres of mature parkland in the
grounds of Galgorm Castle. The
course is bordered by the rivers Main
and Braid which come into play and
include a magnificent oxbow feature and
five landscape lakes. A stimulating
challenge and memorable round for both
novice and low handicap golfers.

COURSE INFORMATION

**Par 72; SSS 72; Length
6,724 yards.
Visitors:** Welcome.
Opening Hours:
8am – 10pm. Saturday, ring to
book.
Green Fees: Weekdays £18;
weekends £24.
Ladies: Welcome.

Juveniles: Welcome, ring in
advance.
Clubhouse Hours:
8.00am – 10.00pm.
Clubhouse Dress: Informal.
Clubhouse Facilities:
Fully licenced bar and
restaurant.

NO.	CHAMP YARDS	MEDAL YARDS	PAR	S.I.	NO.	CHAMP YARDS	MEDAL YARDS	PAR	S.I.
1	452	423	4	6	10	510	483	5	9
2	302	302	4	16	11	475	443	4	1
3	475	475	5	14	12	169	150	3	17
4	323	301	4	10	13	376	350	4	3
5	206	176	3	8	14	177	147	3	13
6	415	371	4	4	15	382	342	4	11
7	141	141	3	18	16	409	362	4	7
8	409	352	4	2	17	446	404	4	5
9	507	484	5	12	18	550	524	5	15
OUT	3,230	3,025	36		IN	3,494	3,205	36	
					TOTAL	6,724	6,230	72	
					STANDARD SCRATCH	72	72		

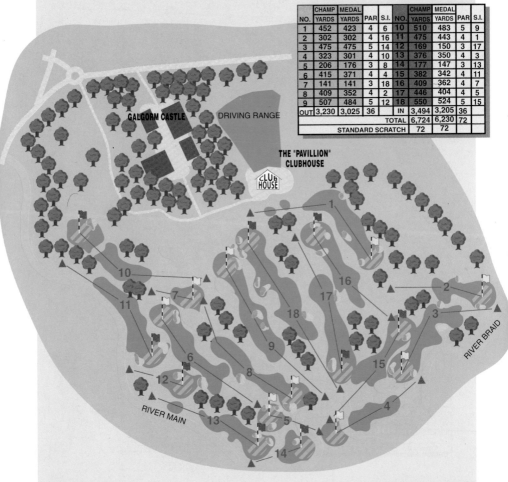

GALGORM CASTLE   DRIVING RANGE

THE "PAVILLION"
CLUBHOUSE

CLUB HOUSE

RIVER BRAID

RIVER MAIN

141 Ballinlea Road, Stranocum, Ballymoney, Co. Antrim, BT53 8PX. Tel: (01265) 751209.

LOCATION: Seven miles north of Ballymoney, fifty minutes from Belfast International Airport and ten minutes from the Causeway Coast.
PROPRIETORS: J&M Gillan.
ARCHITECT: Frank Ainsworth.

Gracehill opened in July 1995 and is a very challenging parkland course which will provide a stern test for even the best golfers. Some of the holes are played over water and many mature trees also come into play. At present there are fourteen holes open and the final ones are scheduled for the Summer of 1998 making it the only eighteen hole championship parkland course in North Antrim.

COURSE INFORMATION

Par 72; SSS 71; Length 6,600 yards.
Avoid: Weekends.
Opening Hours: 8am–Sunset.

Ladies: Restricted on mens' competitions days.
Green Fees: £12 Mon–Tue; £15 Wed–Fri; £18 Sat/Sun.
Juveniles: Must be accompanied by an adult.
Clubhouse Hours: 8am – Sunset.
Clubhouse Dress: Smart / Casual.
Clubhouse Facilities: Full restaurant facilities open to the public everyday from 12noon.

GRACEHILL CLUBHOUSE

CAR PARK

PRACTICE FAIRWAY

NO.	YARDS	PAR	S.I.	NO.	YARDS	PAR	S.I.
1	336	4	8	10	455	4	2
2	356	4	15	11	161	3	13
3	378	4	14	12	482	5	10
4	492	5	11	13	425	4	1
5	442	4	4	14	235	3	6
6	375	4	9	15	500	5	3
7	188	3	12	16	145	3	18
8	386	4	7	17	359	4	17
9	486	5	16	18	405	4	5
OUT	3,439	37		IN	3,167	35	
				TOTAL	6,606	72	
	STANDARD SCRATCH				71		

Bunker and tree positions indicated.

**Greenacres Golf Centre,
153 Ballyrobert Road,
Ballyclare, Co. Antrim.
Tel: (01960) 354111.
Fax: (01960) 354166.**

LOCATION: 8 miles from Belfast city centre.
SECRETARY: Michael Brown.
Tel: (01960) 354111.
PROFESSIONAL: Gary Mercer.

A challenging parkland course designed to fit in with the natural rolling countryside of County Antrim.

COURSE INFORMATION

**Par 71; SSS 69; Length
6,021 yards.
Visitors:** Welcome.
Opening Hours:
8.00am – 9.00pm.
Avoid: Saturday mornings.
Green Fees: £12 Mon - Thurs, £16 Fri, £18 Sat/Sun/Bank hols.
Ladies: Welcome.
Juveniles: Welcome if accompanied by an adult.
Clubhouse Dress:
Smart / Casual.

Clubhouse Facilities:
Full restaurant facilities and bar.
Weekend booking advisable.
Tel. Barnabys (01960) 354151.
20 bay full flood-lit driving range.
Open Competitions: August.

NO.	YARDS	PAR	S.I.	NO.	YARDS	PAR	S.I.
1	252	4	18	10	312	4	15
2	354	4	10	11	153	3	13
3	174	3	16	12	386	4	5
4	330	4	12	13	182	3	11
5	380	4	4	14	340	4	7
6	508	5	6	15	263	4	17
7	173	3	14	16	224	3	3
8	491	5	2	17	333	4	9
9	474	5	8	18	491	5	1
OUT	3,136	37		IN	2,684	34	
				TOTAL	5,820	71	
				STANDARD SCRATCH	69		

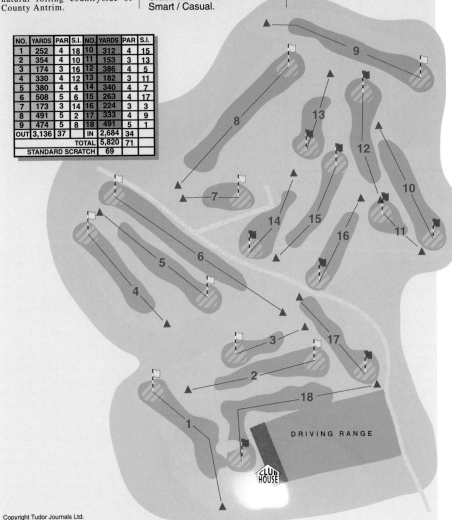

DRIVING RANGE

CLUB HOUSE

GREENISLAND

**156 Upper Road,
Greenisland,
Carrickfergus, BT38 8RW.
Tel: (01232) 862236.**

LOCATION: Eight miles north of Belfast, and two miles from Carrickfergus.
HON. SECRETARY: Jim Wyness. Tel: (01232) 862236.

The course is nestled at the foot of the Knockagh Hill and situated on the edge of Carrickfergus town. One of its features is the scenic views over Belfast Lough.

COURSE INFORMATION

**Par 71; SSS 68; Length 5,536 Metres.
Visitors: Welcome.
Opening Hours:** Sunrise – Sunset.
Avoid: Saurdays until 5.30pm and Club competitions.
Ladies: Saturdays after 5.30pm.
Green Fees: £12 Mon – Fri (£5 with a member); £18 Sat/Sun/All Public Holidays (£7.50 with a member).
Juveniles: Saturdays after

5.30pm. Must be accompanied by an adult. Prior arrangement is required for societies.
Clubhouse Hours: 12.00pm – 11.00pm (summer). Full clubhouse facilities.
Clubhouse Dress: Bar area — casual; Dinning room — jacket, collar and tie.
Clubhouse Facilities:
Tuesday – Sunday: Lunch and evening meals, bar snacks.
Open Competitions: Men's Open – June.
Mixed foursomes – May.

NO.	MEDAL METRES	GEN. METRES	PAR	S.I.	NO.	MEDAL METRES	GEN. METRES	PAR	S.I.
1	312	308	4	3	10	323	308	4	2
2	348	337	4	7	11	360	337	4	6
3	449	443	5	11	12	437	443	5	12
4	304	283	4	13	13	296	283	4	14
5	389	374	4	1	14	484	374	5	8
6	191	170	3	9	15	173	170	3	10
7	326	332	4	5	16	336	332	4	4
8	92	97	3	17	17	87	97	3	18
9	306	286	4	15	18	310	286	4	16
OUT	2,717	2,630	35		IN	2,806	2,630	35	
					TOTAL	5,523	5,260	71	
					STANDARD SCRATCH		69	68	

Bunker and tree positions indicated.

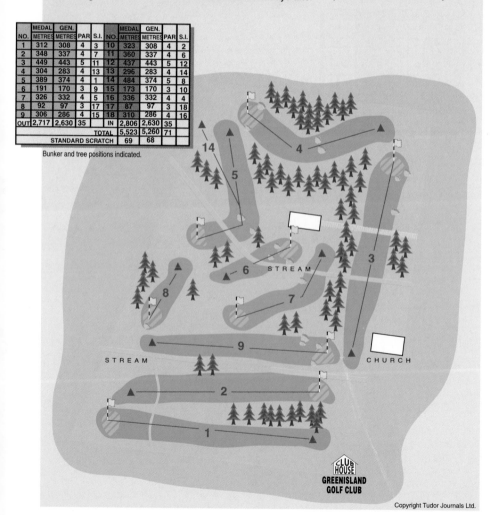

GREENISLAND
GOLF CLUB

LAMBEG

Aberdelghy, Bells Lane, Lambeg, Lisburn.
Tel: (01846) 662738.

LOCATION: Two miles from Lisburn town centre, off the main Lisburn / Belfast Road.
HON. SECRETARY: Frank Hazley.
Tel: (01846) 665750.
PROFESSIONAL: Ian Murdock.
Tel: (01846) 662738.

This parkland course is ideal for medium and high handicap golfers. An interesting feature is the par three 5th which straddles a reservoir. The course was recently upgraded to eighteen holes.

COURSE INFORMATION

Par 66; SSS 62; Length 4,139 metres.
Visitors: Welcome. Municiple course for public use.

Opening Hours: 8am – dusk.
Avoid: Tuesday, Sat/Sun.
Ladies: Welcome.
Green Fees: Mon – Fri £3.50 (18 holes £6.50); Sat / Sun / Public Holidays £4.20 (18 holes £7.50).
Clubhouse Facilities: Limited – no bar. Lessons available by prior arrangement. Club Hire available. Well stocked golf shop.

NO.	Metres	PAR	S.I.	NO.	Metres	PAR	S.I.
1	283	4	15	10	339	4	4
2	180	3	5	11	324	4	10
3	340	4	1	12	99	3	16
4	208	4	11	13	260	4	6
5	118	3	13	14	119	3	14
6	257	4	7	15	339	4	2
7	218	4	3	16	103	3	18
8	93	3	17	17	282	4	12
9	322	4	9	18	255	4	8
OUT	2,019	33		IN	2,120	33	
				TOTAL	4,139	66	
				STANDARD SCRATCH	62		

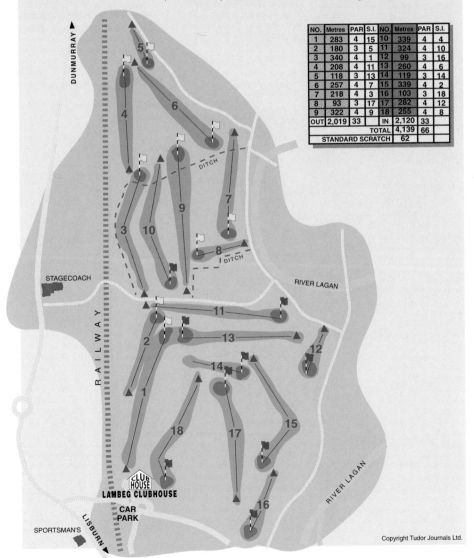

**54 Ferris Bay Road,
Islandmagee, Larne,
Co. Antrim BT40 3RT.
Tel: (01960) 382228.**

LOCATION: Six miles north
of Whitehead.
HON: SECRETARY: Mr Ken
Hedley.
Tel: (01960) 382228.
ARCHITECT: G. L. Bailie.

This course is part links, meadowland
with good views of Larne Lough to
the Maidens. The first five holes are
fairly 'open', and from the 6th the
course becomes tighter with the 7th,

8th and 9th being 'sterner' tests along
the shore. Greens are varied. The 8th
is the most difficult, spoiling many
good cards.

COURSE INFORMATION

**Par 70; SSS 70; Length
6,288 yards.**
Visitors: Welcome.
Opening Hours: Sunrise –
sunset.
Avoid: Friday & Saturday.
Ladies: Welcome Fridays.
Green Fees: £8 Mon – Fri
(with member £4); £15 Sat /
Sun / Bank Hols (w/m £6).

Saturdays – members only.
Juveniles: Mon – Fri before
5.00pm. Not at weekends.
Clubhouse Hours: Mon – Fri
1pm – 11.00pm; Sat 12 noon –
11pm, Sun 12.30pm – 2.30pm
and 5.00pm – 8.00pm. Full
clubhouse facilities.
Clubhouse Dress: Casual,
(no denims). Jacket and
tie for evening.
Clubhouse Facilities: Mon –
Fri bar snacks after 5.00pm by
arrangement. Sunday – as bar
hours.

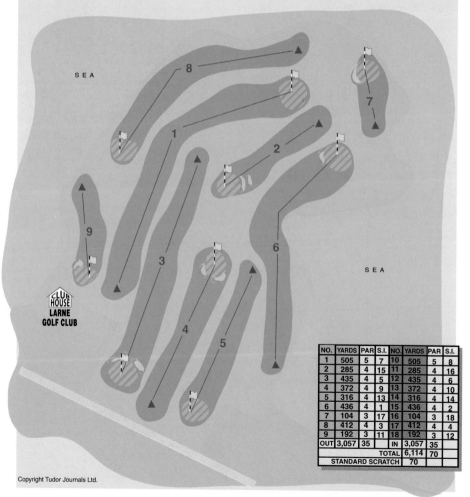

NO.	YARDS	PAR	S.I.	NO.	YARDS	PAR	S.I.
1	505	5	7	10	505	5	8
2	285	4	15	11	285	4	16
3	435	4	5	12	435	4	6
4	372	4	9	13	372	4	10
5	316	4	13	14	316	4	14
6	436	4	1	15	436	4	2
7	104	3	17	16	104	3	18
8	412	4	3	17	412	4	4
9	192	3	11	18	192	3	12
OUT	3,057	35		IN	3,057	35	
				TOTAL	6,114	70	
				STANDARD SCRATCH	70		

Copyright Tudor Journals Ltd.

LISBURN

**68 Eglantine Road,
Lisburn, Co. Antrim.
Tel: (01846) 677216.**

LOCATION: Two miles south of
Lisburn off A1 to Hillsborough.
SECRETARY / MANAGER:
George McVeigh.
Tel: (01846) 677216.
PROFESSIONAL: B.R. Campbell.
Tel: (01846) 677217.
ARCHITECT: F. Hawtree.

Mixture of parkland and
meadowland with reasonably flat
terrain which has an abundance of
trees, some of which have not yet
reached maturity. Landscaped in
recent years, many shrubs are

beginning to feature and enhance the
course. Again, this is a course of
championship standard with a very
difficult finish at 16, 17 and 18, with
the last hole being a spectacular
downhill Par 3 of 195 metres.

COURSE INFORMATION

**Par 72; SSS 72; Length
6,647 yards.**
Visitors: Welcome. Mon,
Wed, Thurs, Fri, Sun. Must
commence before 3.00pm.
Members only Tue & Sat.
Green Fees: £25 Mon – Fri
(with member £10);

£30 Sat / Sun / Bank Holidays
(with member £12).
Juveniles: Mon – Fri £12.50
(with member £5), Sat / Sun /
Bank Holidays £15 (with
member £6). Lessons by prior
arrangements. Club Hire
available. Caddy trolleys
available prior arrangement
required. Telephone club for
details on restricted hours of
play.
Clubhouse Dress:
Jacket and tie after 7.30pm.
Clubhouse Facilities:
Snacks and meals all day.

NO.	MEDAL YARDS	GEN. YARDS	PAR	S.I.	NO.	MEDAL YARDS	GEN. YARDS	PAR	S.I.
1	479	465	5	6	10	461	448	4	3
2	360	344	4	16	11	401	385	4	5
3	375	330	4	10	12	493	484	5	11
4	157	140	3	18	13	160	152	3	17
5	349	344	4	4	14	505	488	5	13
6	164	150	3	12	15	367	358	4	15
7	465	449	4	1	16	375	355	4	7
8	500	488	5	8	17	449	379	4	2
9	370	335	4	14	18	217	200	3	9
OUT	3,219	3,045	36		IN	3,428	3,249	36	
					TOTAL	6,647	6,294	72	
					STANDARD SCRATCH	72	70		

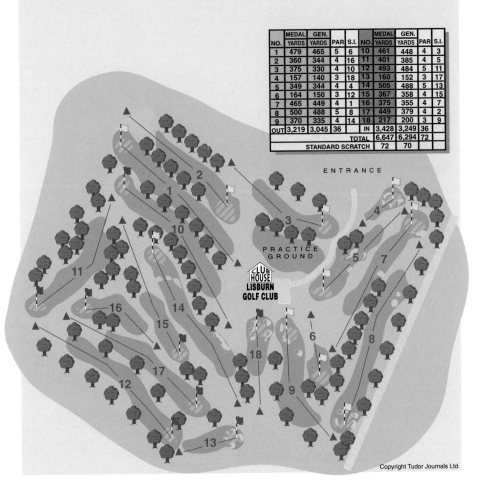

**51 Lough Road, Antrim
BT41 4DQ.
Tel: (01849) 428096.**

LOCATION: Two miles from
Antrim town centre.
SECRETARY/MANAGER: S. Green.
Tel: (01849) 428096
PROFESSIONAL: Jim Smyth.
Tel: (01849) 464074.
ARCHITECT: Mr F. Hawtree.

The first nine holes could be
described as parkland in character
with trees and indigenous scrub. The
second nine holes are adjacent to the
shore of Lough Neagh and are sandy
in nature resembling a links course.
The most difficult holes on the course
are the long Par 4's at the 6th and
17th. A true golf shot from the tee is

essential at the Par 3, 11th which is
well bunkered. The view from the
course takes in Lough Neagh and
Shanes Castle.

COURSE INFORMATION

**Par 72; SSS 71; Length
6,614 Yards.**
Visitors: Welcome.
Opening Hours: 7.30am –
8.00pm (summer); 8.00am –
4.00pm (winter).
Avoid: Sat & Fri mornings.
Ladies: Fridays.
Green Fees: £20 Mon – Fri;
£25 Sat/Sun; Ladies £12 Mon
– Fri; £15 Sat/Sun; Juveniles
£4 Mon – Fri; £7 Sat/Sun.
Juveniles: Mon – Fri; no
teeing off after 4.45pm unless

with an adult. Lessons
available by prior
arrangement. Club hire
available. Societies only need
prior arrangement.
Clubhouse Hours: 11.30am –
11.00pm. Full clubhouse
facilities.
Clubhouse Dress: Casual –
no denims.
Clubhouse Facilities:
Catering facilities: snack
meals and dining room meals
10.30am – 9.30pm (summer);
11.30am – 5.00pm (winter).
Open Competitions: Open
Week: first week in June;
Open Stroke: September.

NO.	MEDAL YARDS	GEN. YARDS	PAR	S.I.	NO.	MEDAL YARDS	GEN. YARDS	PAR	S.I.
1	374	350	4	5	10	510	480	5	14
2	400	384	4	3	11	205	189	3	10
3	130	118	3	17	12	341	329	4	8
4	363	346	4	7	13	415	425	4	2
5	376	360	4	9	14	135	126	3	18
6	460	436	4	1	15	392	377	4	6
7	554	538	5	11	16	496	480	5	16
8	196	187	3	15	17	436	420	4	4
9	329	313	4	13	18	502	487	5	12
OUT	3,182	3,032	35		IN	3,432	3,313	37	
					TOTAL	6,614	6,345	72	
					STANDARD SCRATCH	72	71		

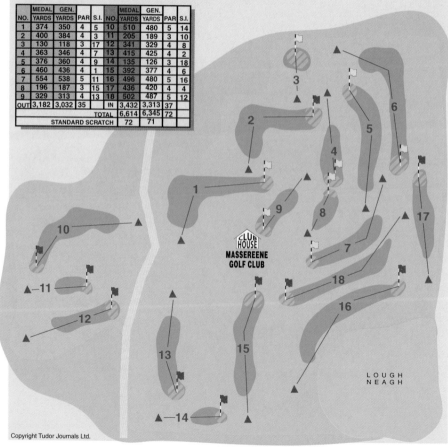

MASSEREENE
GOLF CLUB

LOUGH
NEAGH

**Bushmills Road, Portrush, Co. Antrim BT56 8JQ.
Tel: (01265) 822311.**

LOCATION: One mile from Portrush town towards Bushmills.
SECRETARY: Wilma Erskine.
Tel: (01265) 822311.
Fax: (01265) 823139.
PROFESSIONAL: Dai Stevenson.
Tel: (01265) 823335.
ARCHITECT: Harry Colt.

One of Ireland's most famous links courses. The course is laid out in a marvellous stretch of natural golfing country. Through a tangle of sandhills the course threads its way, with the sweeping contours of dunes lending infinite variety of the game. Situated east of Portrush occupying a triangle

of giant sandhills, from the highest point of which is an amazing varied prospect. The hills of Donegal in the west, the Isle of Islay and southern Hebrides in the north with the Giants Causeway and the Skerries to the east.

COURSE INFORMATION

Par 73; SSS 73; Length 6,641 yards.
Visitors: Welcome on any week day.
Opening Hours: Sunrise – sunset.
Avoid: Wed, Fri pm, Saturday.
Ladies: Welcome.
Green Fees: Mon – Fri £55 (£25 additional round); Sat / Sun / Bank Hols £65.
Juveniles: Play with a member. Lessons by prior arrangements.

Club Hire available; Caddy service available by prior arrangement. A letter of introduction is required and Handicap Certificate required.
Clubhouse Hours: 9am – 11pm. Full clubhouse facilities.
Clubhouse Dress: Casual acceptable; jacket & tie for functions.
Clubhouse Facilities: Limited snacks.
Open Competitions: Antrim Cup: May (Mixed foursomes); Lifeboat Trophy: June; Irish Cup: August (Mixed foursomes); Scott Cup: Sept (Mixed foursomes).

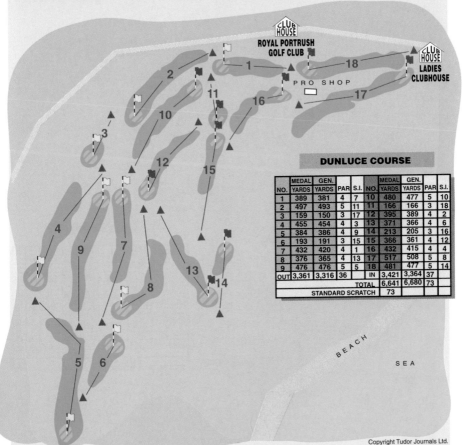

DUNLUCE COURSE

NO.	MEDAL YARDS	GEN. YARDS	PAR	S.I.	NO.	MEDAL YARDS	GEN. YARDS	PAR	S.I.
1	389	381	4	7	10	480	477	5	10
2	497	493	5	11	11	166	166	3	18
3	159	150	3	17	12	395	389	4	2
4	455	454	4	3	13	371	366	4	6
5	384	386	4	9	14	213	205	3	16
6	193	191	3	15	15	366	361	4	12
7	432	420	4	1	16	432	415	4	4
8	376	365	4	13	17	517	508	5	8
9	476	476	5	5	18	481	477	5	14
OUT	3,361	3,316	36		IN	3,421	3,364	37	
					TOTAL	6,641	6,680	73	
					STANDARD SCRATCH	73			

Bushmills Road, Portrush, Co. Antrim. BT56 8JQ.
Tel: (01265) 822311.

LOCATION: One mile from Portrush town towards Bushmills.
SECRETARY: Wilma Erskine.
Tel: (01265) 822311.
Fax: (01265) 823139.
PROFESSIONAL: Dai Stevenson.
Tel: (01265) 823335.
ARCHITECT: Harry Colt.

The Valley lies between the East Strand and the Dunluce course. It is the home of Royal Portrush Ladies Club and the affiliated Rathmore Club. Its characteristics are very much that of a links, undulating sandhills, remarkably dry and in some places below sea level.

COURSE INFORMATION

Par 70; SSS 71: Length 6,273 Yards.
Visitors: Welcome every day except mornings and weekends.
Opening Hours: Dawn – Dusk.
Avoid: Wed (pm); Sat (am) & Sun (before 10.00am).

Ladies: Saturday mornings.
Green Fees: £22 Mon – Fri (additional round £10); £30 Sat/Sun/Bank Hols.
Juveniles: Play with a member.
Clubhouse Hours: 9am – 11pm.
Clubhouse Dress: Smart casual at all times. Jacket and tie required for functions.
Clubhouse Facilities: Full clubhouse facilities. Catering facilities: snacks. R.P.G.C.

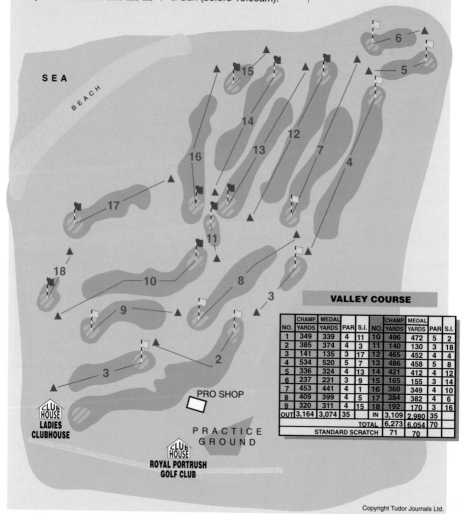

VALLEY COURSE

NO.	CHAMP. YARDS	MEDAL YARDS	PAR	S.I.	NO.	CHAMP. YARDS	MEDAL YARDS	PAR	S.I.
1	349	339	4	11	10	496	472	5	2
2	385	374	4	3	11	140	130	3	18
3	141	135	3	17	12	465	452	4	4
4	534	520	5	7	13	486	458	5	8
5	336	324	4	13	14	421	412	4	12
6	237	231	3	9	15	165	155	3	14
7	453	441	4	1	16	360	349	4	10
8	409	399	4	5	17	384	382	4	6
9	320	311	4	15	18	192	170	3	16
OUT	3,164	3,074	35		IN	3,109	2,980	35	
					TOTAL	6,273	6,054	70	
					STANDARD SCRATCH	71	70		

SEA

BEACH

PRO SHOP

PRACTICE GROUND

CLUB HOUSE
LADIES CLUBHOUSE

CLUB HOUSE
ROYAL PORTRUSH GOLF CLUB

**Temple Golf & Country Club,
60 Church Road, Boardmills,
Lisburn,
Co Antrim, BT27 6UP.
Tel: (01846) 639213.**

LOCATION: Situated within easy access to Belfast / Lisburn.
SECRETARY: David Kinnear.
Tel: (01846) 639213.
ARCHITECT: Paddy Johnson.

A 9 hole challenging golf course with a new innovation of 18 tees, designed to incorporate the panormic views of the Mourne Mountains and the Dromara Hills. Good natural drainage will ensure all year round golf.

COURSE INFORMATION

Par 68; SSS 69; Length 2,552 yards.
Visitors: Welcome every day except Satuday mornings.
Opening Hours: Mon – Fri 9am – 8pm; Sat & Sun 8am – 8pm.
Avoid: Saturday mornings.
Ladies: Welcome.
Green Fees: Weekdays £6 (£5 with member); weekends / Bank Holidays £8 (£7 with member).
Juveniles: Permitted to play until 5.30pm.
Clubhouse Hours: Mon – Thur 12.30 – 9pm; Fri & Sat all day; Saturday night licenced bar hours.

Clubhouse Dress:
Smart / casual.
Clubhouse Facilities:
Fitness suite, steam room, tennis courts, licenced bar & restaurant with conference & function facilities.
Open Competitions:
Varies year to year. Contact Club for details.

NO.	YARDS	PAR	S.I.	NO.	YARDS	PAR	S.I.
1	164	3	15	10	126	3	16
2	361	4	13	11	346	4	14
3	199	3	8	12	199	3	7
4	374	4	4	13	381	4	3
5	321	4	10	14	345	4	9
6	325	4	12	15	325	4	11
7	395	4	2	16	401	4	1
8	281	4	18	17	293	4	17
9	303	4	6	18	312	4	5
OUT	2,723	34		IN	2,728	34	
				TOTAL	5,451	68	
			STANDARD SCRATCH		69		

Bunker & tree positions indicated.

6/15

5/14

7/16

8/17 9/18

4/13

3/12

CLUB HOUSE
TEMPLE CLUBHOUSE

1/10

2/11

McCrae's Brae,
Whitehead, Carrickfergus,
Co. Antrim BT38 9NZ.
Tel: (01960)
353631/353792.

LOCATION: County Antrim coast. 18 miles north of Belfast, midway between Carrickfergus and Larne.
SECRETARY: J. M. Niblock.
Tel: (01960) 353631 (Mon – Fri; 9am – 1pm).
PRO SHOP: C. Farr.
Tel: (01960) 353118.

Parkland course overlooking Blackhead and the Irish Sea. The views from the 4th tee are superb and include Fairhead in the north, the Mourne Mountains to the south and Ailsa Craig to the east.

COURSE INFORMATION

Par 72; SSS 71; Length 6,362 Yards.
Visitors: Welcome Mon – Fri, Sunday with a member only.
Opening Hours: 9am – 6pm (April & Sept); 9am - 5pm (Winter).
Avoid: Saturdays.
Ladies: Mon – Fri unrestricted except 4.15pm – 7.00pm Wed & Fri. Sat after 6.00pm. Sun. unrestricted. Competition Day – Thursday.
Green Fees: £12 Mon – Fri (£7 with a member) £18 Sun, & Public Hols (only with member).
Juveniles: Mon – Fri before 4.15pm. Must be off by

6.00pm. Sunday after 2.30pm. (under 18) £7 Mon – Fri (£5 with a member); £8 Sat/Sun/All public holidays (£4 with a member). Parties 25 plus: £12 Mon – Fri; £18 Sat/Sun/all public holidays.
Clubhouse Hours: Summer: 12am – 11.30pm; Sun 12.30am – 8.30pm. Winter 6pm – 11.30pm. Sun. restricted.
Clubhouse Dress: Casual, except on Sat after 8.00pm – jacket and tie.
Clubhouse Facilities: Mon 12 – 2pm; Tues closed; Wed – Fri 12 – 2pm & 5pm – 9pm.
Open Competitions: August – McKenna Scratch & Open mixed foursomes Open week June/July .

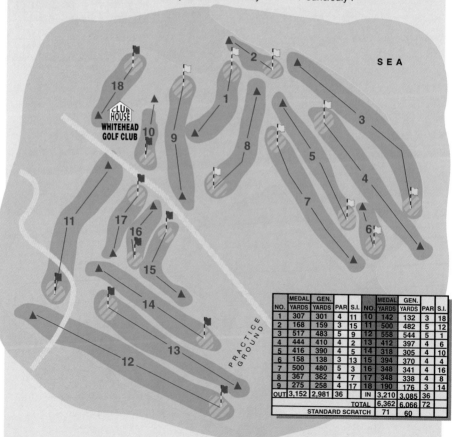

NO.	MEDAL YARDS	GEN. YARDS	PAR	S.I.	NO.	MEDAL YARDS	GEN. YARDS	PAR	S.I.
1	307	301	4	11	10	142	132	3	18
2	168	159	3	15	11	500	482	5	12
3	517	483	5	9	12	558	544	5	1
4	444	410	4	2	13	412	397	4	6
5	416	390	4	5	14	318	305	4	10
6	158	138	3	13	15	394	370	4	4
7	500	480	5	3	16	348	341	4	16
8	367	362	4	7	17	348	338	4	8
9	275	258	4	17	18	190	176	3	14
OUT	3,152	2,981	36		IN	3,210	3,085	36	
					TOTAL	6,362	6,066	72	
					STANDARD SCRATCH	71	60		

SEA

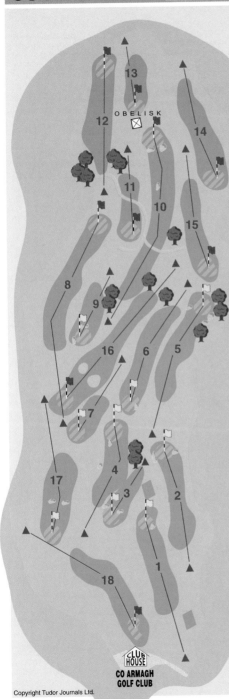

**CO ARMAGH
GOLF CLUB**

Copyright Tudor Journals Ltd.

**The Demense, Newry Road, Armagh.
Tel: (01861) 522501.**

SECRETARY: June McParland.
Tel: (01861) 525861.
PROFESSIONAL: Alan Rankin.
Tel: (01861) 525864.

This wooded parkland course, established in 1893, has nice views from the Obelisk built by Primate Robinson in 1700's. While the 16th might be considered the most difficult, the fifth requires an accurate drive and then an even more accurate second shot down an alley of mature trees, which should be the most rewarding hole to play well.

COURSE INFORMATION

Par 70; SSS 69; Length 5,649 Metres.
Visitors: Welcome Mon – Fri (contact Secretary's office for weekends).
Opening Hours: Sunrise – Sunset.
Avoid: Tues evenings and Thurs (Ladies Day).
Green Fees: £10-£15 weekdays, £15-£20 weekends (depends on numbers). Prior arrangement required if possible. Lessons available by prior arrangement. Caddy cars available.
Ladies Day: Thursday.
Juveniles: Monday – Friday with adult evenings and weekends.
Clubhouse Hours: 9.30am – 11.30pm.
Clubhouse Dress: Smart and neat (no denims or football garments).
Clubhouse Facilities: Full catering and bar facilities except Monday, bar snacks and a la carte available until 9.00pm.
Open Competitions: Open Stableford: May; Open Mixed Greensums: May; Lonsdale Cup: June; Open Mixed Team Competition: June; Open Mixed Greensums: July; Open Family Greensums: Aug; Open Mixed Greensums: Aug; Wood-Webster: Sep; Joshua White Stroke: Sep; Open Mixed Greensums: Sep; Ladies Open: Sep.

NO.	METRES	PAR	S.I.	NO.	METRES	PAR	S.I.
1	366	4	3	10	473	5	4
2	330	4	10	11	160	3	12
3	131	3	13	12	436	5	18
4	354	4	5	13	164	3	15
5	368	4	2	14	335	4	9
6	305	4	17	15	307	4	14
7	136	3	16	16	408	4	1
8	486	5	8	17	358	4	7
9	172	3	11	18	370	4	6
OUT	2,649	34		IN	3,009	36	
				TOTAL	5,658	70	
				STANDARD SCRATCH	69		

Bunker and tree positions indicated.

171

**Freeduff, Cullyhanna,
Co. Armagh.
Tel: (01693) 868180.
Fax:(01693) 868611.**

LOCATION: Two miles from
Crossmaglen.
SECRETARY: James and
Elizabeth Quinn.
PROFESSIONAL: Erill Maney.
ARCHITECT: Frank Ainsworth.

An interesting eighteen hole course
situated in attractive rural
surroundings. Advance notice is

recommended before turning up at
weekends. There are over one
hundred new trees of mature variety
and a man-made lake, and bunkers
on the 17th, 4th, 1st 3rd and 8th.

COURSE INFORMATION

**Par 69; SSS 70; Length
5,616 yards.
Visitors:** Welcome.
Telephone appointment
preferred.
Opening Hours: Summer
8.00am – 10.00pm.

Green Fees: £10 Mon – Fri;
£12 Sat / Sun. Special
reductions for school children,
students, senior citizens,
handicapped persons and
unemployed persons.Special
rates for societies.
Juveniles: Welcome.
Lessons by prior arrangment.
Club Hire available.
Clubhouse Hours:
8.00am – 10.00pm.
Clubhouse Dress: Informal.
Clubhouse Facilities: Meals
and snacks available.

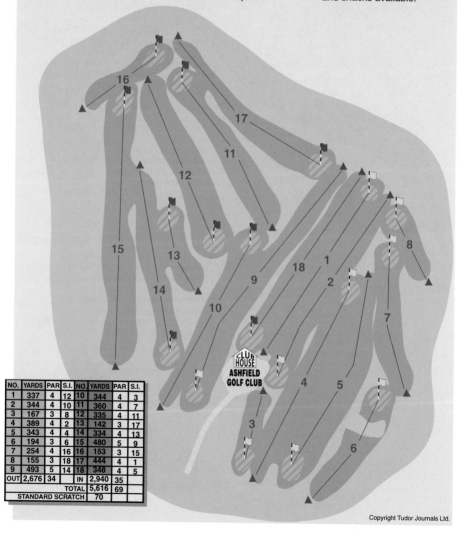

NO.	YARDS	PAR	S.I.	NO.	YARDS	PAR	S.I.
1	337	4	12	10	344	4	3
2	344	4	10	11	360	4	7
3	167	3	8	12	335	4	11
4	389	4	2	13	142	3	17
5	343	4	4	14	334	4	13
6	194	3	6	15	480	5	9
7	254	4	16	16	153	3	15
8	155	3	18	17	444	4	1
9	493	5	14	18	348	4	5
OUT	2,676	34		IN	2,940	35	
				TOTAL	5,616	69	
STANDARD SCRATCH					70		

NO.	MEDAL YARDS	GEN YARDS	PAR	S.I.	NO.	MEDAL YARDS	GEN YARDS	PAR	S.I.
1	550	531	5	5	10	530	502	5	4
2	426	368	4	1	11	186	160	3	10
3	358	330	4	17	12	284	270	4	18
4	168	148	3	13	13	481	470	5	12
5	403	373	4	3	14	401	380	4	2
6	382	372	4	9	15	424	380	4	6
7	195	170	3	11	16	289	269	4	16
8	311	285	4	15	17	184	174	3	8
9	342	322	4	7	18	330	320	4	14
OUT	3,135	2,899	35		IN	3,109	2,925	36	
					TOTAL	6,244	5,824	71	
				STANDARD SCRATCH	70	68		

Drumnabreeze Road,
Magheralin,
Craigavon, Co. Armagh.
Tel: (01846) 611310
Fax: (01846) 613310

LOCATION: Twenty miles from
Belfast, five minutes from
Moira roundabout. Signposted
from Magheralin on main
Moira - Lurgan Road.
SECRETARY: Robert McDowell.
ARCHITECT: Frank Ainsworth.

COURSE INFORMATION

Par 71; SSS 70; Length 6,244
yds.
Visitors: Very welcome.
Opening Hours: 8am –
Sunset.
Avoid: Saturdays before
2.00pm.
Ladies: Welcome.
Green Fees: Weekdays £12;
Saturdays £15.
Juveniles: Welcome. Lessons
can be arranged, telephone for
details.
Clubhouse Dress: Smart.
Clubhouse Facilities: Old Yard
Restaurant (closed Sun),
Showers etc.

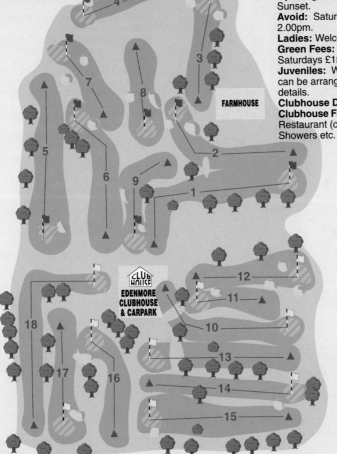

Bunker positions indicated.

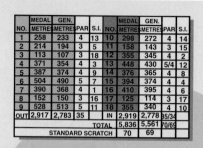

NO.	MEDAL METRES	GEN. METRES	PAR	S.I.	NO.	MEDAL METRES	GEN. METRES	PAR	S.I.
1	258	233	4	13	10	298	272	4	14
2	214	194	3	5	11	158	143	3	15
3	113	107	3	18	12	355	345	4	2
4	371	354	4	3	13	448	430	5/4	12
5	387	374	4	9	14	376	365	4	8
6	504	490	5	7	15	394	374	4	4
7	390	368	4	1	16	410	395	4	6
8	152	150	3	16	17	125	114	3	17
9	528	513	5	11	18	355	340	4	10
OUT	2,917	2,783	35		IN	2,919	2,778	35/34	
					TOTAL	5,836	5,561	70/69	
					STANDARD SCRATCH	70	69		

The Demense, Lurgan BT67 9BN.
Tel: (01762) 322087.

LOCATION: One to two miles from the town centre.
HONORARY SECRETARY: Mr S. McClean.
SECRETARY / MANAGER: Mrs G. Turkington.
Tel: (01762) 322087.
PROFESSIONAL: Des Paul.

Parkland course bordering on Lurgan Lake. Well wooded and greens well trapped. Pond on 7th and 17th fairways, internal out-of-bounds (on some holes), quite a few dog-legs, long straight driving essential. Considered quite a difficult course and well suited for low and middle handicappers.

COURSE INFORMATION

Par 70; SSS 70; Length 6,257 yards.
Visitors: Welcome Mon – Fri.
Opening Hours: 9.00am – 6.00pm.
Avoid: Wednesday (playing by arrangement) and Saturday.
Ladies: £12 (£6 with member).
Green Fees: £15 Mon – Fri (£7.50 with member); £20 Sat / Sun / Bank Holidays (£10 with member).
Juveniles: £5 Must give way to adult members and visitors.
Student: £10 (£5 with member).
Clubhouse Hours: 8.00am – 11.30pm. Professional shop open 9.00am – 6.00pm.
Clubhouse Dress: Smart / casual.
Clubhouse Facilities: Catering facilities: Bar snacks and full menu. Mon: closed; Tues & Thurs 12.00 – 9.00pm; Wed, Fri, Sat and Sun 12.00 – 9.00pm.
Open Competitions: Open week normally May. Handicap certificate required for Open Competition only.

PARK LAKE

CLUB HOUSE
LURGAN GOLF CLUB

192 Gilford Road, Portadown.
Tel: (01762) 355356.

LOCATION: On Gilford Road out of
Portadown, approx. 34 miles from Belfast.
SECRETARY: Mrs. Holloway.
Tel: (01762) 355356.
PROFESSIONAL: Mr. Paul Stevenson.
Tel: (01762) 334655.
ARCHITECT: Clive Henning.

Situated on the edge of Portadown this parkland
course has one of the holes actually played over
the River Bann (9th). Trees come into play on
many of the holes, and the course is generally flat.

COURSE INFORMATION

Par 70; SSS 70; Length 5,621 Metres.
Visitors: Welcome.
Opening Hours: 9.00am – 9.30pm.
Ladies: Tuesday (No green fees on
Tuesdays).
Green Fees: £17 Mon – Fri (£10 with
member); £21 Sat / Sun, Bank Holidays
(£11 with member); Ladies: £15 Mon –
Fri (£9 with member); £19 Sat / Sun (£9
with member); Juveniles: 50% off listed
price.
Juveniles: Mon, Wed, Fri until 4.00pm;
Thur after 12.00 noon Sat before
5.00pm; resricted on Sun. Club Hire
available.
Clubhouse Hours: Office: 9.00am –
5.00pm. Bar: 12.00 noon – 11.00pm. Full
Clubhouse facilities.
Clubhouse Dress: Neat dress essential.
No jeans, shorts or sleeveless shirts both
on the course or clubhouse.
Clubhouse Facilities: Full catering, a
la carte, snacks and functions 12.00 –
9.00pm. Closed Mondays.
Open Competitions: Opens run
throughout the season.

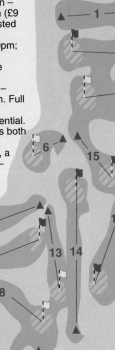

PORTADOWN
GOLF CLUB

RIVER
BANN

NO.	METRES	PAR	S.I.	NO.	METRES	PAR	S.I.
1	247	4	18	10	334	4	12
2	297	4	14	11	376	4	9
3	392	4	1	12	378	4	4
4	150/143	3	13	13	173	3	7
5	398	4	3	14	259	4	15
6	113	3	17	15	129	3	16
7	346	4	8	16	329	4	10
8	371	4	5	17	504	5	6
9	452	5	11	18	401	4	2
OUT	2,766	35		IN	2,883	35	
				TOTAL	5,621	70	
		STANDARD SCRATCH			70		

SILVERWOOD

U L S T E R

ARMAGH

**Tormoyra Lane, Silverwood,
Lurgan, BT66 6NG.
Tel: (01762) 326606.**

LOCATION: The Golf/Ski Centre is
located at Silverwood, just off the
M1 Lurgan roundabout.
MANAGER: Vincent P. McCorry.
ASS. MANAGER: Geoff Coupland.
PROFESSIONAL: Part-time, Mr D. Paul.
Tel: (01762) 326606.

The course has sand-based, well irrigated
greens making ideal winter putting conditions
and is ideally suited for the middle and high
handicap golfers. One of it's main features are
the lakes which are incorporated into the third
and tenth holes. The course has already
proved extremely popular with golfing
societies for tournaments.

COURSE INFORMATION

Par 72; SSS 72; Length 6,496 yards.
Visitors: Welcome to play: municipal
course for public use.
Opening Hours: Daylight hours.
Green Fees: £10.50 Mon – Fri; £13.50
Sat, Sun & Bank Hols. Club Hire
available.
Clubhouse Hours: Monday – Sunday
9.00am – 7.00pm.
Clubhouse Facilities: New clubhouse
open. Full restaurant available. Driving
range Par 3 Course.
Open Competitions: June / July.

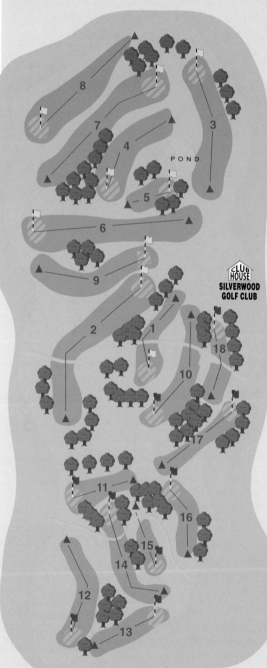

NO.	YARDS	PAR	S.I.	NO.	YARDS	PAR	S.I.
1	401	4	5	10	484	5	11
2	529	5	9	11	188	3	10
3	390	4	8	12	369	4	6
4	320	4	16	13	284	4	17
5	161	3	18	14	464	4	1
6	433	4	4	15	212	3	3
7	444	4	2	16	321	4	13
8	387	4	7	17	326	4	15
9	477	5	12	18	306	4	14
OUT	3,542	37		IN	2,954	35	
				TOTAL	6,496	72	
			STANDARD SCRATCH		72		

**Markethill Rd, Tandragee.
Tel: (01762) 840727.**

LOCATION: Six miles from Portadown, 15 miles from Newry.
SECRETARY/MANAGER: Brian Carson. Tel: (01762) 841272.
PROFESSIONAL: Paul Stevenson. Tel: (01762) 841761.

Parkland course — complete with beautiful old trees and pleasant views of the Mourne Mountains and South Armagh hills.

COURSE INFORMATION

Par 71; SSS 70; Length 5,589 metres.
Visitors: Welcome.
Opening Hours: Dawn – dusk.
Avoid: After 4.00pm Mon – Fri. Sat and Sun.
Green Fees: £14 weekdays; £21 Sat / Sun / Public Holidays.
Ladies: £10 weekdays; £18 weekends.
Juveniles: £5 weekdays.

Clubhouse Hours:
9.00am – 11.00pm. Full clubhouse facilities.
Clubhouse Dress: Casual; jacket & tie on function nights.
Clubhouse Facilities: Full catering from 12.30pm. Last orders 9pm.
Open Competitions: May Holiday, August Bank Holiday and Dixon Cup – June (one day). Handicap certificate required for competitions.

NO.	METRES	PAR	S.I.	NO.	METRES	PAR	S.I.
1	346	4	4	10	305	4	15
2	273	4	14	11	380	4	1
3	490	5	6	12	350	4	5
4	307	4	18	13	363	4	9
5	168	3	11	14	140	3	17
6	322	4	16	15	304	4	7
7	388	4	2	16	157	3	10
8	456	5	12	17	474	5	13
9	182	3	8	18	342	4	3
OUT	2,932	36		IN	2,815	35	
				TOTAL	5,747	71	
			STANDARD SCRATCH		70		

Bunker and tree positions indicated.

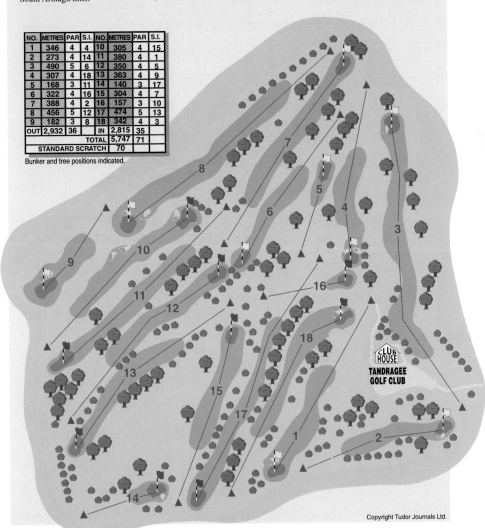

TANDRAGEE
GOLF CLUB

**518 Lisburn Road,
Belfast BT9 6GX.
Tel: (01232) 381514.**

LOCATION: Two to three miles south of Belfast City Centre on main Lisburn Road, next to King's Hall.
MANAGER: R. McConkey.
PROFESSIONAL: G. Bleakley.
Tel: (01232) 667747.

A flat undulating course with thirty plus bunkers, and a stream to contend with when playing. The greens are generally excellent and approached by tree-lined fairways.

Situated beside the Royal Ulster Agricultural Society, the course is particularly convenient to Belfast city centre.

COURSE INFORMATION

**Par 69; SSS 70;
Length 5,702 Metres.
Visitors:** Welcome.
Green Fees: £20 Mon – Fri (£24 Wed.) £10 with member. £30 weekends & public holidays (£10 with a member).
Ladies: £16 Mon - Fri; £20 weekends; £9 with a member / Public holidays.
Juveniles: £7 and restricted on weekends. Lessons by prior

arrangement.
Clubhouse Hours: 9.00am - 11.00pm
Clubhouse Dress: Smart casual (no jeans) up to 8.00pm. After 7.30pm jacket and tie for gentlemen.
Catering Facilities: Lunch 12.30pm - 2.30pm; Evening meal 6.30pm - 10.00pm. Full a la carte menu. (Last orders 9.30pm).
Open Competitions: Several throughout the golfing season.
Convenient Hotel: Balmoral Hotel, Blacks road, Dunmurry, Belfast, (01232) 301234.

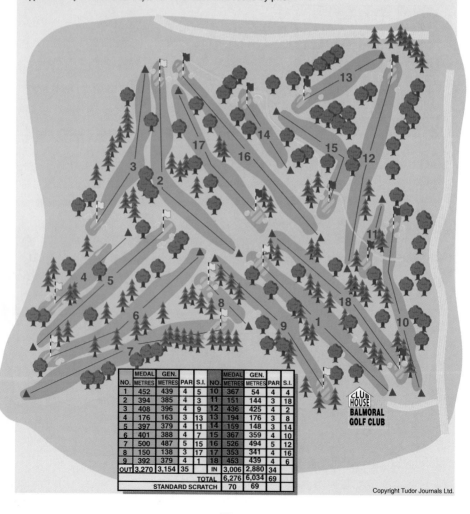

BALMORAL GOLF CLUB

NO.	MEDAL METRES	GEN. METRES	PAR	S.I.	NO.	MEDAL METRES	GEN. METRES	PAR	S.I.
1	452	439	4	5	10	367	54	4	4
2	394	385	4	3	11	151	144	3	18
3	408	396	4	9	12	436	425	4	2
4	176	163	3	13	13	194	176	3	8
5	397	379	4	11	14	159	148	3	14
6	401	388	4	7	15	367	359	4	10
7	500	487	5	15	16	526	494	5	12
8	150	138	3	17	17	353	341	4	16
9	392	379	4	1	18	453	439	4	6
OUT	3,270	3,154	35		IN	3,006	2,880	34	
					TOTAL	6,276	6,034	69	
					STANDARD SCRATCH		70	69	

Newtownbreda, Belfast BT8 4AN.
Tel: (01232) 491693.
Fax: (01232) 646113.

LOCATION: Four miles south of city centre.
SECRETARY: K.H. Graham.
Tel: (01232) 491693.
Fax: (01232) 646113.
PROFESSIONAL: Maurice Kelly.
Tel: (01232) 646714.

Considered one of the best inland courses with fair but tight fairways and good greens. Rarely closed due to water logging. The course has extensive mature woods and many scenic views.

COURSE INFORMATION

Par 71; SSS 71; Length 6,476 Yards.
Visitors: Welcome Mon, Tues, Thur and Sun.
Opening Hours: 8am – dusk.
Avoid: Wednesday & Saturday (competiton days). Friday is Ladies Day, prior arrangement is preferred.
Ladies Day: Friday.
Green Fees: Weekdays excluding Wed – £33. Weekends and Bank Holidays – £38.
Clubhouse Dress: Jacket, collar and tie after 7.30pm.
Clubhouse Facilities: Catering facilities 10.30am – 9.30pm.
Open Competitions: Mixed foursomes in June; Open week – July.
Clubhouse Hours: 10am – 11pm.

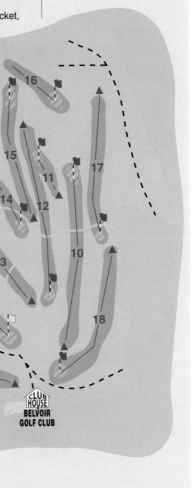

BELVOIR GOLF CLUB

NO.	MEDAL YARDS	GEN. YARDS	PAR	S.I.	NO.	MEDAL YARDS	GEN. YARDS	PAR	S.I.
1	284	260	4	18	10	480	439	5	5
2	398	364	4	6	11	181	166	3	15
3	428	391	4	2	12	462	422	4	1
4	190	174	3	8	13	370	338	4	9
5	491	449	5	14	14	167	153	3	13
6	393	359	4	10	15	507	464	5	11
7	440	402	4	3	16	204	187	3	7
8	140	128	3	16	17	449	411	4	4
9	484	443	5	12	18	407	372	4	17
OUT	3,249	2,970	36		IN	3,227	2,952	35	
					TOTAL	6,476	5,922	71	
	STANDARD SCRATCH		71						

CLIFTONVILLE ULSTER BELFAST

NO.	YARDS	PAR	S.I.	NO.	YARDS	PAR	S.I.
1	181	3	7	10	181	3	8
2	406	4	1	11	406	4	2
3	327	4	13	12	327	4	14
4	137	3	15	13	137	3	16
5	341	4	3	14	341	4	4
6	350	4	9	15	350	4	10
7	331	4	5	16	331	4	6
8	439	5	17	17	439	5	18
9	324	4	11	18	324	4	12
OUT	2,836	35		IN	2,836	35	
				TOTAL	5,672	70	
				STANDARD SCRATCH		70	

Bunker and tree positions indicated.

**44 Westland Road, Belfast
BT14 6NH.
Tel: (01232) 744158.**

LOCATION: Situated between Cavehill
Road and Cliftonville Circus.
SECRETARY: J. M. Henderson.
Tel: (01232) 746595.

Parkland course on rising ground with
exstensive views of Belfast Lough. Course is
played around the waterworks complex.

COURSE INFORMATION

**Par 70; SSS 70; Length 5,672 Yards.
Visitors:** Welcome to play up to 5.00pm.
Opening Hours: 8.30am – sunset.
Avoid: Tuesday afternoons and
Sunday mornings. Members only —
Saturday, (visitors can only be
accompanied by a member after 6.00pm.
Ladies: Tuesday.
Green Fees: £12 weekdays (w/m £8);
£15 Sat, Sun / Bank Holidays (w/m £10).
Juveniles: £5 weekdays only. Full
clubhouse facilities.
Clubhouse Hours: 8.30am – midnight.
Clubhouse Dress: No denims. Jacket
and tie in lounge after 9.00pm.
Clubhouse Facilities: Snacks, meals
12.00 - 3.00pm and a la carte 5.00pm -
9.00pm. No catering on Monday except
by arrangement.

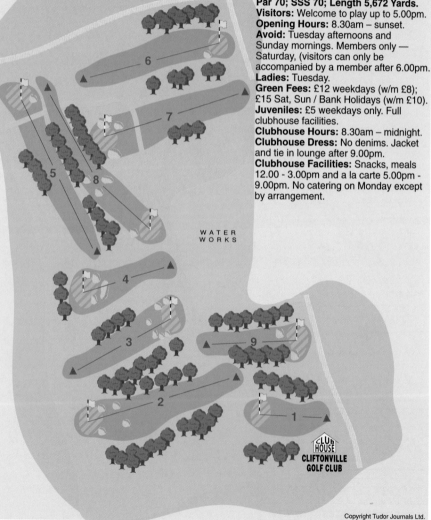

WATER
WORKS

CLUB HOUSE
CLIFTONVILLE
GOLF CLUB

Copyright Tudor Journals Ltd.

**91 Dunmurry Lane,
Dunmurry, Belfast.
Tel: (01232) 610834.**

LOCATION: Between Upper
Malone Road and Lisburn Rd.
SECRETARY/MANAGER: Ian McBride.
Tel: (01232) 610834.
PROFESSIONAL: J. Dolan.
ASSISTANT: G. Morrow.
Tel: (01232) 621314.

The course lies astride Dunmurry
Lane and consists of rolling
parkland in all directions. Since its
opening in 1983 it has matured
well and is a popular venue for
many golfers. The lake at the tenth
makes it a very interesting hole.

COURSE INFORMATION

**Par 69; SSS 68; Length
5,832 Yards.**
Visitors: Welcome Mon –
Thur by arrangement.
Opening Hours: Dawn to
dusk.
Ladies: Welcome Friday.
Green Fees: £17
weekdays; £26.50
weekends.
Juveniles: Must be
accompanied by an adult.
Lessons, Club Hire and
Caddy trolleys (limited)
available.

Clubhouse Dress: Jacket
and tie after 7.00pm and all
day Sunday, otherwise smart /
casual.
Clubhouse Facilities: Full
clubhouse facilities all week
during summer months.
Snacks and meals: Mon – Fri
12.00 – 2.30pm and 6.00pm –
9.30pm; Sat 12.00 – 9.00pm;
Sun 12.00 – 2.30pm and
5.30pm – 8.00pm. No catering
on Mon during the winter.
Open Competitions: Open
Week: 2nd – 10th Aug. Various
other semi opens during the
summer.

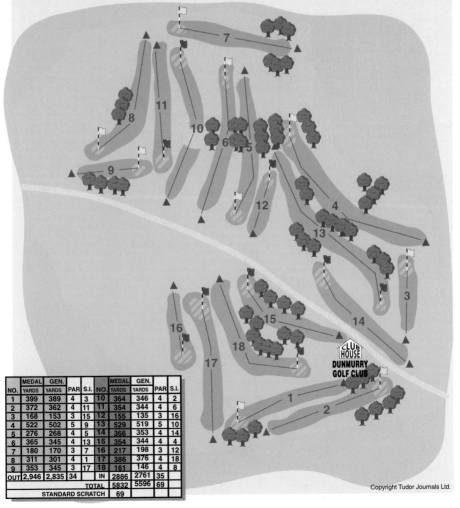

NO.	MEDAL YARDS	GEN. YARDS	PAR	S.I.	NO.	MEDAL YARDS	GEN. YARDS	PAR	S.I.
1	399	389	4	3	10	364	346	4	2
2	372	362	4	11	11	354	344	4	6
3	168	153	3	15	12	155	135	3	16
4	522	502	5	9	13	529	519	5	10
5	276	268	4	5	14	366	353	4	14
6	365	345	4	13	15	354	344	4	4
7	180	170	3	7	16	217	198	3	12
8	311	301	4	1	17	386	376	4	18
9	353	345	3	17	18	161	146	4	8
OUT	2,946	2,835	34		IN	2886	2761	35	
					TOTAL	5832	5596	69	
					STANDARD SCRATCH		69		

**Downview Avenue,
Belfast BT15 4EZ.
Tel: (01232) 370770.**

LOCATION: Off Antrim Rd,
Belfast.
HONORARY SECRETARY:
Michael Purdy.
Tel: (01232) 370770.
PROFESSIONAL: Peter Hanna.
Tel: (01232) 770980.
ARCHITECT: H. Colt.

The course is dominated by the
picturesque and heavily wooded
'Cavehill' which rises to over 1,000
feet above sea level, making an
attractive background to many

shots throughout the round. There
is quite a height difference between
the top and bottom of the course,
which in itself is divided into two
parts by Grays Lane.

COURSE INFORMATION

**Par 70; SSS 69; Length
5,973 Yards.**
Visitors: Welcome Mon - Fri.
Opening Hours: 8.30 – Dusk.
Ladies: £19 Mon – Fri (£12
with a member) £23 Sat / Sun
/ Bank holidays (£14 with a
member).
Ladies Day: Monday &
Friday.
Green Fees: £21 Mon – Fri

(£13 with a member) £28 Sat
/ Sun / Bank holidays (£15
with a member).
Juveniles: Can play all day
Mon, Tues, Thur, Fri & Sun.
Restricted hours Wed & Sat –
telephone club for details.
Clubhouse Hours: 9.00am –
11.30pm everyday.
Clubhouse Dress: October –
March jacket and tie after
9.00pm. April - September
casual smart dress (no
denims).
Open Competitions: Open
Week – August; plus various
other open competitions.

NO.	YARDS	PAR	S.I.	NO.	YARDS	PAR	S.I.
1	421	4	7	10	195	3	10
2	329	4	9	11	378	4	8
3	437	4	1	12	131	3	18
4	314	4	17	13	377	4	2
5	474	5	11	14	502	5	12
6	169	3	15	15	315	4	14
7	311	4	3	16	345	4	4
8	421	4	5	17	150	3	16
9	272	4	13	18	432	4	6
OUT	3,148	36		IN	2,825	34	
				TOTAL	5,973	70	
STANDARD SCRATCH		69					

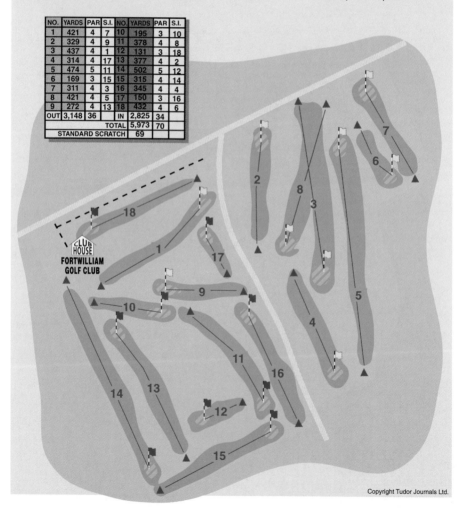

FORTWILLIAM
GOLF CLUB

Copyright Tudor Journals Ltd.

Summerfield, Dundonald, Belfast.
BT16 0QX.
Tel: (01232) 482249.

LOCATION: Five miles east of Belfast on the Upper Newtownards Road.
SECRETARY / MANAGER: Mr Managh.
Tel: (01232) 483251.
PROFESSIONAL: Gordon Fairweather.
Tel: (01232) 483825.

Parkland course with numerous large and small trees with the additional hazard of several deep bunkers. The 8th is an interesting hole with a river immediately fronting the green. The course is situated on the eastern suburbs of the city adjacent to Dundonald village.

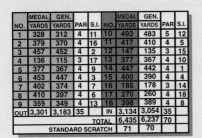

NO.	MEDAL YARDS	GEN. YARDS	PAR	S.I.	NO.	MEDAL YARDS	GEN. YARDS	PAR	S.I.
1	328	312	4	11	10	493	483	5	12
2	379	370	4	16	11	417	410	4	5
3	457	452	4	2	12	147	135	3	15
4	136	115	3	17	13	377	367	4	10
5	377	367	4	9	14	447	442	4	1
6	453	447	4	3	15	400	390	4	4
7	402	374	4	7	16	185	178	3	14
8	410	397	4	6	17	270	260	4	18
9	359	349	4	13	18	398	389	4	8
OUT	3,301	3,183	35		IN	3,134	3,054	35	
					TOTAL	6,435	6,237	70	
					STANDARD SCRATCH	71	70		

COURSE INFORMATION

Par 70; SSS 71; Length 6,435 Yards.
Visitors: Welcome Mon – Fri & Sun.
Avoid: Tues & Sat.
Ladies: Anytime except after 4pm Wed & before 4pm Sat.
Ladies Day: Tuesday.
Green Fees: £20 Mon – Fri; £25 Sun & Public Holidays.
Juveniles: Anytime except after 4pm Wed & before 4pm Sat. Lessons by prior arrangement. Club hire available.
Clubhouse Dress: Smart casual dress throughout the clubhouse, except after 7.00pm on Saturdays when jacket and tie are required.
Clubhouse Facilities: Full catering facilities. Snacks and meals available all day.
Open Competitions: Open week – June.

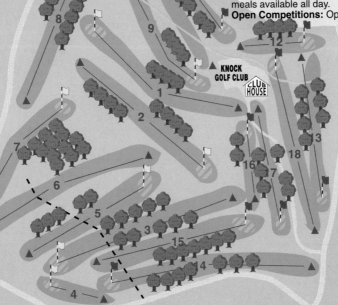

KNOCK
GOLF CLUB
CLUB HOUSE

MOUNT OBER

**Mount Ober Golf and
Country Club,
24 Ballymaconaghy Road,
Knockbracken, Belfast.
Tel: (01232) 792108.
Fax: (01232) 705862.**

LOCATION: 15 minutes from
the city centre, off the
Saintfield Road.
SECRETARY/MANAGER: P. Laverty.
Tel: (01232) 792108.
PROFESSIONAL: Geoff Loughrey.
Tel: (01232) 792108.

Hillside course with narrow, but
open fairways. It has several other
sporting facilities on location. There
is a large Golf Driving Range at the
complex, which is ideal for practice
and a Golf Academy with shop and
teaching professionals.

COURSE INFORMATION

**Par 67; SSS 68; Length
5,321 Metres.
Visitors:** Welcome anytime.
Avoid: Saturday all day and
Sunday 8am – 10.30am.
Ladies: Welcome anytime.

Green Fees: £11 Mon – Fri;
£14 Sat & Sun.
Juveniles: Weekdays and
after 3pm Sat & Sun.
Lessons by prior
arrangements. Club Hire
available. Caddy cars are
also available.
Clubhouse Dress: Smart
casual wear after 7.30pm.
Clubhouse Facilities: Full
clubhouse facilities.Snacks
and meals all day for up to 100
people. All weather barbecue
available also.

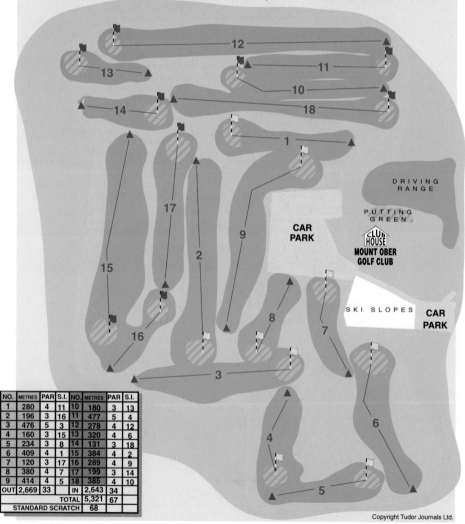

NO.	METRES	PAR	S.I.	NO.	METRES	PAR	S.I.
1	280	4	11	10	180	3	13
2	196	3	16	11	477	5	4
3	476	5	3	12	278	4	12
4	160	3	15	13	320	4	6
5	234	3	8	14	131	3	18
6	409	4	1	15	384	4	2
7	120	3	17	16	289	4	9
8	380	4	7	17	199	3	14
9	414	4	5	18	385	4	10
OUT	2,669	33		IN	2,643	34	
				TOTAL	5,321	67	
				STANDARD SCRATCH		68	

240 Upper Malone Road, Dunmurry, Belfast BT17 9LB.
Tel: (01232) 612695.

LOCATION: Five miles from centre of Belfast.
SECRETARY: M H Turnbull.
Tel: (01232) 612758.
MANAGER: Nick Agate.
PROFESSIONAL: Michael McGee.
Tel: (01232) 614917.
CATERER: (01232) 614916.

One of the most picturesque inland golf courses in the Province with many mature trees and flowering shrubs. This course is of championship standard and has a very high standard of course maintenance. The greens on the course are large with many undulations and an exceptionally good putting surface. The course is quite long and demanding and is classed as one of the best inland courses in Ireland. A real pleasure to play. Malone is now a 27 hole golf club.

COURSE INFORMATION

Par 71; SSS 71; Length 6,599 Yards.
Visitors: Welcome, although letter of introduction or handicap preferred.
Opening Hours: 8am – Dusk.
Avoid: Wednesday pm – members only. No visitors before 5pm Sat.
Ladies Day: Tuesday.
Green Fees: £32 Mon – Fri (£15 with member); £37 Sat / Sun, Wed & Bank Holidays (£17 with member). Lessons by prior arrangements. Caddy trolleys available. Society & Company book through office Mon & Thurs only.
Juveniles: Restricted on main course.
Clubhouse Hours: From 8.00am. Full club facilities when with a member.
Clubhouse Dress: Jacket and tie in mixed lounge, otherwise smart / casual. No denim, tee shirts or training shoes on main course.
Clubhouse Facilities: Full catering by arrangement with caterer. Lunch and bar snacks.
Open Competitions: Open Week: 18th – 25th July. Open Scratch Foursomes in June.

NO.	MEDAL YARDS	SOCIETY YARDS	PAR	S.I.	NO.	MEDAL YARDS	SOCIETY YARDS	PAR	S.I.
1	382	361	4	9	10	404	390	4	10
2	505	483	5	5	11	394	365	4	16
3	522	480	5	17	12	193	181	3	4
4	158	147	3	7	13	397	380	4	14
5	440	400	4	3	14	419	403	4	2
6	195	156	3	13	15	132	134	3	18
7	468	455	4	1	16	309	296	4	8
8	366	340	4	15	17	525	476	5	6
9	365	354	4	11	18	425	388	4	12
OUT	3,401	3,176	36		IN	3,198	3,013	35	
					TOTAL	6,599	6,189	71	
					STANDARD SCRATCH	71	69		

Bunker and tree positions indicated.

MALONE GOLF CLUB

CLUB HOUSE

PRO SHOP

LAKE

RIVER LAGAN

50 Park Road,
Belfast
BT7 2FX.
Tel: (01232) 641069.
Fax: (01232) 646250.

LOCATION: Alongside Ravenhill Road and Park Road, adjacent to Ormeau Road.
SECRETARY / MANAGER: Robin Kirk.
SHOP MANAGER: Bertie Wilson.
Tel: (01232) 640999.
PROFESSIONAL: Bertie Wilson.

A parkland setting on the edge of Ormeau Park, this course is tree-lined on all holes, with a realistic out of bounds on eight of the nine holes.

Nearest golf course to Belfast city centre, although situated in a quiet residential area. New clubhouse recently constructed.

COURSE INFORMATION

Par 68; SSS 66; Length 5,308 Yards, 4,850 Metres.
Visitors: Welcome except Tuesday evening, (Ladies competition) and Saturdays until 4.30pm.
Opening Hours: 9.00am – 11.00pm seven days per week.
Avoid: Visitors play up to 5pm every day except Tuesday.
Ladies: Can play up to 5.00pm every day except Sat.

Ladies Day: Tuesday.
Green Fees: £12 Weekdays; £14.50 Weekends. Telephone for special offers – golfers free fry etc.
Juveniles: Can play up to 5pm every day. Except on Wednesday. Otherwise accompanied by an adult.
Clubhouse Hours: Mon – Sat 11.30am – 11.00pm. Sun 12.30pm – 10pm.
Clubhouse Dress: Smart / casual. Jacket, collar and tie after 7.30pm on Sat.
Clubhouse Facilities: Restaurant, lounge bar & snooker.

NO.	METRES	PAR	S.I.	NO.	METRES	PAR	S.I.
1	261	4	15	10	261	4	16
2	265	4	13	11	265	4	14
3	465	5	3	12	465	5	4
4	92	3	17	13	92	3	18
5	414	4	1	14	414	4	2
6	173	3	7	15	173	3	8
7	274	4	9	16	274	4	10
8	202	3	5	17	202	3	6
9	279	4	11	18	279	4	12
OUT	2,425	34		IN	2,425	34	
			TOTAL		4,850	68	
	STANDARD SCRATCH				66		

Bunkers and tree positions indicated.

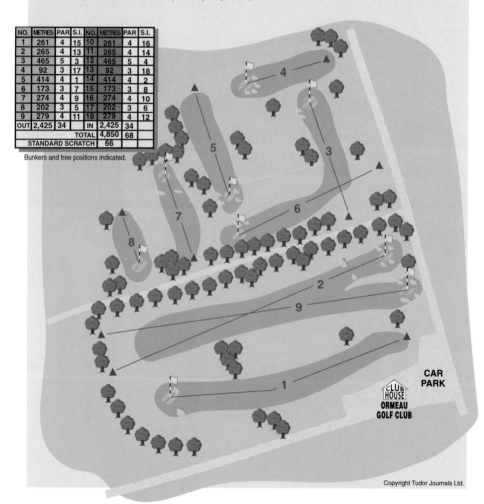

CAR PARK

ORMEAU GOLF CLUB

ROCKMOUNT

**28 Drumalig Road,
Carryduff, Co.Down.
Tel: (01232) 812279.**

LOCATION: Seven miles south of Belfast.
SECRETARY: R & D. Patterson.
Tel: (01232) 812279.

18 hole Drumlin Course set in the beauty and quiet of the countryside with scenic views of the Mourne Mountains. The course has been designed to ensure that the land's natural features are incorporated throughout the 18 holes.

COURSE INFORMATION

Par 72; SSS 71; Length 6,373 yards.
Visitors: Welcome any day.
Opening Hours: 8am – Dusk.
Avoid: Saturday (members only).
Ladies: Welcome.
Green Fees: Mon – Fri £18 & Sundays £22.
Juveniles: Welcome, must be accompanied by an adult.
Clubhouse Hours: 8.00am – 11.30pm. (Seasonal).

Clubhouse Facilities: Restaurant open to the public. Grill & A La Carte menu available. Function room & professional shop.
Clubhouse Dress: Smart / Casual, No Denims.

NO.	CHAMP YARDS	MEDAL YARDS	PAR	S.I.	NO.	CHAMP YARDS	MEDAL YARDS	PAR	S.I.
1	301	289	4	12	10	358	345	4	5
2	496	485	5	4	11	397	381	4	2
3	213	199	3	6	12	157	147	3	15
4	287	280	4	16	13	353	340	4	9
5	541	513	5	8	14	361	343	4	11
6	489	473	5	18	15	554	511	5	7
7	410	384	4	1	16	193	157	3	17
8	349	338	4	10	17	360	336	4	13
9	129	121	3	14	18	425	412	4	3
OUT	3,215	3,082	37		IN	3,158	2,972	35	
					TOTAL	6,373	6,054	72	
					STANDARD SCRATCH	71	72		

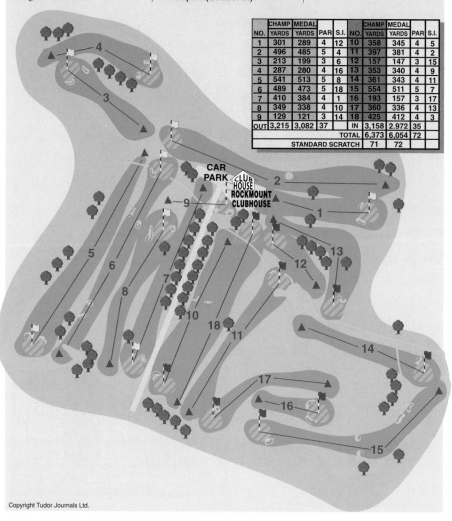

SHANDON

**73 Shandon Park,
Belfast
BT5 6NY.
Tel: (01232) 793730.**

LOCATION: Three miles from city centre.
GENERAL MANAGER: Michael Corsar.
Tel: (01232) 401856.
PROFESSIONAL: B. Wilson.
Tel: (01232) 797859.

Situated in eastern suburbs of Belfast this is a well known lush parkland course with true greens. Irrespective of handicap, golfers will find that it offers an enjoyable challenge to their golfing prowness. The course is generally flat and trees come into play on some of the holes.

COURSE INFORMATION

Par 70; SSS 70; Length 6,282 yards.
Visitors: Welcome.
Opening Hours:
8.30am – sunset.
Avoid: Saturdays and Wednesdays.
Ladies: Welcome Tuesdays.
Green Fees: £22 Mon – Fri; £27 Sat / Sun / all Public Holidays.
Juveniles: Accompanied by a member. Lessons by prior arrangement.

Sun. Full clubhouse facilities.
Clubhouse Dress: Jacket and tie. Casual in Men's Bar.
Clubhouse Facilities: 12.00 – 3.00pm all week, 5.30pm – 10.00pm Mon – Sat and 5.30pm – 9.30pm High tea (Sun).
Open Competitions: Open Week; 18th – 25th July.
Clubhouse Hours: 12 noon – 11.00pm Mon – Sat; 12.30pm – 2.00pm; 4.30pm – 8.00pm

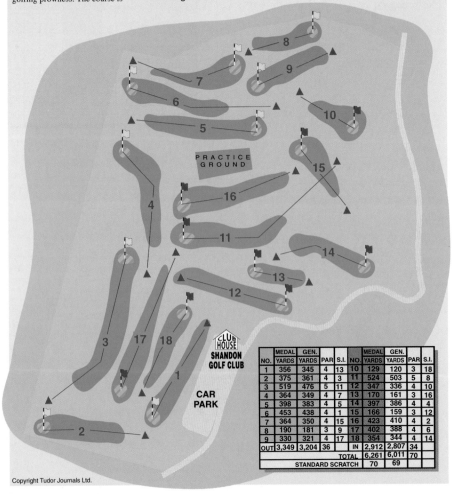

NO.	MEDAL YARDS	GEN. YARDS	PAR	S.I.	NO.	MEDAL YARDS	GEN. YARDS	PAR	S.I.
1	356	345	4	13	10	129	120	3	18
2	375	361	4	3	11	524	503	5	8
3	519	476	5	11	12	347	336	4	10
4	364	349	4	7	13	170	161	3	16
5	398	383	4	5	14	397	386	4	4
6	453	438	4	1	15	166	159	3	12
7	364	350	4	15	16	423	410	4	2
8	190	181	3	9	17	402	388	4	6
9	330	321	4	17	18	354	344	4	14
OUT	3,349	3,204	36		IN	2,912	2,807	34	
					TOTAL	6,261	6,011	70	
					STANDARD SCRATCH		70	69	

**Erne Hill, Belturbet,
Co. Cavan.
Tel: (049) 22287.**

LOCATION: Just outside town on main Cavan Road.
SECRETARY: Peter Coffey.
Tel: (049) 22498.

Most of the holes at Belturbet are played to elevated greens. Out of the eighteen holes the 5th, 7th and 9th holes are considered to be the toughest on the whole course.

COURSE INFORMATION

Par 72; SSS 65; Length 5,180 yards.
Visitors: Welcome any day, including weekends.
Opening Hours:
9.00am – dusk each day.
Avoid: Major club competitions and selected Open Competitions.
Green Fees: £10 Mon – Sun. Letter of introduction required, or Handicap Certificate required

if wishing to compete in Open Competitions.
Clubhouse Hours: Normal bar hours except mornings.
Clubhouse Dress: Informal.
Clubhouse Facilities: Snooker, darts. Catering facilities by arrangement.
Open Competitions: 17th & 18th April; 8th & 9th May; Open Week: 18th – 25th July inclusive; 20st – 22nd August inclusive; 18th & 19th September.

NO.	YARDS	PAR	S.I.	NO.	YARDS	PAR	S.I.
1	277	4	15	10	277	4	16
2	378	4	3	11	378	4	4
3	477	5	11	12	477	5	12
4	175	3	7	13	175	3	8
5	340	4	5	14	340	4	6
6	115	3	17	15	115	3	18
7	415	4	1	16	415	4	2
8	272	4	13	17	272	4	14
9	141	3	9	18	141	3	10
OUT	2,590	34		IN	2,590	34	
				TOTAL	5,180	72	
			STANDARD SCRATCH	65			

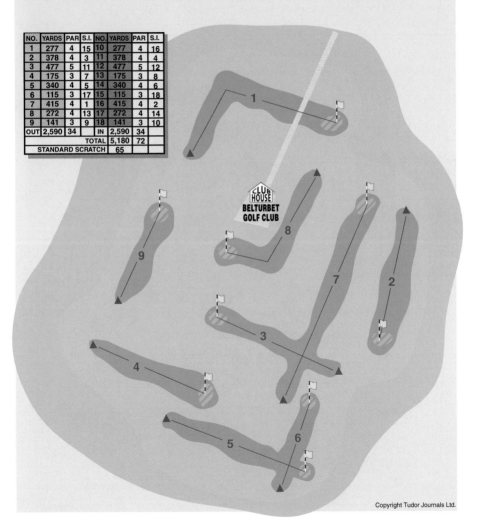

CLUB HOUSE
BELTURBET GOLF CLUB

**Toam, Blacklion,
Co. Cavan.
Tel: (072) 53024.**

LOCATION: At Blacklion
Village on the main
Enniskillen – Sligo Road
(A4 / N15).
HON. SECRETARY: Patsy
Ferguson.
Tel: (01365) 348796.
ARCHITECT: E. Hackett.

The course is bordered on two sides
by Lough McNean which can come
into play on three holes. Typical
inland course, which is playable all
year. Out of bounds on two holes,
some thick shrubbery comes into
play on two holes. Reasonably easy
for the straight hitter!

COURSE INFORMATION

**Par 72; SSS 69; Length
6,170 yards, 5,642 metres.**
Visitors: Welcome any day,
but prior arrangement is
preferred.
Opening Hours:
Sunrise – sunset.
Avoid: Sunday morning and
early afternoon. Certain club
competitions, which are
posted in clubhouse.
Ladies: Welcome Thursdays.
Green Fees: £8 weekdays
(£6 with member); £10.00
Sat / Sun and all public
holidays (£8 with member).
Juveniles: Welcome when
accompanied by an adult.
Lessons available by prior
arrangement.
Clubhouse Hours: 2.00pm
– 10.00pm.
Clubhouse Dress: Informal.
Clubhouse Facilities: Bar
snacks throughout the day.
Meals for small parties by
prior arrangement.
Open Competitions: 1st
Monday in June; Open Week
in mid June.

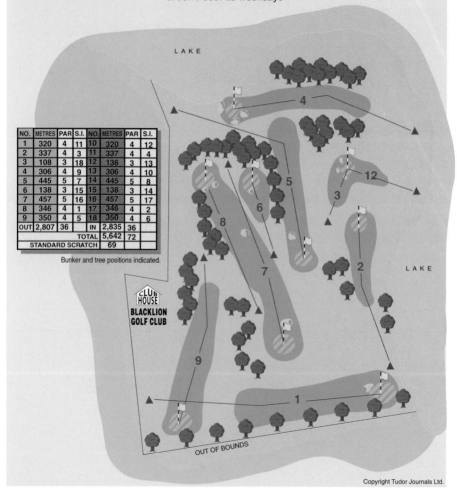

NO.	METRES	PAR	S.I.	NO.	METRES	PAR	S.I.
1	320	4	11	10	320	4	12
2	337	4	3	11	337	4	4
3	108	3	18	12	136	3	13
4	306	4	9	13	306	4	10
5	445	5	7	14	445	5	8
6	138	3	15	15	138	3	14
7	457	5	16	16	457	5	17
8	346	4	1	17	346	4	2
9	350	4	5	18	350	4	6
OUT	2,807	36		IN	2,835	36	
				TOTAL	5,642	72	
				STANDARD SCRATCH	69		

Bunker and tree positions indicated.

BLACKLION
GOLF CLUB

**Kingscourt, Co. Cavan.
Tel: (042) 67030.**

LOCATION: Kingscourt,
Co Cavan.
SECRETARY / MANAGER: Howard
Corscadden.
Tel: (042) 67030.
Fax: (042) 67039.

Cabra Castle Golf Club may not be
the hardest golf course that you
will play, but it can be surprisingly
difficult and will provide a reasonable
test of golf.

COURSE INFORMATION

**Par 70; SSS 68; Length 5,308
Metres.
Visitors:** Welcome to play at all
times.
Opening Hours: Daylight.
Avoid: Sunday morning and
Tuesday.
Ladies Day: Tuesday.

Green Fees: £9 Mon – Fri;
£9 Sat / Sun.Green Fees: £9
Mon – Fri; £9 Sat / Sun.
Juveniles: Must be
accompanied by an adult.
Clubhouse Hours: Cabra
Castle Hotel 7am – 12
midnight.
Clubhouse Dress: Casual.
Clubhouse Facilities: Full
catering and bar facilities.
Open Competitions: Open
Week – June 14th – 20th.

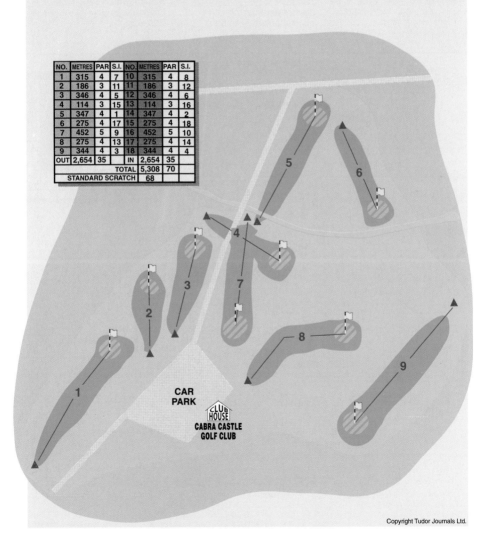

NO.	METRES	PAR	S.I.	NO.	METRES	PAR	S.I.
1	315	4	7	10	315	4	8
2	186	3	11	11	186	3	12
3	346	4	5	12	346	4	6
4	114	3	15	13	114	3	16
5	347	4	1	14	347	4	2
6	275	4	17	15	275	4	18
7	452	5	9	16	452	5	10
8	275	4	13	17	275	4	14
9	344	4	3	18	344	4	4
OUT	2,654	35		IN	2,654	35	
				TOTAL	5,308	70	
				STANDARD SCRATCH	68		

CAR
PARK

CABRA CASTLE
GOLF CLUB

CO. CAVAN

**Arnmore House,
Drumelis, Cavan,
Co. Cavan.
Tel: (049) 31283.**

LOCATION: One mile from
Cavan town, on the
Killeshandra Road.
SECRETARY: J. Sheridan.
Tel: (049) 32045.

A Parkland course in the suburbs of
Cavan town that offers a good test of
golf, with several interesting holes a
feature of the course. Three of the
holes (8th, 13th and 14th) have
recently been modified.

COURSE INFORMATION

**Par 70; SSS 69; Length 5,634
metres.**
Visitors: Welcome to play at
any time.
Opening Hours: Daylight
hours.
Avoid: Sundays and
Wednesdays.
Ladies: Welcome
Wednesdays.
Green Fees: £12 Mon – Fri;
£14 Sat / Sun & Public
Holidays.
Juveniles: Must be
accompanied by an adult.

Club Hire and Caddy cars
available by prior arrangement.
Clubhouse Hours: Normal
licensing hours.
Clubhouse Dress: Casual.
Clubhouse Facilities: Bar,
meals and snooker room.
Catering facilities available any
day May – Sep. (prior
arrangements may be made
with resident steward or
caterer).
Open Competitions: Open
Week – July; Open Junior
Scratch Cup – Sep; Open
Intermediate Scratch
Cup – Sep.

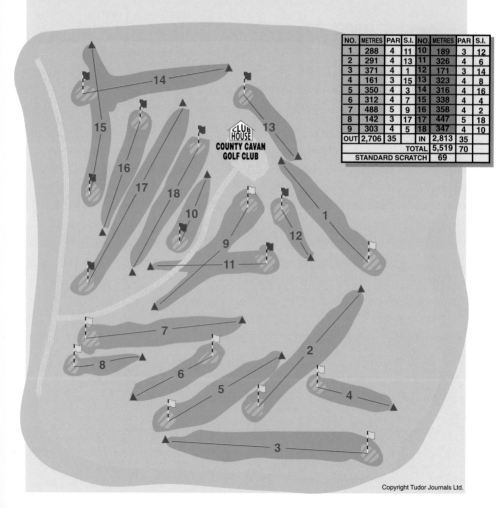

**COUNTY CAVAN
GOLF CLUB**

NO.	METRES	PAR	S.I.	NO.	METRES	PAR	S.I.
1	288	4	11	10	189	3	12
2	291	4	13	11	326	4	6
3	371	4	1	12	171	3	14
4	161	3	15	13	323	4	8
5	350	4	3	14	316	4	16
6	312	4	7	15	338	4	4
7	488	5	9	16	358	4	2
8	142	3	17	17	447	5	18
9	303	4	5	18	347	4	10
OUT	2,706	35		IN	2,813	35	
				TOTAL	5,519	70	
				STANDARD SCRATCH	69		

**The Slieve Russell,
Golf and Country Club,
Ballyconnell, Co. Cavan.
Tel: (049) 26444.
Fax: (049) 26474/26511.**

LOCATION: Two hours from both
Dublin and Belfast.
GOLF DIRECTOR:
Mr P.J. Creamer.
ARCHITECT: Paddy Merrigan.
PROFESSIONAL: Liam McCool.
SECRETARY: Michael Ryan.

An 18 hole championship course is set in
300 acres of parkland including 50 acres of
lake. The unique style of the Slieve Russell
fits and complements the Cavan Drumlin
landscape multiple tee positions facilitate
all categories of golfer.

COURSE INFORMATION

**Par 72; SSS 72; Length
7,013 yards.
Visitors:** Welcome.
Opening Hours: 8am –11pm
(seasonal opening times).
Avoid: Saturday.
Ladies: Welcome.
Juveniles: Over 12yrs full green
fees payable.
Green Fees: Non-resident rates
–£28 (Sun – Fri) & £36 (Sat).
Clubhouse Hours: 10.30am
–11pm.
Clubhouse Dress: Dress code
in operation.
Clubhouse Facilities: Attached
to the Slieve Russell Hotel,
clubhouse restaurant and bar
also available.
Additional Facilities:
9 hole Par 3 course; Flood lit
driving range; Golf Tuition
available.

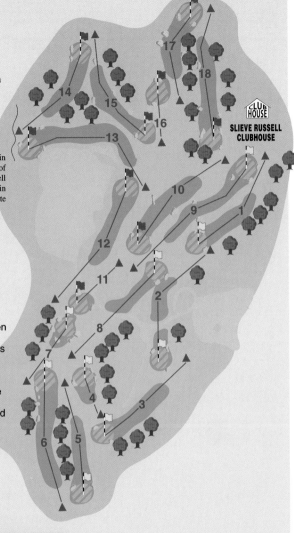

SLIEVE RUSSELL
CLUBHOUSE

NO.	CHAMP YARDS	MEDAL YARDS	PAR	S.I.	NO.	CHAMP YARDS	MEDAL YARDS	PAR	S.I.
1	382	355	4	8	10	376	360	4	2
2	397	373	4	1	11	176	154	3	13
3	364	339	4	6	12	404	397	4	4
4	152	145	3	18	13	484	459	5	12
5	399	377	4	3	14	342	326	4	16
6	468	449	5	15	15	414	390	4	5
7	201	179	3	10	16	161	151	3	9
8	356	309	4	14	17	338	315	4	17
9	505	466	5	11	18	494	474	5	7
OUT	3,224	2,992	36		IN	3,189	3,026	36	
					TOTAL	6,413	6,018	72	
			STANDARD SCRATCH			74	72		

Bunker & tree positions indicated.

Virginia, Co Cavan.
Tel: (049) 48066.

LOCATION: Fifty miles N.W. of Dublin on Virginia – Ballyjamesduff Road on the grounds of the Park Hotel.
SECRETARY: Joe Greene.
Tel: (049) 40223.
CAPTAIN: Oliver O'Dwyer.

A compact nine hole course situated adjacent to the picturesque Lough Ramor. Fairways are narrow and divided by trees. Involves accuracy and a delicate touch around the greens. The course is located in the grounds of the Park Hotel.

COURSE INFORMATION

Par 64; SSS 62; Length 4,139 Metres.
Visitors: Welcome to play on any day except Ladies Day on Thurs.
Opening Hours: Daylight hours.
Avoid: Sunday mornings – Men's competitions.

Ladies: Welcome Thursdays (except on Competition Days).
Green Fees: £8 (£4 with a member).
Ladies day: Thursday.
Juveniles: Not allowed after 5.00pm or on Sun. or Thur. Club Hire and Caddy service available by prior arrangement.
Clubhouse Facilities: Available in the Park Hotel.
Open Competitions: Open Week: 7th June – 14th June.

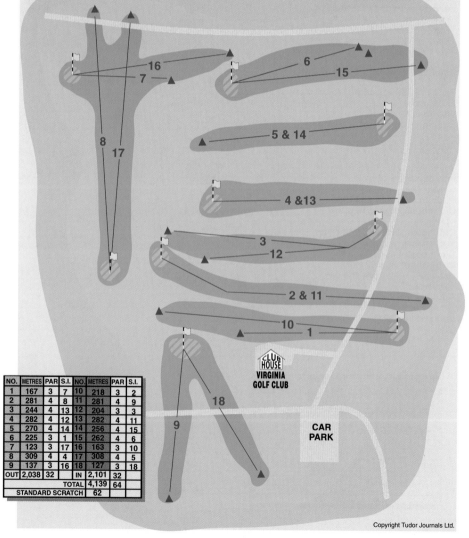

NO.	METRES	PAR	S.I.	NO.	METRES	PAR	S.I.
1	167	3	7	10	218	3	2
2	281	4	8	11	281	4	9
3	244	4	13	12	204	3	3
4	282	4	12	13	282	4	11
5	270	4	14	14	256	4	15
6	225	3	1	15	262	4	6
7	123	3	17	16	163	3	10
8	309	4	4	17	308	4	5
9	137	3	16	18	127	3	18
OUT	2,038	32		IN	2,101	32	
				TOTAL	4,139	64	
	STANDARD SCRATCH				62		

VIRGINIA
GOLF CLUB

CAR PARK

Ballybofey, Co. Donegal.
Tel: (074) 31093.

LOCATION: Lough Alan, Stranorlar, off Strabane/Stranorlar main road.
SECRETARY: A. Harkin.
Tel: (074) 31228.
ARCHITECT: P.C. Carr.
CAPTAIN: Brian McDermott.

Undulating parkland course with picturesque views of the Donegal Hills and Valley of River Finn. The course is located on the shores of Lough Alan, yet follows the rolling contours of the surrounding countryside. A satisfying course and one that is popular with societies.

COURSE INFORMATION

Par 68; SSS 69; Length 5,399 metres.
Visitors: Welcome. Booking essential for weekends. Please telephone (074) 31093.
Opening Hours: 9.00am – sunset. New shop.

Avoid: Mon & Tue evenings from 4.30pm.
Green Fees: £15 Mon – Fri. Sat / Sun; £14 Societies.
Clubhouse Hours: 12.00 noon – 11.00 p.m.
Clubhouse Dress: Informal.
Clubhouse Facilities: A new clubhouse with full facilities.
Open Competitions: Annual Open Week 29th May –7th June.

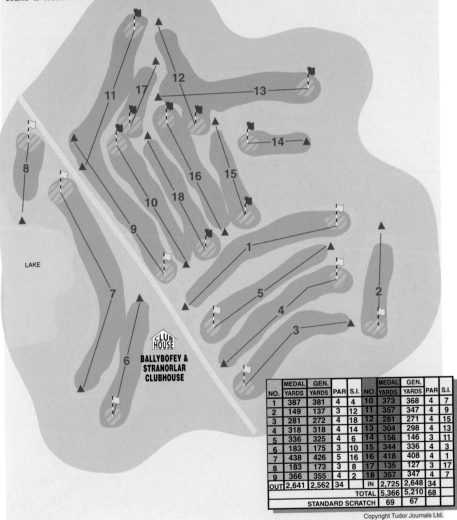

LAKE

CLUB HOUSE
BALLYBOFEY &
STRANORLAR
CLUBHOUSE

NO.	MEDAL YARDS	GEN. YARDS	PAR	S.I.	NO.	MEDAL YARDS	GEN. YARDS	PAR	S.I.
1	387	381	4	4	10	373	368	4	7
2	149	137	3	12	11	357	347	4	9
3	281	272	4	18	12	281	271	4	15
4	318	318	4	14	13	304	298	4	13
5	336	325	4	6	14	156	146	3	11
6	183	175	3	10	15	344	336	4	3
7	438	426	5	16	16	418	408	4	1
8	183	173	3	8	17	135	127	3	17
9	366	355	4	2	18	357	347	4	7
OUT	2,641	2,562	34		IN	2,725	2,648	34	
					TOTAL	5,366	5,210	68	
					STANDARD SCRATCH	69	67		

Copyright Tudor Journals Ltd.

**Ballyliffin Golf Club,
Clonmany,
Co. Donegal.
Tel: (077) 76119.
Fax: (077) 76672.**

LOCATION: 6 miles from
Cardonagh.
HON. SECRETARY: Karl O'Doherty.
Tel: (077) 76119.
ARCHITECT: Tom Craddock & Pat
Ruddy.

To play The Old Links at Ballyliffin is
to experience golf on one of natures
most beautiful stages. All around are
dramatic hills and mountains with
magnificent views of the bay, the
ocean and the course. Very difficult
3rd hole with narrow fairway and

sloping green. The 5th hole is an
interesting par 3 known locally as
"The Tank." Also, the Glashedy course
opened in 1995.

COURSE INFORMATION

**Par 72; SSS 73; Length
6,837 yards.
Visitors:** Welcome.
Opening Hours: Daylight.
Avoid: Sat & Sun afternoons.
Ladies: Welcome Tuesdays and
4.00pm – 6.00pm Sat & Sun.
Green Fees: Mon – Fri £22:
weekends / Bank holidays £27. Old
Link: Mon – Fri £17. Weekend £25.

Glashedy Mon – Fri £25.
Weekend £30.
Juveniles: By arangement.
Caddy service available by prior
arrangement.
Clubhouse Hours:
9.00am – 11.30pm.
Clubhouse Facilities: Bar,
snacks, showers. Catering
facilities by arrangement and
most weekends.
Open Competitions: Contact
office for details.

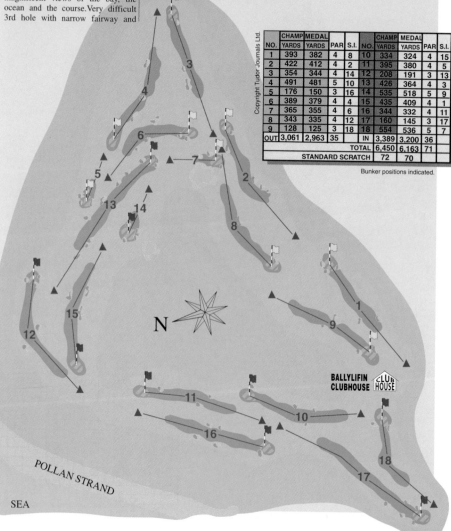

Copyright Tudor Journals Ltd.

NO.	CHAMP YARDS	MEDAL YARDS	PAR	S.I.	NO.	CHAMP YARDS	MEDAL YARDS	PAR	S.I.
1	393	382	4	8	10	334	324	4	15
2	422	412	4	2	11	395	380	4	5
3	354	344	4	14	12	208	191	3	13
4	491	481	5	10	13	426	364	4	3
5	176	150	3	16	14	535	518	5	9
6	389	379	4	4	15	435	409	4	1
7	365	355	4	6	16	344	332	4	11
8	343	335	4	12	17	160	145	3	17
9	128	125	3	18	18	554	536	5	7
OUT	3,061	2,963	35		IN	3,389	3,200	36	
					TOTAL	6,450	6,163	71	
					STANDARD SCRATCH	72	70		

Bunker positions indicated.

N

BALLYLIFIN
CLUBHOUSE CLUB HOUSE

POLLAN STRAND

SEA

BUNDORAN

Bundoran, Co. Donegal.
Tel: (072) 41302.

Location: 25 miles North of Sligo on coast.
Secretary: John McGagh.
Tel: (072) 41302.
Professional: David Robinson.
Tel: (072) 41302.
Architect: Harry Vardon.

A combination of links and a treeless parkland course in undulating terrain. The greens and approaches are well protected by bunkers. A picturesque course with the middle holes playing

alongside the impressive Atlantic coast and beautiful strands. The course is sited on the edge of Bundoran and literally surrounds the Great Northern Hotel.

COURSE INFORMATION

Par 69; SSS 70; Length 5,689 metres.
Visitors: Welcome to play especially on weekdays.
Opening Hours: 9.00am – 6.00pm (winter) 8.00am – 8.00pm (summer).
Green Fees: £16 Mon – Fri;

£18 at weekends. Club Hire available.
Clubhouse Hours: Bar 4.30pm – 11.30pm (winter) 12noon – 11.30pm (summer).
Clubhouse Dress: Casual.
Clubhouse Facilities: Snacks only. Open all day, snacks available. Hotel on course.
Open Competitions: All weekends from May to October. Open Week. Letter of introduction required for competitions.

NO.	CHAMP METRES	MEDAL METRES	PAR	S.I.	NO.	CHAMP METRES	MEDAL METRES	PAR	S.I.
1	327	327	4	8	10	364	358	4	1
2	459	437	5	16	11	384	374	4	5
3	117	107	3	18	12	316	316	4	11
4	331	291	4	6	13	212	179	3	9
5	197	156	3	10	14	366	343	4	7
6	180	180	3	2	15	390	371	4	3
7	325	276	4	12	16	142	132	3	17
8	356	324	4	4	17	453	453	5/4	15
9	356	333	4	13	18	324	291	4	14
OUT	2,738	2,431	34		IN	2,951	2,817	35/34	
					TOTAL	5,689	5,248	69/68	
					STANDARD SCRATCH	70	68		

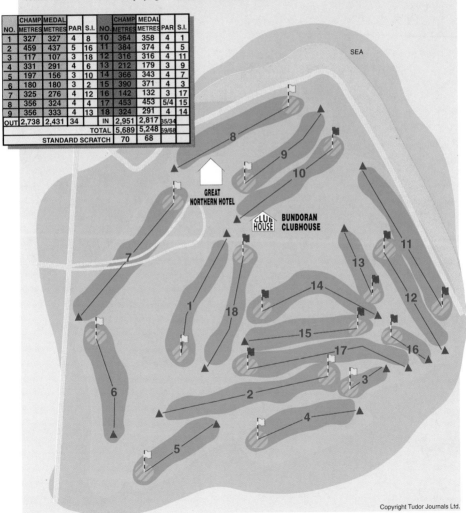

SEA

GREAT NORTHERN HOTEL

BUNDORAN CLUBHOUSE

Copyright Tudor Journals Ltd.

**Cloughaneely Golf Club,
Ballyconnell, Falcarragh,
Co. Donegal.
Tel: (074) 65416.**

LOCATION: Ballyconnell,
Falcarragh, Co. Donegal.
SECRETARY: Noel O'Gallchoir.
Tel: (074) 35305.
ARCHITECT: Michael
Doherty.

Opened in 1997 this is an
undulating inland course set in an
old estate with mature woodlands.

COURSE INFORMATION

**Par 70; SSS 69; Length
6,088 yards.**
Visitors: Welcome.
Opening Hours:
8.30am – 10.00pm.
Avoid: Sunday mornings.
Green Fees: Weekdays £7;
weekends / Bank Holidays £9.
Juveniles: Welcome.
Clubhouse Hours:
9.00am – 11.00pm.
Clubhouse Dress: Informal.
Clubhouse Facilities: Tea,

coffee, sandwiches, and
snacks. Full catering by
arrangement. Additional
facilities nearby at Ballyconnell
House Complex include family
accommodation, catering or
self-catering.
Open Competitions:
Bank Holiday weekends /
Open Week 12th – 20th July.

NO.	YARDS	PAR	S.I.	NO.	YARDS	PAR	S.I.
1	408	4	1	10	408	4	2
2	195	3	15	11	195	3	16
3	334	4	13	12	334	4	14
4	345	4	9	13	345	4	10
5	381	4	11	14	381	4	12
6	362	4	5	15	362	4	6
7	147	3	17	16	147	3	18
8	501	5	7	17	501	5	8
9	371	4	3	18	371	4	4
OUT	3,044	35		IN	3,044	35	
					TOTAL	6,088	70
				STANDARD SCRATCH		69	

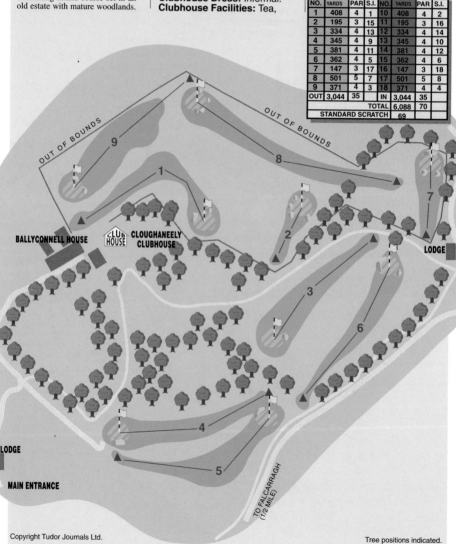

BALLYCONNELL HOUSE

CLUB HOUSE CLOUGHANEELY CLUBHOUSE

LODGE

LODGE

MAIN ENTRANCE

TO FALCARRAGH (1/2 MILE)

OUT OF BOUNDS

OUT OF BOUNDS

Copyright Tudor Journals Ltd.

Tree positions indicated.

Kincasslagh, Co Donegal.
Tel: (075) 43296.

LOCATION: Two miles outside village of Kincasslagh.
SECRETARY: D. Devenney.
Tel: (075) 48151.

A breathtaking 9 hole links course perched precariously on the edge of the Atlantic Ocean and accessible only by a bridge which joins it to the mainland and the village of Kincasslagh. The crowning glory of the course is the magnificent Par 3 6th hole where nerves of steel are required to hit over a deep cove and land on a small green which as a sheer drop into the sea behind for anyone who over clubs it.

COURSE INFORMATION

Par 68; SSS 64; Length 4,860 metres.
Visitors: Welcome anytime. Prior arrangement required for parties in excess of 12 people.
Avoid: Club Competitions Sunday mornings; Ladies Competitions Saturday mornings.
Ladies: Welcome Thursdays.

Green Fees: £7 weekdays; £10 weekends (£5 with a member); £10 July/August all week (Subject to change).
Juveniles: Welcome. No restrictions.
Clubhouse Hours: June/Sept 10.00am – dusk.
Clubhouse Facilities: Bar, locker rooms. Catering facilities, meals available. Prior arrangement required for larger parties.

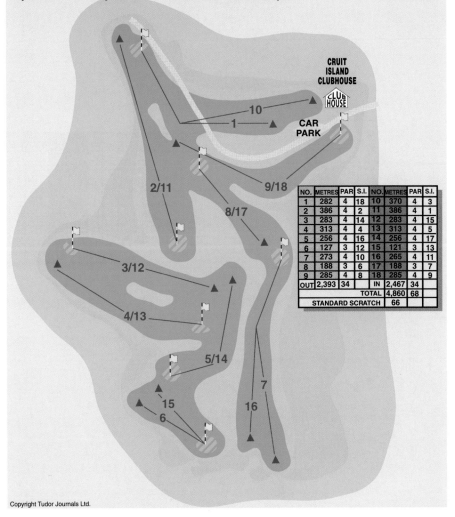

NO.	METRES	PAR	S.I.	NO.	METRES	PAR	S.I.
1	282	4	18	10	370	4	3
2	386	4	2	11	386	4	1
3	283	4	14	12	283	4	15
4	313	4	4	13	313	4	5
5	256	4	16	14	256	4	17
6	127	3	12	15	121	3	13
7	273	4	10	16	265	4	11
8	188	3	6	17	188	3	7
9	285	4	8	18	285	4	9
OUT	2,393	34		IN	2,467	34	
				TOTAL	4,860	68	
				STANDARD SCRATCH	66		

**Murvagh, Laghey,
Ballintra, Co Donegal
Tel:** (073) 34054
Fax: (073) 34377.

LOCATION: Halfway between
Rossnowlagh &
Donegal Town.
ADMINISTRATOR: John McBride.
ARCHITECT: Eddie Hackett.

Challenging links course fit to test the best. Superbly scenic between sea and mountains, the holes are a mixture of testing Par 5's, tricky Par 4's and memorable Par 3's.

COURSE INFORMATION

**Par 73; SSS 73; Length
6,249 metres.
Visitors:** Welcome. Every day
except special events as per
fixture card.
Opening Hours: Dawn –
dusk.
Avoid: Sunday.
Ladies: Welcome Mondays.
Green Fees: £18 weekdays;
£25 Weekends and bank
holidays. Husband & Wife
weekday rate £28.

Juveniles: Welcome 1/2 price
– restrictions at weekends.
Clubhouse Hours: 9.00am –
11.00pm.
Clubhouse Dress: Informal
but neat.
Clubhouse Facilities:
Available to visitors, include
buggy hire £20 per round,
caddy carts £1.50, bar,
snooker, locker rooms and
showers. Snacks available at
all times full meals by prior
arrangement with caterer.
Open Competitions: Phone
for details.

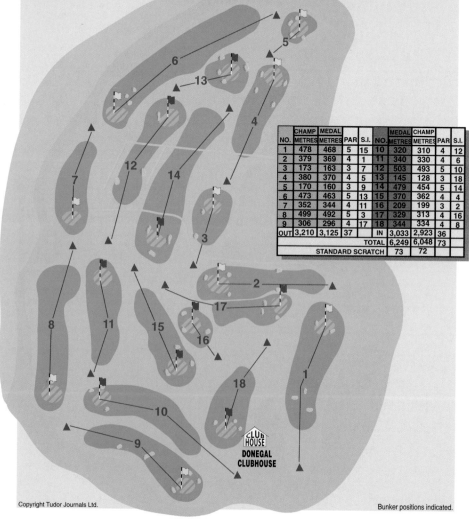

	CHAMP	MEDAL				MEDAL	CHAMP		
NO.	METRES	METRES	PAR	S.I.	NO.	METRES	METRES	PAR	S.I.
1	478	468	5	15	10	320	310	4	12
2	379	369	4	1	11	340	330	4	6
3	173	163	3	7	12	503	493	5	10
4	380	370	4	5	13	145	128	3	18
5	170	160	3	9	14	479	454	5	14
6	473	463	5	13	15	370	362	4	4
7	352	344	4	11	16	209	199	3	2
8	499	492	5	3	17	329	313	4	16
9	306	296	4	17	18	344	334	4	8
OUT	3,210	3,125	37		IN	3,033	2,923	36	
					TOTAL	6,249	6,048	73	
					STANDARD SCRATCH		73	72	

**DONEGAL
CLUBHOUSE**

Bunker positions indicated.

**Kill, Dunfanaghy.
Tel: (074) 36335.**

LOCATION: Less than a mile from Dunfanaghy on the main road to Letterkenny.
SECRETARY/MANAGER: Sam Sterritt. Tel: (074) 36335.

This is a course suited for high and middle handicappers. It improves each year and provides a fair test. The most notable improvement of recent years is the removal of fences and sheep from the course and a notable feature is the view from the 7th tee, looking west across the bay to Horn Head.

COURSE INFORMATION

**Par 68; SSS 66; Length 5,066 metres.
Visitors:** Welcome anytime.
Opening Hours: 9.00am – 10.00pm.
Ladies: Welcome Tuesdays.
Green Fees: Mon – Fri £12.50 (£8 with a member); £14.50 Sat, Sun & Bank Hols (£8 with a member).
Juveniles: Welcome.
Clubhouse Hours: 9.00am onwards.
Clubhouse Dress: Informal.
Clubhouse Facilities: Bar and snacks available all day.
Open Competitions: Hickey Clarke & Largan Open Stableford April. Open Week July / Aug. Carrig Rua Classic 27th & 28th September. Caravana Classic 9th August.

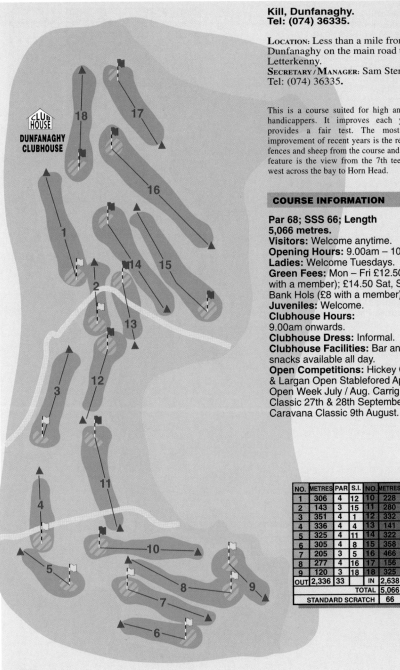

DUNFANAGHY
CLUBHOUSE

NO.	METRES	PAR	S.I.	NO.	METRES	PAR	S.I.
1	306	4	12	10	228	4	13
2	143	3	15	11	280	4	17
3	351	4	1	12	332	4	2
4	336	4	4	13	141	3	14
5	325	4	11	14	322	4	3
6	305	4	8	15	358	4	7
7	205	3	5	16	466	5	6
8	277	4	16	17	156	3	9
9	120	3	18	18	325	4	10
OUT	2,336	33		IN	2,638	35	
				TOTAL	5,066	68	
				STANDARD SCRATCH	66		

Maghergallon, Derrybeg, Letterkenny.
Tel: (075) 31140/81013.

LOCATION: North west of Letterkenny.
SECRETARY: Bryan Gormley.
Tel: (075) 82280.
ARCHITECT: E. Hackett.

A scenic course sited along the very pleasant shores of the Insihowen Pennisula in the north of Donegal.

NO.	MEDAL METRES	GEN. METRES	PAR	S.I.	NO.	MEDAL METRES	GEN. METRES	PAR	S.I.
1	312	312	4	11	10	488	474	5	6
2	386	344	4	1	11	165	155	3	8
3	138	138	3	13	12	311	299	4	10
4	428	414	4	3	13	440	420	5	16
5	319	264	4	7	14	350	350	4	4
6	285	285	4	9	15	103	103	3	18
7	119	119	3	15	16	366	350	4	2
8	265	265	4	17	17	277	255	4	14
9	294	279	4	5	18	165	153	3	12
OUT	2,546	2,420	34		IN	2,665	2,559	35	
					TOTAL	5,211	4,979	69	
					STANDARD SCRATCH	66	66		

COURSE INFORMATION

Par 69; SSS 66; Length 5,211 metres.
Visitors: Welcome.
Opening Hours: Daylight.
Ladies: Welcome.
Green Fees: £10 Mon –Fri, (£8 with member); £15 Sat / Sun & Bank Hols (£10 with member).
Juveniles: Welcome.
Clubhouse Hours:
11.00am – 11.00pm.
Clubhouse Dress: Informal.
Clubhouse Facilities: Available Thurs & Weekends in summer. Full Clubhouse Facilities.
Open Competitions: Open Week June. Open Competitions various weekends.

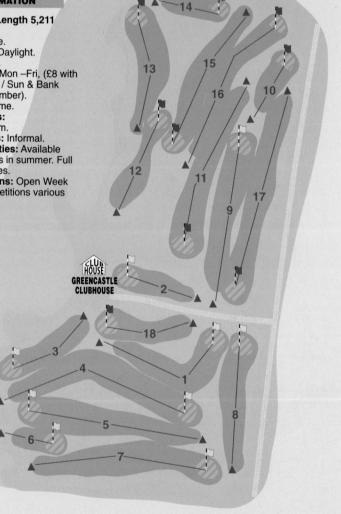

Maghergallon, Derrybeg, Letterkenny, Co Donegal.
Tel: (075) 31140.

LOCATION: North west of Letterkenny.
SECRETARY / MANAGER: Eric Campbell.

An attractive nine hole, seaside course which is quite challenging for players of all handicaps. The course is not physically taxing and the setting is attractive.

COURSE INFORMATION

Par 71; SSS 69; Length 6,201 metres.
Visitors: Welcome.
Opening Hours: All day.
Ladies: Welcome.
Green Fees: Mon - Fri £7; Sat, Sun & Bank Hols £8 (with member £5). Caddy service available by prior arrangement.

Juveniles: Sat mornings.
Clubhouse Hours: Normally 10am – 12 midnight.
Clubhouse Dress: Informal.
Clubhouse Facilities: Showers, Cloakrooms. Catering facilities; daily during summer months. Weekends for remainder of the year.

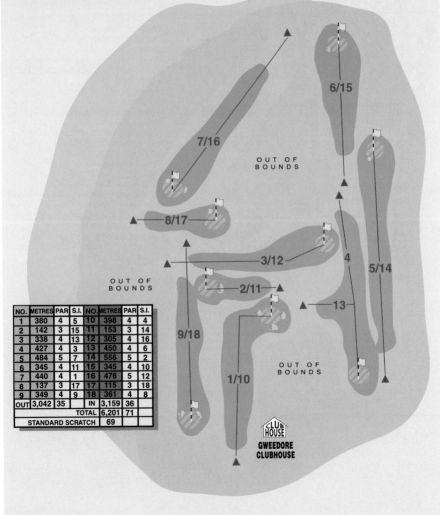

NO.	METRES	PAR	S.I.	NO.	METRES	PAR	S.I.
1	380	4	5	10	398	4	4
2	142	3	15	11	153	3	14
3	338	4	13	12	305	4	16
4	427	4	3	13	450	4	6
5	484	5	7	14	556	5	2
6	345	4	11	15	345	4	10
7	440	4	1	16	476	5	12
8	137	3	17	17	115	3	18
9	349	4	9	18	361	4	8
OUT	3,042	35		IN	3,159	36	
				TOTAL	6,201	71	
STANDARD SCRATCH		69					

NO.	MEDAL METRES	GEN METRES	PA	S.I.	NO.	MEDAL METRES	GEN METRES	PA	S.I.
1	368	354	4	14	10	396	384	4	9
2	530	516	5	12	11	415	397	4	2
3	364	354	4	8	12	343	343	4	11
4	362	352	4	6	13	209	195	3	7
5	138	128	3	18	14	337	325	4	13
6	423	413	4	2	15	420	406	4	5
7	388	378	4	4	16	151	151	3	17
8	170	170	3	16	17	400	368	4	1
9	370	354	4	10	18	508	508	5	15
OU T	3,113	3,019	35		IN	3,179	3,077	35	
					TOTAL	6,292	6,096	70	
					STANDARD SCRATCH	71	70		

**Barnhill Golf Club,
Letterkenny Co Donegal.
Tel: (074) 21150.**

LOCATION: One – two miles from outskirts of Letterkenny town.
SECRETARY: Barry Ramsay.
Tel: (074) 24491 (home) (074) 21022.

An attractive eighteen hole golf course in which the first eleven holes are played on relatively flat ground, the remaining seven holes are played on a plateau above the others. The course is a good challenge with a demanding finishing hole.New Clubhouse open from June

COURSE INFORMATION

Par 70; SSS 71; Length 6,292 metres.
Visitors: Welcome.
Opening Hours: Call in advance to check.
Avoid: Tuesdays and Wednesdays after 5pm. Timesheets in use most weekends.
Ladies: Welcome Tuesdays and Thursdays.
Green Fees: £12 weekdays & £15 weekends.
Juveniles: Welcome. Lessons by appointment. Club Hire and trolleys available.
Clubhouse Hours: 12.00 noon – 11.30pm.
Clubhouse Dress: Informal.
Clubhouse Facilities: New clubhouse opens May 1998. Full catering and bar facilities all week during summer (only at weekends in winter).
Open Competitions: Weekends in summer. Open Week – June. Phone clubhouse for further details.

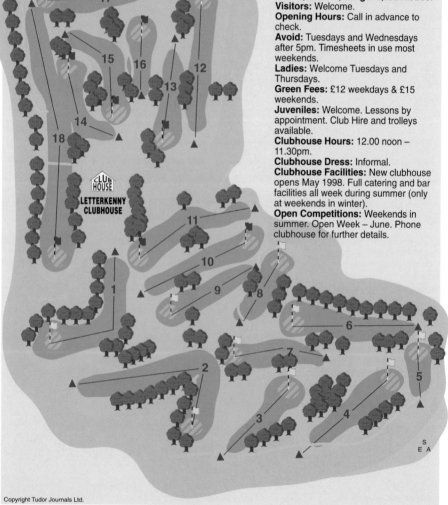

LETTERKENNY
CLUBHOUSE

NARIN & PORTNOO ULSTER **DONEGAL**

Narin, Portnoo, Co Donegal.
Tel: (074) 45107.

LOCATION: Narin / Portnoo, Co
Donegal.
SECRETARY: Enda Bonner.
Tel: (074) 24668.
PROFESSIONAL: None.
ARCHITECT: P Carr, Ballybofey.

Beautiful scenery and a quiet course,
although it is particularly popular in the
summer months as it is located in a holiday
area. Set amidst beautiful scenery on the
extreme west coast of Donegal, providing
well deserved praise from both low and high
handicappers. A very popular location with
the best of links and inland characteristics.

COURSE INFORMATION

Par 69; SSS 68; Length
5,766 yards.
Visitors: Welcome.
Opening Hours: Daylight hours.
Avoid: Sunday (sometimes
available – ring before).
Ladies: Welcome.
Green Fees: £13 daily, £16
weekends. £12 Societies
(twenty plus).
Juveniles: Welcome.
Clubhouse Hours:
9.00am – 12.00pm.
Clubhouse Dress: Casual.
Clubhouse Facilities: Bar and light
refreshments.
Open Competitions: Open Week –
June; Open Competitions evey
second weekend during July &
August.

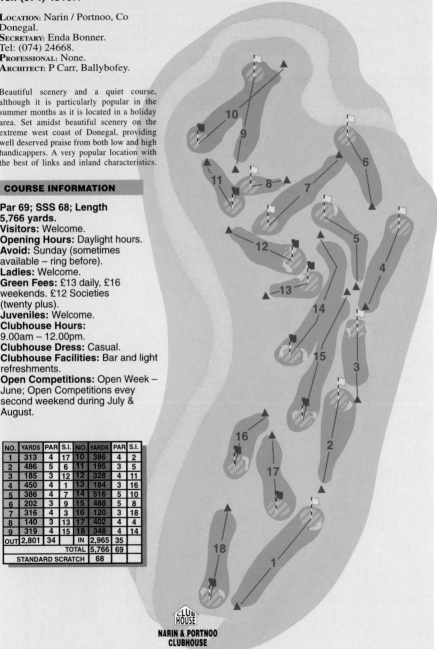

NO.	YARDS	PAR	S.I.	NO.	YARDS	PAR	S.I.
1	313	4	17	10	386	4	2
2	486	5	6	11	195	3	5
3	185	3	12	12	328	4	11
4	450	4	1	13	184	3	16
5	386	4	7	14	516	5	10
6	202	3	9	15	488	5	8
7	316	4	3	16	120	3	18
8	140	3	13	17	402	4	4
9	319	4	15	18	348	4	14
OUT	2,801	34		IN	2,965	35	
				TOTAL	5,766	69	
STANDARD SCRATCH		68					

NARIN & PORTNOO
CLUBHOUSE

**Lisfannon, Fahan,
Co. Donegal.
Tel: (077) 61027/61715.**

LOCATION: At Lisfannon which
is two miles from Buncrana
and eight miles from Derry.
SECRETARY: Dudley Coyle.
PROFESSIONAL: Seamus
McBriarty.

The course lies between the sea and
the picturesque Mouldy Mountain.
The holes are varied, with many
sandy knolls and pleasing
undulations, but the general
tendency is flattish. There are two
loops of nine holes, each loop
terminating at the Clubhouse.

COURSE INFORMATION

**Par 70; SSS 69; Length
6,239 yards.
Visitors:** Welcome Mon-Fri
and Weekends by
arrangement.
Opening Hours: 8.00am
till dark.
Avoid: Weekends during
October – March, 12.00 –
2.00pm Saturday and 8.30am
– 11pm Sunday's.
Ladies: Welcome.
Green Fees: £15 Mon – Fri
(£10 with member); £20 Sat,
Sun & Bank Hols

(£15 with member). Caddy
cars always available.
Lessons available by prior
arrangement.
Juveniles: Welcome.
Clubhouse Dress: Casual.
Clubhouse Facilities: Locker
room, showers. Catering
facilities all week at 1.00pm.
Open Competitions: Whit
Open May; Open Week July.
Handicap certificate required.

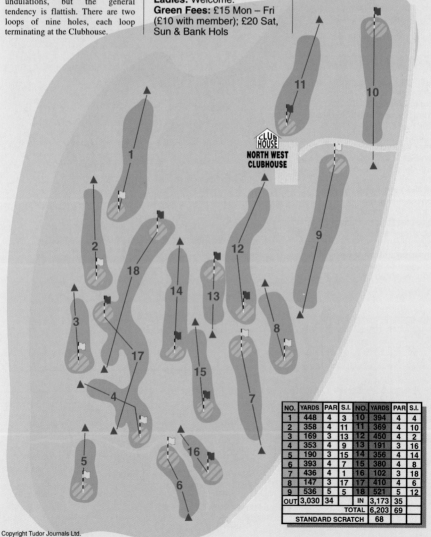

**NORTH WEST
CLUBHOUSE**

NO.	YARDS	PAR	S.I.	NO.	YARDS	PAR	S.I.
1	448	4	3	10	394	4	4
2	358	4	11	11	369	4	10
3	169	3	13	12	450	4	2
4	353	4	9	13	191	3	16
5	190	3	15	14	356	4	14
6	393	4	7	15	380	4	8
7	436	4	1	16	102	3	18
8	147	3	17	17	410	4	6
9	536	5	5	18	521	5	12
OUT	3,030	34		IN	3,173	35	
				TOTAL	6,203	69	
				STANDARD SCRATCH	68		

Portsalon, Letterkenny, Co. Donegal.
Tel: (074) 59459.
Fax: (074) 59459.

LOCATION: Twenty miles north of Letterkenny on western shore of Lough Swilly.
SECRETARY: Frank McAteer.
Tel: (074) 59459.

A popular seaside links with quite narrow fairways. Greens are well protected with bunkers, streams and natural sand dunes all coming into play. Course runs in clockwise direction, so the out-of-bounds is generally on left. The club celebrated its Centenary in 1991 and in the same year built a new clubhouse. The 7th, 8th and 9th holes have been modified.

COURSE INFORMATION

Par 69; SSS 68; Length 5,880 metres.
Visitors: Welcome (ring in advance).
Opening Hours: Sunrise – Sunset.
Green Fees: £12 (weekdays), £15 (weekends), weekly tickets on request.
Ladies: Welcome.
Juveniles: Should be accompanied by an adult.
Clubhouse Hours: 8.30 – 11.30pm.
Clubhouse Facilities: Bar snacks and meals available everyday (April – October). Normal clubhouse facilities.
Open Competitions: Open Week 11th – 19th July. All Bank Holiday weekends.

NO.	METRES	PAR	S.I.	NO.	METRES	PAR	S.I.
1	340	4	2	10	330	4	7
2	180	3	12	11	296	4	15
3	320	4	14	12	170	3	11
4	316	4	4	13	391	4	1
5	185	3	10	14	142	3	13
6	327	4	8	15	356	4	9
7	472	5	6	16	260	4	17
8	150	3	18	17	479	5	5
9	291	4	16	18	371	4	3
OUT	2,581	34		IN	2,795	35	
				TOTAL	5,376	69	
				STANDARD SCRATCH		68	

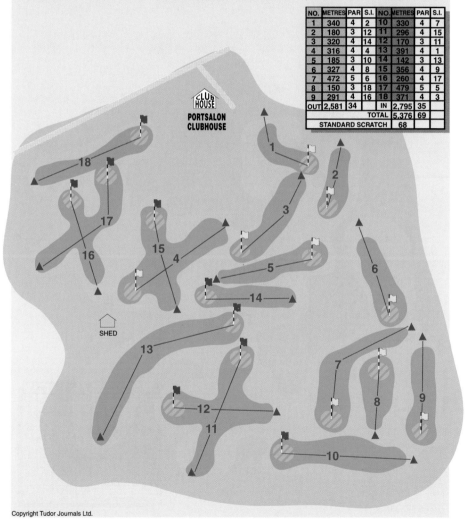

PORTSALON CLUBHOUSE

SHED

REDCASTLE   ULSTER   DONEGAL

Redcastle, Moville, Co. Donegal.
Tel: (077) 82073.

Location: Beside hotel.
Secretary: Danny McCartney.
Tel: (077) 350510.

A difficult course set in a very picturesque area on the shores of Lough Foyle, with the advantage of its own hotel. The two Par 3 holes are quite difficult and should be approached with the necessary respect.

COURSE INFORMATION

Par 72; SSS 69; Length 6,046 yards.
Visitors: Welcome to play midweek.
Opening Hours: All day, all year.
Ladies: Welcome.
Green Fees: £8 Mon – Fri (£7 with member); £12 Sat / Sun & Bank Holidays (£11 with member).
Juveniles: Welcome if accompanied by an adult. Fee – £3.50. Students – £5 (must present student I. D.).
Clubhouse Hours: 9.00am – 11.30pm.
Clubhouse Dress: Casual
Clubhouse Facilities: Bar and catering from 11.30am – 7pm.
Open Competitions: Various throughout the season. Information on request.

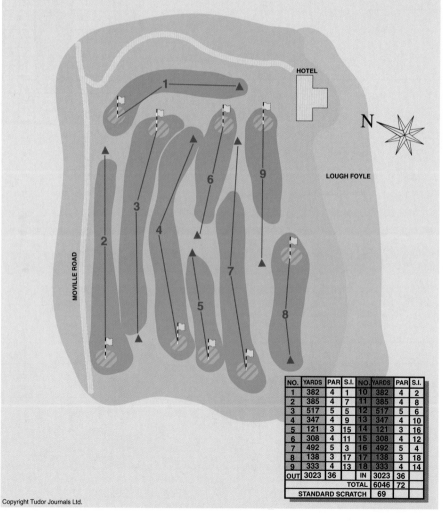

NO.	YARDS	PAR	S.I.	NO.	YARDS	PAR	S.I.
1	382	4	1	10	382	4	2
2	385	4	7	11	385	4	8
3	517	5	5	12	517	5	6
4	347	4	9	13	347	4	10
5	121	3	15	14	121	3	16
6	308	4	11	15	308	4	12
7	492	5	3	16	492	5	4
8	138	3	17	17	138	3	18
9	333	4	13	18	333	4	14
OUT	3023	36		IN	3023	36	
				TOTAL	6046	72	
				STANDARD SCRATCH	69		

ROSAPENNA

**Rosapenna Golf Club,
Downings.
Co. Donegal.
Tel: (074) 55301.**

LOCATION: Two miles north of Carrigart.
SECRETARY: Frank Casey.
ARCHITECT: Original Course (1893) – Tom Morris.

This championship length links course is set in north west Donegal at Downings. The first nine are played along a majestic stretch of beach and have many large sandhills with some bunkers. The second nine begins and ends with a second shot over the main Downings–Carrigart Road.

Looping around a large bluff the second nine have inland characteristics. Very popular with visiting societies as the Rosapenna Golf Hotel is situated on the course and and offers special golf breaks. A new alternative back eight was added in 1997 that double back behind the giant dunes. The new holes are more in the links character of the first 10.

COURSE INFORMATION

**Old course distances; Par 70;
SSS 71; Length 5,719 metres.
Visitors:** Welcome.
Opening Hours: Dawn to Dusk.
Ladies: Welcome.
Green Fees: £20 weekdays;

£25 Saturday and Sunday.
Juveniles: Must be accompanied by an adult.
Clubhouse Facilities: Full catering facilities at Rosapenna Golf Hotel.
Open Competition: Open week 9th – 16th August.

OLD COURSE CARD

NO.	YARDS	PAR	S.I.	NO.	YARDS	PAR	S.I.
1	298	4	11	10	543	5	10
2	428	4	5	11	427	4	2
3	446	4	1	12	342	4	14
4	386	4	9	13	455	5	6
5	255	4	15	14	128	3	18
6	167	3	17	15	418	4	4
7	367	4	3	16	216	3	16
8	485	5	7	17	358	4	12
9	185	3	13	18	367	4	8
OUT	3,017	35		IN	3,254	35	
				TOTAL	6,271	70	
			STANDARD SCRATCH		71		

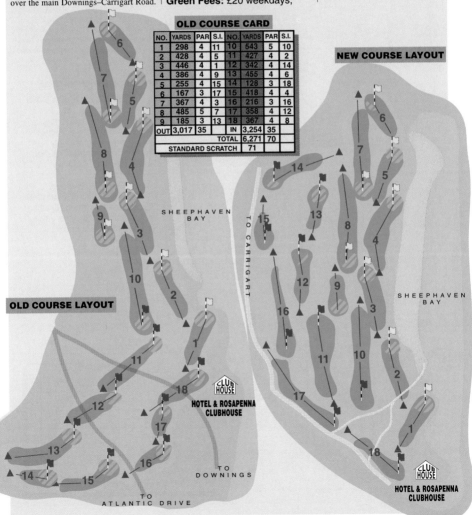

NEW COURSE LAYOUT

OLD COURSE LAYOUT

SHEEPHAVEN BAY

TO CARRIGART

SHEEPHAVEN BAY

CLUB HOUSE

HOTEL & ROSAPENNA CLUBHOUSE

HOTEL & ROSAPENNA CLUBHOUSE

TO DOWNINGS

TO ATLANTIC DRIVE

Castle Place, Ardglass.
Co. Down.
Tel: (01396) 841219.
Fax: (01396) 841219.

LOCATION: Approx 7 miles
from Downpatrick on B1.
CLUB MANAGER:
Debbie Polly.
Tel: (01396) 841219.
PROFFESSIONAL: Philip Farrell.
Tel: (01396) 841022.

A seaside course with superb views
over St. Johns Point, Killough Harbour
and lying to the west, the Mourne
Mountains. The 2nd (Howds) hole a
147 Metres, Par 3 is played over a
gaping gorge to an elevated green.
Another Par 3, the 11th is played from
an elevated tee looking down to Coney
Island. Both provide two memorable
golf holes.

COURSE INFORMATION

**Par 70; SSS 69; Length 5,498
metres.**
Visitors: Welcome Monday,
Tuesday, Thursday & Friday.
Avoid: Arrangement only
Wednesday, Saturday, Sunday.
Green Fees: £14 Mon – Fri; £20
weekends.
Ladies Day: Wednesday.
Clubhouse Dress: Smart dress.
Clubhouse Facilities: Snacks
are available during the day.
Evening meals by prior
arrangement.

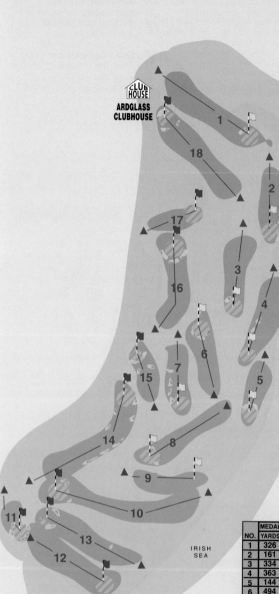

NO.	MEDAL YARDS	GEN. YARDS	PAR	S.I.	NO.	MEDAL YARDS	GEN. YARDS	PAR	S.I.
1	326	292	4	10	10	439	430	4	1
2	161	173	3	6	11	181	142	3	5
3	334	269	4	14	12	397	371	4	7
4	363	351	4	4	13	382	362	4	11
5	144	135	3	12	14	492	480	5	13
6	494	485	5	16	15	392	384	4	3
7	514	507	5	18	16	361	361	4	9
8	404	394	4	2	17	119	114	3	17
9	219	205	3	8	18	345	321	4	15
OUT	2,959	2,811	35		IN	3,106	2,965	35	
					TOTAL	6,065	5,776	70	
					STANDARD SCRATCH	69	68		

IRISH
SEA

Bunker positions indicated.
Copyright Tudor Journals Ltd.

210

BANBRIDGE

**Huntly Road, Banbridge.
Co. Down.
Tel: (018206) 62342 /
62211.**

LOCATION: 1 mile from town
centre on Huntly Road.
HON / SECRETARY: Thomas Fee.
SECRETARY / MANAGER: H.
Carson.
ADMINISTRATOR: Mrs J. A.
Anketell.
Tel: (018206) 62211.

The course has been extended to 18
holes the new holes designed by
Frank Ainsworth and include a very
exciting 'pond hole', 6th. The
redesigned Par 5, 14th calls for an
accurate shot over a ravine. The Par
3, 10th is tricky primarily as it is
quite long at 201 metres and
secondly, the green is very close to
the boundary hedge.

COURSE INFORMATION

**Par 69; SSS 67; Length 5,003
metres.**

Visitors: Welcome to play on
most days, contact office to
make arrangements.
Green Fees: £15 Mon – Fri
(£8 with member); £20
weekends (£10 with member).
Ladies Day: Tuesday.
Clubhouse Dress: Casual.
Clubhouse Facilities: By
arrangement.
Open Competitions:
Telephone Club for details.

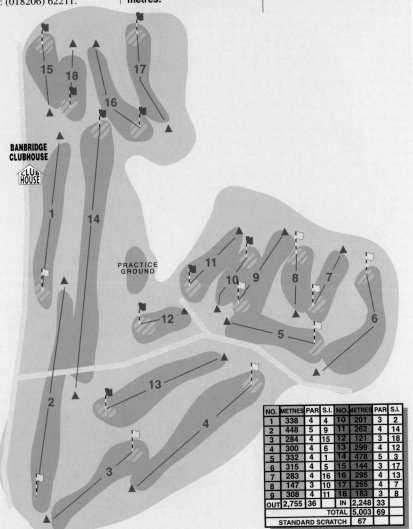

NO.	METRES	PAR	S.I.	NO.	METRES	PAR	S.I.
1	338	4	4	10	201	3	2
2	448	5	9	11	262	4	14
3	284	4	15	12	121	3	18
4	300	4	6	13	299	4	12
5	332	4	1	14	478	5	3
6	315	4	5	15	144	3	17
7	283	4	16	16	295	4	13
8	147	3	10	17	265	4	7
9	308	4	11	18	183	3	8
OUT	2,755	36		IN	2,248	33	
				TOTAL	5,003	69	
				STANDARD SCRATCH		67	

NO.	MEDAL YARDS	GEN. YARDS	PAR	S.I.	NO.	MEDAL YARDS	GEN. YARDS	PAR	S.I.
1	351	341	4	14	10	438	417	4	3
2	493	482	5	10	11	319	309	4	15
3	359	339	4	18	12	194	175	3	7
4	471	461	5	6	13	384	374	4	5
5	463	455	4	2	14	175	163	3	13
6	354	344	4	16	15	408	398	4	1
7	192	182	3	12	16	510	482	5	11
8	409	391	4	4	17	159	149	3	17
9	392	384	4	8	18	339	323	4	9
OUT	3,484	3,379	37		IN	2,926	2,790	34	
					TOTAL	6,410	6,169	71	
	STANDARD SCRATCH					71	70		

Bunker and tree positions indicated.

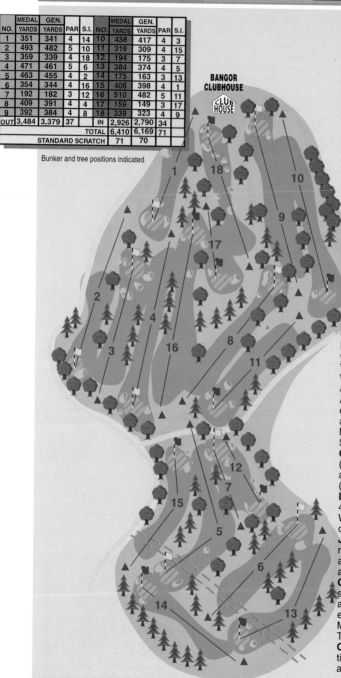

BANGOR CLUBHOUSE

**Broadway, Bangor.
Co. Down.
Tel: (01247) 270922.**

LOCATION: 1 mile from town centre off Donaghadee Road.
SECRETARY: David Ryan.
Tel: (01247) 270922.
PROFESSIONAL:
Blake Campbell.
Tel: (01247) 462164.
ARCHITECT: James Braid.

Bangor Golf Course is a pleasant, well-groomed, scenic parkland course. The four 'pitch' holes balance the three Par 5's, and the long and difficult Par 4, 5th hole. Recent improvements in fairway drainage and in the treatment of greens have resulted in the course returning to its previous year-round excellence. A major tree planting programme has been undertaken. It remains a challenge and a pleasure to both 'single-figure' and less serious players.

COURSE INFORMATION

Par 71; SSS 71; Length 6,410 yards.
Visitors: Welcome, Monday, Wednesday, Thursday, Friday & Sunday.
Avoid: 1.00pm – 2.00pm everyday; Wednesday, Friday after 4.00pm; Sunday morning. Members only Tuesday and Saturday.
Green Fees: £17.50 Mon – Fri (£10 with member); £25 Sun / all bank holidays. Weekends (£10 with member).
Ladies: No visitors after 4.00pm Monday and Wednesday or Saturday all day.
Juveniles: Weekdays up to 12 noon only. Lessons by prior arrangements. Golf trolleys available.
Clubhouse Facilities: Bar snacks up to 7.30pm. Lunch and evening meal – booking is essential. No catering on Mondays from Oct – Mar. Tel: (01247) 270483.
Clubhouse Dress: Jacket and tie in dining room. No denim at any time.

BLACKWOOD

Crawfordsburn Rd,
Clandeboye, Co. Down,
BT19 1GB.
Tel: (01247) 852706.

LOCATION: Ten miles from Belfast –
three miles from Bangor, Co. Down.
GENERAL MANAGER: Richard Gibson.
Tel: (01247) 853581.
PROFESSIONAL: Tony White.
Tel: (01247) 852706.
ARCHITECT: Simon Gidman.

NO.	MEDAL YARDS	GEN. YARDS	PAR	S.I.	NO.	MEDAL YARDS	GEN. YARDS	PAR	S.I.
1	354	343	4	12	10	436	421	4	3
2	540	529	5	4	11	354	341	4	15
3	212	206	3	6	12	166	152	3	9
4	306	295	4	18	13	436	415	4	1
5	419	398	4	2	14	491	475	5	11
6	332	321	4	14	15	404	385	4	7
7	165	165	3	16	16	180	164	3	5
8	325	305	4	10	17	355	340	4	13
9	480	471	5	8	18	349	331	4	17
OUT	3,133	3,033	36		IN	3,171	3,024	35	
					TOTAL	6,304	6,057	71	

STANDARD SCRATCH

Blackwood Golf Centre is Ulster's
foremost pay and play golf facility.
Opened in 1994, the centre comprises
Hamilton course – an eighteen hole
championship standard course, Temple
course – an eighteen hole, par 3 course,
plus a twenty bay covered, floodlit driving
range. The centre also boasts Shanks
Restaurant, bar & grill and a salon privé
(private function room) sponsored by
Guinness Northern Ireland.

COURSE INFORMATION

HAMILTON COURSE SSS 70
Par 71; Length 6,304 yards.
Visitors: Welcome.
Opening Hours: 8am – 10pm.
Green Fees: £14 midweek & £18
weekends and Bank Holidays
(booking advised).

TEMPLE COURSE
Par 54; Length 2,492 yards.
Greens Fees: £7 midweek & £9
weekends and Bank Holidays.
Opening hours: 8 a.m –10 p.m.
Golf Centre Hours: 10am –11pm.
Golf Centre Dress: Smart /casual.
Golf Centre Facilities: Top rated
restaurant (telephone booking for
evening service is recommended),
bar and grill (with lunch menu) and
private function room – available for
private hire.

YARDS	PAR	S.I.	NO.	YARDS	PAR	S.I.
75	3	16	10	185	3	1
182	3	6	11	101	3	13
108	3	14	12	176	3	3
83	3	18	13	129	3	15
116	3	8	14	154	3	7
116	3	12	15	125	3	11
147	3	4	16	163	3	9
177	3	2	17	129	3	17
132	3	10	18	174	3	5
T 1,136	27		IN	1,356	27	
	TOTAL	2,492	54			

STANDARD SCRATCH

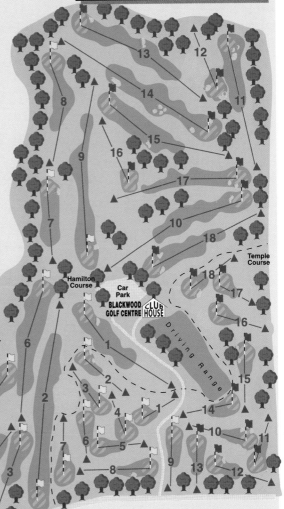

Temple
Course

Hamilton
Course

Car
Park

BLACKWOOD
GOLF CENTRE

CLUB
HOUSE

Driving Range

BRIGHT CASTLE ULSTER · DOWN

14 Coniamstown Road, Bright, Downpatrick, Co. Down.
Tel: (01396) 841319.

LOCATION: 5 miles south of Downpatrick off B1 to Ardglass, take road to Bright.
SECRETARY: John McCaul.
Tel: (01396) 841319.
ARCHITECT: Mr A. Ennis (Sen).

Inland course on high ground with splendid views of the Mourne Mountains from the 2nd green. A long course with four Par 5's, 16th a par 6 (735 yards – the longest golf hole in Europe) and an abundance of young trees which are maturing well. Stamina is important on this course.

COURSE INFORMATION

Par 74; SSS 74; Length 7,143 yards.

Visitors: Welcome anytime.
Opening Hours: Sunrise – sunset.
Green Fees: £10 Mon – Fri; £12 Sat / Sun / Bank Holidays
Clubhouse Dress: Casual.
Clubhouse Facilities: Changing rooms only. snacks from 9am – 8pm, golfers frys available, fish & chips, sausage bacon, chips etc.
Open Competitions: Open Week August.

NO.	YARDS	PAR	S.I.	NO.	YARDS	PAR	S.I.
1	550	5	8	10	565	5	13
2	560	5	2	11	345	4	11
3	475	4	6	12	455	4	1
4	440	4	4	13	455]	4	5
5	285	4	16	14	320	4	7
6	340	4	12	15	210	3	15
7	330	4	14	16	735	6	3
8	355	4	10	17	395	4	9
9	140	3	18	18	188	3	17
OUT	3,475	37		IN	3,668	37	
				TOTAL	7,143	74	
	STANDARD SCRATCH				74		

BRIGHT CASTLE
GOLF CLUB

CARNALEA

Station Road, Bangor, Co. Down.
Tel: (01247) 465004.

LOCATION: 2 Miles West of Bangor.
SECRETARY: J.H. Crozier.
Tel: (01247) 270368.

The course is situated on rising ground by the shores of Belfast Lough and the turf is of inland variety. The railway line runs parallel and adjacent to the 1st hole so one has to be careful not to be playing three off the tee! If your game is not working on all cylinders you can enjoy the scenery instead.

COURSE INFORMATION

Par 68; SSS 67; Length 5,574 yards.
Visitors: Welcome any day.
Avoid: Saturday.
Ladies: Welcome.

Green Fees: £13 Mon - Fri; £17 Sat / Sun.
Juveniles: Must be accompanied by an adult. Lessons available by prior arrangement. Club Hire and Caddy cars available.
Clubhouse Dress: Informal except Saturday night. Jacket and tie after 8.00pm.
Clubhouse Facilities: Full facilities. Lunches, snacks 11.30am - 2.30pm. Snacks, high tea, a la carte 5.00pm - 10.00pm.

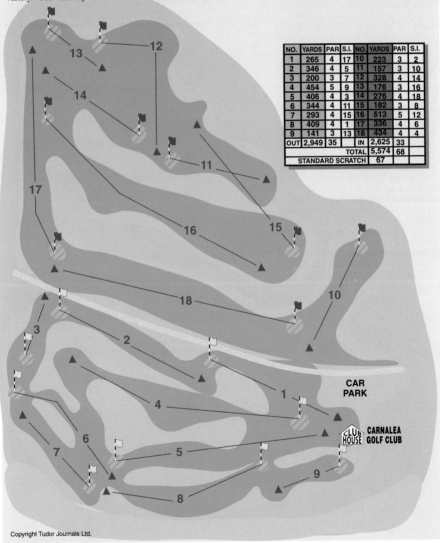

NO.	YARDS	PAR	S.I.	NO.	YARDS	PAR	S.I.
1	265	4	17	10	223	3	2
2	346	4	5	11	157	3	10
3	200	3	7	12	328	4	14
4	454	5	9	13	176	3	16
5	406	4	3	14	276	4	18
6	344	4	11	15	182	3	8
7	293	4	15	16	513	5	12
8	409	4	1	17	336	4	6
9	141	3	13	18	434	4	4
OUT	2,949	35		IN	2,625	33	
				TOTAL	5,574	68	
STANDARD SCRATCH		67					

CAR PARK

CARNALEA GOLF CLUB

**Tower Road, Conlig,
Newtownards. BT23 5PN.
Tel: (01247) 271767.**

LOCATION: Above Conlig Village off A21 between Bangor and Newtownards.
GENERAL MANAGER: Bill Donald.
PROFESSIONAL: Peter Gregory.
Tel: (01247) 271750.
ARCHITECT: William Rennick Robinson, Dr Von Limburger.

The second course at Clandeboye, the Ava, although much shorter than the 'Dufferin' is a complete contrast and is different in its own right. The 2nd hole is considered one of the most attractive in Irish golf and is a true test of any players game.

NO.	MEDAL YARDS	GEN. YARDS	PAR	S.I.	NO.	MEDAL YARDS	GEN. YARDS	PAR	S.I.
1	346	335	4	9	10	175	150	3	12
2	524	506	5	1	11	432	421	4	2
3	166	156	3	7	12	178	167	3	10
4	319	274	4	5	13	495	479	5	14
5	310	303	4	17	14	359	345	4	4
6	183	171	3	15	15	131	120	3	18
7	312	305	4	3	16	317	303	4	6
8	542	496	5	13	17	329	315	4	16
9	309	294	4	11	18	328	317	4	8
OUT	3,011	2,840	36		IN	2,744	2,625	34	
					TOTAL	5,755	5,465	70	
					STANDARD SCRATCH	68	67		

COURSE INFORMATION

Par 70; SSS 68; Length 5,755 yards.
Visitors: Welcome on weekdays. Must be with member at weekends.
Green Fees: £20 Mon - Fri (with member £9); £15 after 4.00pm April – September. Societies – £20 (meals inclusive). Lessons available by prior arrangment. Club Hire and Caddy cars also available.
Clubhouse Dress: Smart / Casual.
Clubhouse Facilities: Full facilities (except during the winter closed on Mon). Prior arrangement required. Snacks, meals 10.00am - 10.00pm.
Open Competitions: Numerous throughout the year. Letter of introduction required, if possible.

AVA COURSE

CLANDEBOYE CLUBHOUSE

Tower Road, Conlig, Newtownards.
BT23 5PN.
Tel: (01247) 271767.

LOCATION: Above Conlig Village off A21 between Bangor and Newtownards.
GENERAL MANAGER: Bill Donald.
PROFESSIONAL: Peter Gregory. Tel: (01247) 271750.
ARCHITECT: William Rennick Robinson, Dr Von Limburger.

One of North Down's most popular golf clubs, Clandeboye, has two courses – the Ava and the Dufferin. The latter being the Championship one, the short Par 4, 1st giving no indication of the stern test ahead. The course is laid out on the hills above Conlig village and has superb views over Belfast Lough and the Irish Sea. This course is now recognised as one of the great inland golfing experiences in Ireland.

COURSE INFORMATION

Par 71; SSS 71; Length 6,548 yards.
Visitors: Welcome on weekdays. Must be with member at weekends.
Green Fees: £25 Mon – Fri (with member £10). Lessons available by prior arrangement. Club Hire and

Caddy cars available.
Clubhouse Facilities: Full facilities. Prior arrangement required. Snacks, meals 10.00am – 10.00pm.
Open Competitions: Co. Down Senoirs Open; 5th & 6th May: Clandeboye Open Week; 18th – 24th May: Bank of Ireland Open Stroke; 17th August (36 holes): Ferguson Cup Open Stroke; 24th August: Hosting Irish Ladies Open in 1998. Letter of introduction required, if possible, for open competitons.

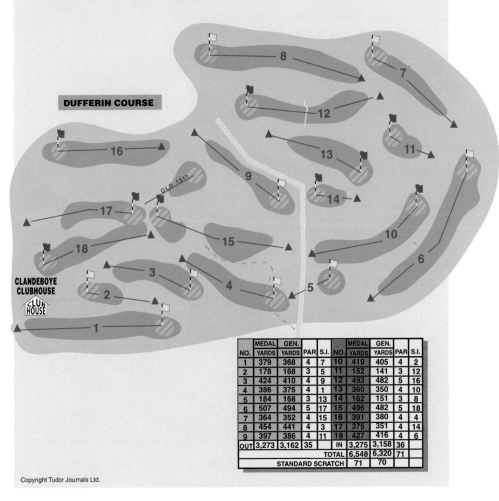

DUFFERIN COURSE

CLANDEBOYE CLUBHOUSE

NO.	MEDAL YARDS	GEN. YARDS	PAR	S.I.	NO.	MEDAL YARDS	GEN. YARDS	PAR	S.I.
1	379	368	4	7	10	419	405	4	2
2	178	168	3	5	11	152	141	3	12
3	424	410	4	9	12	493	482	5	16
4	386	375	4	1	13	360	350	4	10
5	184	168	3	13	14	162	151	3	8
6	507	494	5	17	15	496	482	5	18
7	364	352	4	15	16	391	380	4	4
8	454	441	4	3	17	375	351	4	14
9	397	386	4	11	18	427	416	4	6
OUT	3,273	3,162	35		IN	3,275	3,158	36	
					TOTAL	6,548	6,320	71	
					STANDARD SCRATCH		71	70	

**84 Warren Road,
Donaghadee,
Co. Down.
Tel: (01247) 883624.**

LOCATION: 5 miles south of
Bangor on A2 on Coast Road.
SECRETARY: Mr K. Patton.
Tel: (01247) 883624.
PROFESSIONAL: Gordon Drew.
Tel: (01247) 882392.

A part links and part inland open
course with little rough but several
water hazards which can catch the
unthinking shot. The 18th with
out-of-bounds on both left and right
can be intimidating. Lovely views
over the Copeland Islands to the

Scottish Coast, particularly from the
16th tee. Well appointed clubhouse.

COURSE INFORMATION

**Par 71; SSS 69; Length
5,570 metres.
Visitors:** Welcome on any
weekday and Sunday.
Members only on Saturday.
Avoid: Saturdays and
Bank Holidays.
Ladies: Welcome Tuesday.
Green Fees: £14 Mon – Fri;
£18 Sunday. Special rates
for societies.
Juveniles: Mon – Fri and
Sun. Must be accompanied by
an adult. Lessons available by

prior arrangement. Club Hire
available also.
Clubhouse Dress: Saturday
after 8.00pm in mixed lounge
and dining room – jacket and
tie. Otherwise smart / casual
(no denims).
Clubhouse Facilities: Full
facilities; 11.00am – 9.00pm
Tues – Sun during winter; 7
days a week in summer.
Open Competitions: Open
week: 30th May – 6th June;
Coca Cola Youth Tournament:
10th – 14th Aug. Various
others throughout the season;
telephone club for details.

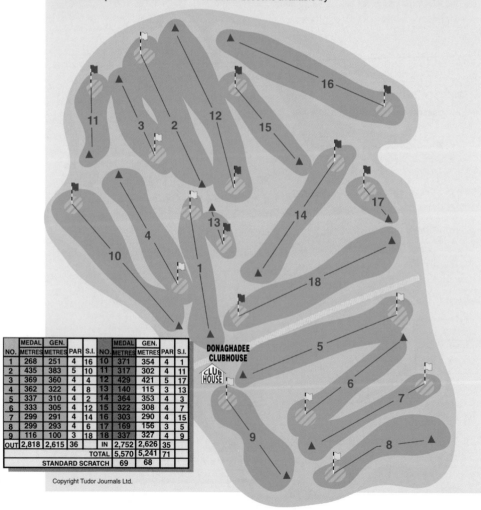

NO.	MEDAL METRES	GEN. METRES	PAR	S.I.	NO.	MEDAL METRES	GEN. METRES	PAR	S.I.
1	268	251	4	16	10	371	354	4	1
2	435	383	5	10	11	317	302	4	11
3	369	360	4	4	12	429	421	5	17
4	362	322	4	8	13	140	115	3	13
5	337	310	4	2	14	364	353	4	3
6	333	305	4	12	15	322	308	4	7
7	299	291	4	14	16	303	290	4	15
8	299	293	4	6	17	169	156	3	5
9	116	100	3	18	18	337	327	4	9
OUT	2,818	2,615	36		IN	2,752	2,626	35	
					TOTAL	5,570	5,241	71	
					STANDARD SCRATCH	69	68		

DONAGHADEE CLUBHOUSE

**43 Saul Road,
Downpatrick, Co. Down
BT30 6PA
Tel: (01396)
612152/615947.**

LOCATION: 25 miles south of Belfast on (A7) and 1 & 1/2 miles south east of Downpatrick town centre.
SECRETARY: Mr A. Carson.
Tel: (01396) 615947.
ARCHITECT: Martin Hawtree.

Recently upgraded, challenging parkland course. 5th hole particularly challenging. Excellent drainage so open all year round.

COURSE INFORMATION

Par 69; SSS 69; Length 6,100 yards.
Visitors: Welcome any day by prior arrangment.
Ladies: Anyday except Sunday.
Green Fees: £15 Mon – Fri; £20 Sat / Sun.
Juveniles: No non - members allowed on course. Lessons available. Club Hire and Caddy cars available.
Clubhouse Hours: 11.00am – 11.00pm.

Clubhouse Dress: Jacket and tie after 7pm.
Clubhouse Facilities: Full facilities snooker, bowls, TV lounge. Meals available all day; everyday (except Monday) during season. Winter months 12pm – 3pm.
Open Competitions: Bank of Ireland – June; Guinness Open – July; Heart of Down – September.

NO.	MEDAL YARDS	GEN. YARDS	PAR	S.I.	NO.	MEDAL YARDS	GEN. YARDS	PAR	S.I.
1	374	368	4	3	10	362	326	4	10
2	298	293	4	17	11	181	170	3	12
3	506	500	5	11	12	544	538	5	4
4	176	166	3	13	13	390	379	4	6
5	457	457	4	5	14	424	390	4	2
6	330	324	4	9	15	171	168	3	16
7	437	427	4	1	16	364	338	4	14
8	135	129	3	15	17	278	270	4	18
9	337	325	4	7	18	336	330	4	8
OUT	3050	2989	35		IN	3050	2909	34	
					TOTAL	6100	5898	69	
					STANDARD SCRATCH		69		

DOWNPATRICK CLUBHOUSE

Golf Road, Helens Bay, Bangor, Co Down.
Tel: (01247) 852601.

LOCATION: 9 miles east of Belfast on A2.
SECRETARY: L. W. L. Mann.
Tel: (01247) 852815.
Fax: (01247) 852815.

This popular course is compact with the layout encircling the Clubhouse. The turf is of the inland variety, greens are small making scoring more difficult than first impressions would suggest. There are extensive views of the Antrim Hills across Belfast Lough. The 4th hole, a short pitch over trees to a green protected by bunkers on three sides, is a particularly interesting one.

COURSE INFORMATION

Par 68; SSS 67; Length 5,176 metres.
Visitors: Welcome to play; Mon, Wed, Thurs up to 5.00pm. Fri and Sun.
Avoid: Tue, Thur (after 1.30pm) Sat before 6.00pm.
Ladies: Tuesday – members only.
Green Fees: £12 Mon Fri; £15 Sun / Public Holidays.
Juveniles: Under 18's must be accompanied by an adult and unable to play after 6.00pm Mon – Fri.

Clubhouse Hours: 9.00am – 11.30am.
Clubhouse Dress: Smart casual dress is permitted until 7.30pm. After 7.30pm gentlemen must wear a jacket, collar and tie. Tee shirts or denim jeans are not acceptable on the course or in the Clubhouse.
Clubhouse Facilities: Full facilities. Evening meals until 9.00pm.
Open Competitions: Open week; 12th – 18th July. Numerous other competitions – telephone for details.

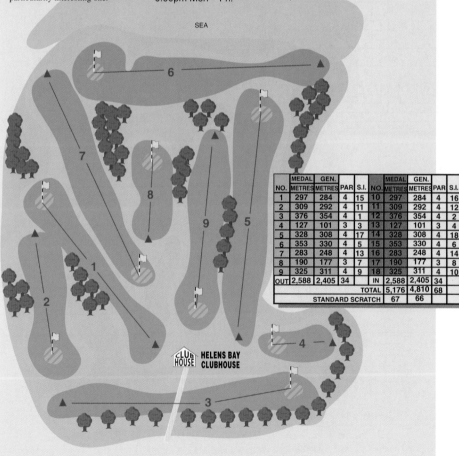

SEA

NO.	MEDAL METRES	GEN. METRES	PAR	S.I.	NO.	MEDAL METRES	GEN. METRES	PAR	S.I.
1	297	284	4	15	10	297	284	4	16
2	309	292	4	11	11	309	292	4	12
3	376	354	4	1	12	376	354	4	2
4	127	101	3	3	13	127	101	3	4
5	328	308	4	17	14	328	308	4	18
6	353	330	4	5	15	353	330	4	6
7	283	248	4	13	16	283	248	4	14
8	190	177	3	7	17	190	177	3	8
9	325	311	4	9	18	325	311	4	10
OUT	2,588	2,405	34		IN	2,588	2,405	34	
					TOTAL	5,176	4,810	68	
					STANDARD SCRATCH		67	66	

HELENS BAY CLUBHOUSE

**Demense Road,
Holywood, Co Down.
Tel: (01232) 422138.**

LOCATION: 5 miles east of
Belfast on A2.
SECRETARY: S. Melville
Tel: 423135.
PROFESSIONAL: Michael Bannon.
Tel: 425503.

Hilly parkland course over-looking
Holywood, and with excellent views
over Belfast Lough. The first nine play
on the slopes of the Holywood Hills,
whilst the back nine are more varied
with some interesting tee shots and
some steep hills and valleys. Most of
the greens run toward the sea. The
back nine are a strenuous test begining

with a very steep climb to the 10th
green.

COURSE INFORMATION
**Par 69; SSS 68; Length
5,425 metres.
Opening hours:** Sunrise -
Sunset.
Visitors: Welcome to play;
Mon, Wed, Thu, Fri and Sun
after 2.15pm. (members only
1.30pm - 2.15pm.)
Avoid: Public holidays.
Ladies: Welcome Tuesday.
Green Fees: £15 Mon / Fri,
£21 Sun; Ladies £9 Mon / Fri,
£21 Sun; Societies £20 Sun.
Juveniles: Lessons available
by prior arrangments. Club

Hire and Caddy service
available.
Clubhouse Hours: 9.00am
11.30pm.
Clubhouse Dress: Smart /
casual, no denims or training
shoes on course. Jacket and
tie in mixed lounge after
7.30pm on Saturday.
Clubhouse Facilities: Full
facilities. Snacks, evening
meals all day everyday.
Open Competitions: Open
Week in June. Various other
open competitions throughout
the summer – telephone club
for details.

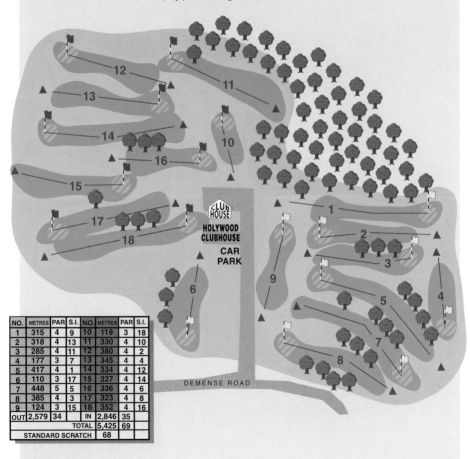

NO.	METRES	PAR	S.I.	NO.	METRES	PAR	S.I.
1	315	4	9	10	119	3	18
2	318	4	13	11	330	4	10
3	285	4	11	12	380	4	2
4	177	3	7	13	345	4	4
5	417	4	1	14	334	4	12
6	110	3	17	15	327	4	14
7	448	5	5	16	336	4	6
8	385	4	3	17	323	4	8
9	124	3	15	18	352	4	16
OUT	2,579	34		IN	2,846	35	
				TOTAL	5,425	69	
	STANDARD SCRATCH				68		

Tree positions indicated.

Mourne Park, Ballyardle, Kilkeel, Co Down.
Tel: (016937) 65095.
Fax: (016937) 65095.

LOCATION: Three miles from Kilkeel on main Newry Road.
SECRETARY: S. C. McBride.
Tel: (016937) 65095.
ARCHITECT: Lord Justice Babington (original nine holes); Mr. E. Hackett (new development).

Situated at the foot of Knockcree Mountain, the course is ringed by woodlands and masses of rhododendron shrubs in an area that might well be described as the Garden of Mourne. The course was enlarged in 1993 from seven old holes to 18 holes.

COURSE INFORMATION

Par 72; SSS 72; Length 6,615 yards.
Opening hours: Sunrise – sunset.
Visitors: Welcome Mon, Wed, Thurs, Fri and Sun.
Avoid: Tues & Sat.
Ladies: Welcome Tuesday.

Green Fees: £16 Mon – Fri; £18 weekends.
Juveniles: up to 5.00pm. Caddy cars available by prior arrangment. A Handicap Certificate is required for open competitions.
Clubhouse Dress: Jacket and tie in main lounge.
Clubhouse Facilities: Full facilities. Snacks, evening meals all day during summer or by prior arrangment.
Open Competitions: Several throughout the year.

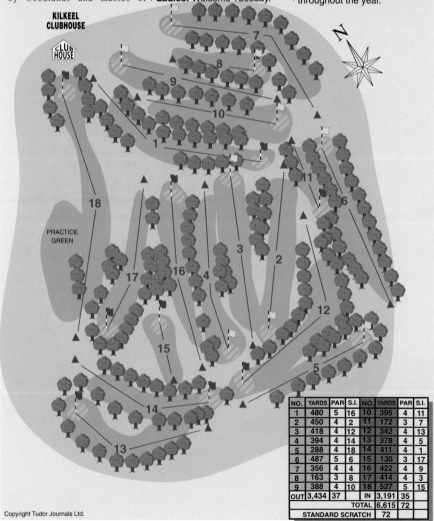

KILKEEL CLUBHOUSE

PRACTICE GREEN

NO.	YARDS	PAR	S.I.	NO.	YARDS	PAR	S.I.
1	480	5	16	10	395	4	11
2	450	4	2	11	172	3	7
3	418	4	12	12	342	4	13
4	394	4	14	13	378	4	5
5	288	4	18	14	411	4	1
6	487	5	6	15	130	3	17
7	356	4	4	16	422	4	9
8	163	3	8	17	414	4	3
9	388	4	10	18	527	5	15
OUT	3,434	37		IN	3,191	35	
				TOTAL	6,615	72	
				STANDARD SCRATCH		72	

Copyright Tudor Journals Ltd.

KIRKISTOWN CASTLE

**142 Main Road,
Cloughey, Newtownards,
Co Down.
Tel: (01247) 771233**

Location: 16 miles south east
of Newtownards on A2.
Secretary: George Graham.
Tel: (01247) 771233.
Professional: J. Peden.
Tel: (01247) 771004.
Architect: J Braid.

Eighteen hole links course having
the distinct advantage due to its
dryness of being open for play
when many other courses are
closed due to inclement weather.
An open course that offers much
forgiveness for errant shots.
Adjacent to the Irish Sea coastline.

COURSE INFORMATION

**Par 69; SSS 69; Length
5,596 metres.
Opening hours:** 8am - Dusk.
Visitors: Welcome any
weekday.
Avoid: Friday mornings.
Green Fees: £13 Mon – Fri;
(£9 with a member); £20 Sat /
Sun / All public holidays (£12
with a member).
Juveniles: £3 Mon – Fri; £8 –
Sat / Sun, must be
accompanied

by an adult. Can play anytime.
Clubhouse Hours: 8am –
11.30pm.
Clubhouse Dress: Casual,
jacket and tie after 7.30pm.
Clubhouse Facilities: Full
facilities up to 5.00pm and
evening meals must be
ordered before commencing
play.
Open Competitions:
Throughout the season. Open
Week July / August.

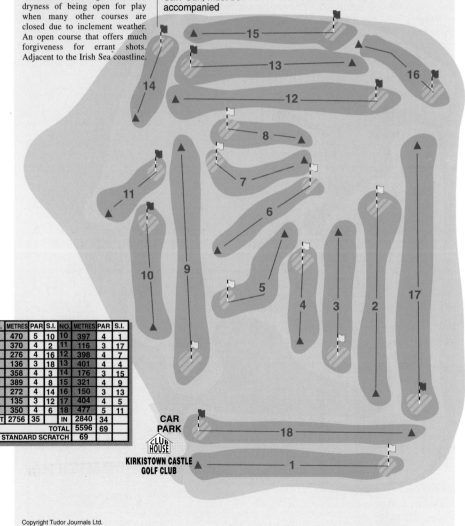

NO.	METRES	PAR	S.I.	NO.	METRES	PAR	S.I.
1	470	5	10	10	397	4	1
2	370	4	2	11	116	3	17
3	276	4	16	12	398	4	7
4	136	3	18	13	401	4	4
5	358	4	3	14	176	3	15
6	389	4	8	15	321	4	9
7	272	4	14	16	150	3	13
8	135	3	12	17	404	4	5
9	350	4	6	18	477	5	11
OUT	2756	35		IN	2840	34	
				TOTAL	5596	69	
				STANDARD SCRATCH	69		

CAR
PARK

CLUB
HOUSE

KIRKISTOWN CASTLE
GOLF CLUB

Copyright Tudor Journals Ltd.

223

Comber, Newtownards, Co Down.
Tel: (01238) 541234.

LOCATION: Take Killyleagh Road from Comber, in less than a mile take a road to left, signposted Ardmillan. Bear left for 6 miles to Mahee Island.
SECRETARY: Tom Reid.
Tel: (01238) 541234.
SHOP: A McCracken.
Tel: (01238) 541234.
ARCHITECT: Mr Robinson, Bangor.

A nine hole course sited on an island in Strangford Lough with excellent views for 360 degrees. The course is parkland with luscious fairways and well manicured greens. The undulating fairways and tricky approach shots make this a good test of golf. The course record stands at 65 so it is no pushover. One to visit, not only for the golf enthusiast, but for the views.

COURSE INFORMATION

Par 68; SSS 68; Length 5,588 yards 5,108 metres.
Opening hours:
9.00am – 9.00pm.
Visitors: Welcome to play.
Avoid: Sat before 4.30pm and Wed after 4.30pm.

Ladies: Welcome Mondays.
Green Fees: £10 Mon – Fri; £15 Sat / Sun / Bank hols.
Juveniles: Play Thur. Not Sat. Club Hire available. Handicap Certificate required for Open Competitions only. Prior arrangement required.
Clubhouse Hours: 9.00am – 5.30pm.
Clubhouse Dress: Casual to 7pm. Jacket and tie at all functions.
Clubhouse Facilities: Meals by prior arrangement. No bar.
Open Competitions: July each year.

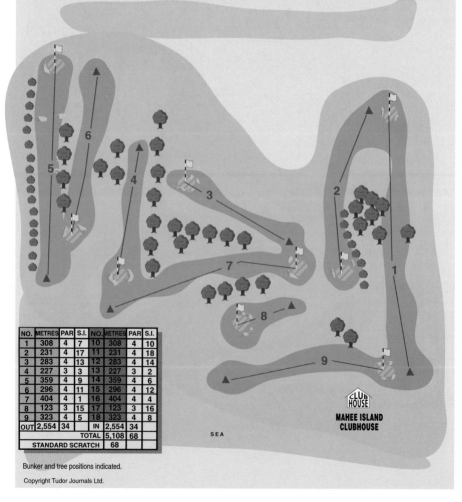

NO.	METRES	PAR	S.I.	NO.	METRES	PAR	S.I.
1	308	4	7	10	308	4	10
2	231	4	17	11	231	4	18
3	283	4	13	12	283	4	14
4	227	3	3	13	227	3	2
5	359	4	9	14	359	4	6
6	296	4	11	15	296	4	12
7	404	4	1	16	404	4	4
8	123	3	15	17	123	3	16
9	323	4	5	18	323	4	8
OUT	2,554	34		IN	2,554	34	
				TOTAL	5,108	68	
STANDARD SCRATCH		68					

MAHEE ISLAND CLUBHOUSE

SEA

Bunker and tree positions indicated.

NO.	MEDAL METRES	GEN. METRES	PAR	S.I.	NO.	MEDAL METRES	GEN. METRES	PAR	S.I.
1	322	320	4	4	10	292	309	4	1
2	261	261	4	12	11	91	252	3	13
3	309	303	4	11	12	282	309	4	6
4	176	174	3	5	13	312	162	4	7
5	427	423	5	9	14	108	383	3	15
6	313	291	4	2	15	323	291	4	14
7	277	276	4	10	16	124	277	3	16
8	121	121	3	17	17	277	121	4	8
9	291	288	4	18	18	392	273	4	3
OUT	2,497	2,455	35		IN	2,201	2,377	33	
					TOTAL	4,698	4,754	68	
					STANDARD SCRATCH		66		

Ringdufferin Road, Toye, Killyleagh, Co Down.
Tel: (01396) 828812.

LOCATION: Three miles north of Killyleagh off Comber Road.
SECRETARY: Helen Lindsay.
Tel: (01396) 828812.

A nine hole course with excellent views. The course runs over drumlins (rounded hills) and will be converting to 18 holes late in 1997 / early 1998. The undulating fairways and tricky approach shots make this a testing course to play on. Idyllic views over Strangford Lough from some of the elevated tees.

COURSE INFORMATION

Par 68; SSS 66; Length 4,698 metres.
Visitors: Welcome.
Opening Hours:
8.00am – 9.00pm.
Avoid: Telephone for available tee times on Saturday.
Ladies: Welcome.
Green Fees: £5 Mon – Fri (9 holes), £8 (18 holes); Sat & Sun £6 (9 holes), £10 (18 holes).
Juveniles: Permitted.
Clubhouse Hours:
8.00am – 9.00pm.
Clubhouse Dress: Casual.
Clubhouse Facilities: Light snacks and society meals by prior arrangement.
Open week: June

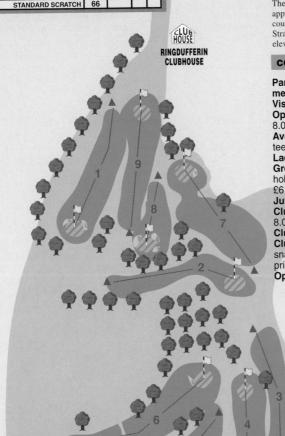

CLUB HOUSE
RINGDUFFERIN CLUBHOUSE

Bunker and tree positions indicated.
Copyright Tudor Journals Ltd.

**Station Road, Craigavad,
Holywood,
Co Down.
Tel: (01232) 428165.**

LOCATION: 7 miles east of
Belfast on A2.
SECRETARY: Susanna Morrison.
Tel: (01232) 428165.
PROFESSIONAL: Chris Spence.
Tel: (01232) 428586
ARCHITECT: H. C. Colt.

Eighteen hole parkland course rolls
gently to the shores of Belfast Lough.
The course is very picturesque with
many mature trees and many carefully
placed bunkers. The greens are
undulating and generally run towards
the sea. A very pleasant course that
presents a challenge to any handicap of
golfer.

COURSE INFORMATION

**Par 70; SSS 71; Length
6,274 yards.**
Visitors: Welcome any day
except Wednesday, Saturday
before 4.30pm and the 1st Mon
of each month
Opening Hours: 8.30am –
7.30pm.

Avoid: Wednesday.
Ladies: Welcome Wednesday,
Saturdays before 4.30pm and
the 1st Mon of each month.
Green Fees: £30 Mon – Fri;
£40 Sat / Sun / all public
holidays.
Clubhouse Dress: Smart /
casual.
Juveniles: Must be
accompanied by an adult.
Lessons available by prior
arrangement.
Clubhouse Facilities: Full
catering and bar. Pool / snooker.

NO.	MEDAL YARDS	GEN. YARDS	PAR	S.I.	NO.	MEDAL YARDS	GEN. YARDS	PAR	S.I.
1	417	414	4	7	10	303	299	4	14
2	404	400	4	3	11	165	162	3	8
3	372	359	4	13	12	433	430	4	4
4	143	140	3	15	13	360	357	4	12
5	555	550	5	9	14	187	184	3	10
6	351	348	4	11	15	410	407	4	2
7	184	164	3	17	16	485	476	5	16
8	394	392	4	5	17	193	190	3	18
9	409	406	4	1	18	509	506	5	6
OUT	3,229	3,173	35		IN	3,045	3,011	35	
					TOTAL	6,274	6,184	70	
		STANDARD SCRATCH					71	70	

ROYAL BELFAST
CLUBHOUSE

NO.	MEDAL YARDS	GEN. YARDS	PAR	S.I.	NO.	MEDAL YARDS	GEN. YARDS	PAR	S.I.
1	506	502	5	13	10	197	189	3	14
2	421	385	4	9	11	448	425	4	8
3	474	474	4	3	12	525	479	5	10
4	212	212	3	15	13	443	421	4	2
5	438	416	4	7	14	213	203	3	12
6	396	369	4	11	15	464	450	4	4
7	145	135	3	17	16	276	265	4	18
8	429	425	4	1	17	427	400	4	16
9	486	425	4	5	18	547	547	5	6
OUT	3,507	3,343	35		IN	3,530	3,379	36	
					TOTAL	7,037	6,722	71	
		STANDARD SCRATCH				74	72		

Newcastle, Co. Down.
Tel: (013967) 23314.
Fax: (013967) 26281.

LOCATION: 30 miles south of Belfast, 1 mile from Newcastle.
HON / SECRETARY: H. B. Mercer.
SECRETARY: P. E. Rolph.
Tel: (013967) 23314.
PROFESSIONAL: Kevan J. Whitson.
Tel: (013967) 22419.
ARCHITECT: Tom Morris.

Founded in 1889, the course offers an exhilerating challenge to even the most experienced golfers. The setting of this links course is continually remarked upon for its outstanding beauty. The Mountains of Mourne in all their glory rise up from the

Irish Sea. The fact that this course has five blind tee shots and several partially obscured approach shots makes it all the more formidable challenge to play. This is in addition to its well positioned bunkers. Professional golfers from all over the world rate Royal County Down as one of the best.

COURSE INFORMATION

Par 71; SSS 74; Length 7,037 yards.
Visitors: Welcome to play every weekday, except Wed; (limited hours) Sun, make prior arrangements.
Opening Hours: 8am – sunset.
Avoid: Wed & weekends. Prior arrangement preferred. Sat (members only).
Ladies: Welcome.
Green Fees: £60 Mon – Fri; (£35 – winter); £70 weekends (£45 winter). Reduced green fees with a member. Club Hire available, Caddy service available by prior arrangement and Caddy cars available. No open competitions.
Juveniles: With a member only.
Clubhouse Hours: 7.30am – 9pm except at weekends when members only. (Centenary Room; 9am – 9pm).
Clubhouse Dress: Jacket and tie at all times except in the Centenary Room where casual dress is permitted.
Clubhouse Facilities: Available in the Centenary Room from 9.30am – 6.30pm weekdays.

ROYAL COUNTY DOWN GOLF CLUB

CLUB HOUSE

PRO SHOP

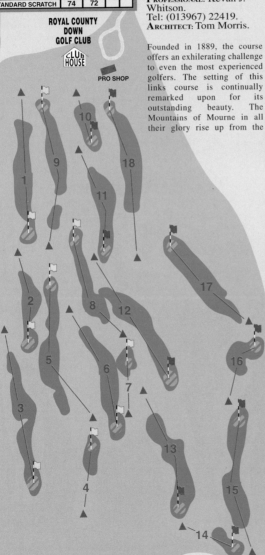

**233 Scrabo Road,
Newtownards, Co Down.
BT23 4SL.
Tel: (01247) 812355.
Fax: (01247) 822919.**

LOCATION: 10 miles from Belfast off the main Belfast to Newtownards carriageway, (follow signs for scrabo country park).
SECRETARY: Christine Hamill.
Tel: (01247) 812355.
PROFESSIONAL: Paul McCrystal.
Tel: (01247) 817848.

The course winds its way around Scrabo Hill and Tower, one of the well-known Co Down landmarks. Fabulous views over Strangford Lough and Mourne

Mountains (the 2nd hole is called Mourne View). Narrow fairways bordered by health and gorse call for accurate driving. The terrain around Scrabo Hill makes it a strenuous course for golfers.

COURSE INFORMATION

**Par 71; SSS 71; Length
5,699 metres.**
Visitors: Welcome.
Opening Hours: 9.00am – sunset.
Avoid: Saturday & Wednesday afternoons.
Ladies: Welcome Wednesday.
Green Fees: £15.00 Mon – Fri; £20.00weekend.

Societies: Special rates.
Juveniles: Not to play after 5.30pm. Must be accompanied by an adult member. Lessons and Caddy service available by prior arrangements. Club Hire available also. by prior arrangements.
Clubhouse Hours: 8.30am – 12 midnight. Full clubhouse facilities.
Clubhouse Dress: Informal. Jacket & Tie after 7.30pm in Dining Room.
Clubhouse Facilities: Tues 11.30am – 2.30pm; Wed – Fri 11.30am – 2.30pm & 6pm – 9.30pm. Sat / Sun 11.30am – 9.30pm. Excellent Cuisine.

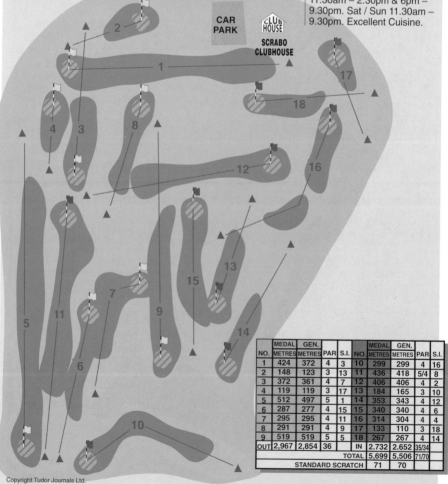

	MEDAL	GEN.				MEDAL	GEN.		
NO.	METRES	METRES	PAR	S.I.	NO.	METRES	METRES	PAR	S.I.
1	424	372	4	3	10	299	299	4	16
2	148	123	3	13	11	436	418	5/4	8
3	372	361	4	7	12	406	406	4	2
4	119	119	3	17	13	184	165	3	10
5	512	497	5	1	14	353	343	4	12
6	287	277	4	15	15	340	340	4	6
7	295	295	4	11	16	314	304	4	4
8	291	291	4	9	17	133	110	3	18
9	519	519	5	5	18	267	267	4	14
OUT	2,967	2,854	36		IN	2,732	2,652	35/34	
					TOTAL	5,699	5,506	71/70	
		STANDARD SCRATCH				71	70		

20 Grove Road, Ballynahinch, Co. Down.
Tel: (01238) 562365.

Location: 11 miles south of Belfast on the main road to Newcastle.
Hon. Secretary: Norman Morrow. Tel: (01238) 562365.
Secretary / Manager: Terry Magee.

Each fairway is lined with trees, and several high points on the course give scenic views of the countryside. The 8th and 17th give panoramic views of the Mourne Mountains. This is a relatively new eighteen hole golf course which has been laid out adjacent to the Monalto

Estate. Not physically demanding and many of the views on the course overlook the Mourne Mountains. Wildlife is also a great feature of the course.

COURSE INFORMATION

Par 72; SSS 72; Length 6,003 metres.
Visitors: Welcome any day.
Green Fees: £15.00 Mon – Fri; £20.00 Sun / Bank Holidays.
Ladies: Welcome.
Ladies: Competition – Friday.
Juveniles: Must be accompanied by an adult at

weekends and off the course by 6.00pm during weekdays.
Clubhouse Hours: 8.30am – 11.30pm.
Clubhouse Facilities: Full clubhouse facilities all week. Bar snacks from 12noon – 3.00pm. Arrangements for parties.
Clubhouse Dress: Casual – no denims.
Open Competitions: Open Week; 18th – 25th July. Open Stroke 6th & 20th June.

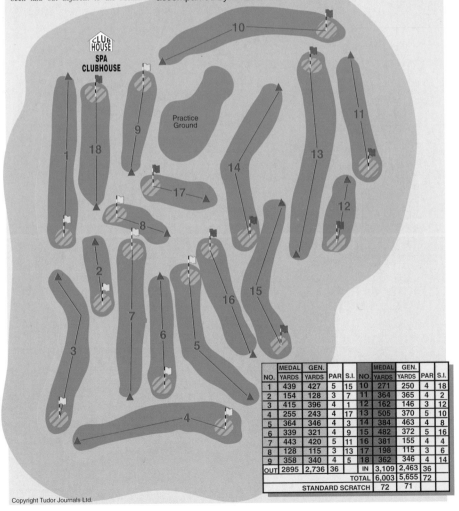

NO.	MEDAL YARDS	GEN. YARDS	PAR	S.I.	NO.	MEDAL YARDS	GEN. YARDS	PAR	S.I.
1	439	427	5	15	10	271	250	4	18
2	154	128	3	7	11	364	365	4	2
3	415	396	4	1	12	162	146	3	12
4	255	243	4	17	13	505	370	5	10
5	364	346	4	3	14	384	463	4	8
6	339	321	4	9	15	482	372	5	16
7	443	420	5	11	16	381	155	4	4
8	128	115	3	13	17	198	115	3	6
9	358	340	4	5	18	362	346	4	14
OUT	2895	2,736	36		IN	3,109	2,463	36	
					TOTAL	6,003	5,655	72	
					STANDARD SCRATCH	72	71		

Lower Dromore Road, Warrenpoint, Co. Down. Tel: (01693) 753695.

SECRETARY / MANAGER: John McMahon.
Tel: (01693) 753695.
PROFESSIONAL: Nigel Shaw.
Tel: (01693) 752371.

The course is set in parkland with picturesque views of the Carlingford Mountains. Although not a long course, it demands from the golfer straight driving and skill around the greens. There are five par 3's and four par 5's so it offers plenty of variety.

COURSE INFORMATION

Par 71; SSS 70; Length 5,618 metres.
Visitors: Welcome Mon, Thurs & Fri. By arrangement Wed & Sun. Avoid: Tues & Sat.
Green Fees: £18 Mon – Fri; £24 Sat / Sun / Bank Holidays.
Juveniles: Must be accompanied by an adult. Lessons available by prior arrangement. Club Hire available. Caddy cars available by prior arrangement.
Clubhouse Hours: 8.30am – 12midnight.
Clubhouse Facilities: Full clubhouse facilities everyday. Catering 11.30am – 9.30pm.
Clubhouse Dress: Respectable dress essential.
Open Competitions: Open Week June. Handicap certificate is required for open competitions.

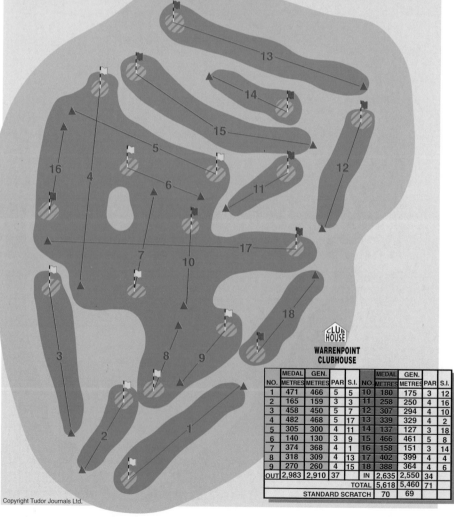

WARRENPOINT
CLUBHOUSE

NO.	MEDAL METRES	GEN. METRES	PAR	S.I.	NO.	MEDAL METRES	GEN. METRES	PAR	S.I.
1	471	466	5	5	10	180	175	3	12
2	165	159	3	3	11	258	250	4	16
3	458	450	5	7	12	307	294	4	10
4	482	468	5	17	13	339	329	4	2
5	305	300	4	11	14	137	127	3	18
6	140	130	3	9	15	466	461	5	8
7	374	368	4	1	16	158	151	3	14
8	318	309	4	13	17	402	399	4	4
9	270	260	4	15	18	388	364	4	6
OUT	2,983	2,910	37		IN	2,635	2,550	34	
					TOTAL	5,618	5,460	71	
					STANDARD SCRATCH	70	69		

Copyright Tudor Journals Ltd.

230

NO.	MEDAL METRES	GEN. METRES	PAR	S.I.	NO.	MEDAL METRES	GEN. METRES	PAR	S.I.
1	325	320	4	13	10	360	345	4	14
2	150	145	3	15	11	450	435	5	10
3	445	430	5	5	12	125	125	3	12
4	160	150	3	7	13	390	375	4	2
5	385	360	4	3	14	455	430	5	6
6	475	450	5	11	15	150	140	3	16
7	360	355	4	1	16	375	365	4	4
8	325	320	4	9	17	310	300	4	8
9	345	340	4	17	18	310	300	4	18
OUT	2,975	2,870	36		IN	2,925	2,815	36	
					TOTAL	5,941	5,685	72	
			STANDARD SCRATCH				72		

Castle Hume, Enniskillen, Co. Fermanagh.

LOCATION: Four miles from Enniskillen on the Belleek Road.
SECRETARY: Helen Keenan.
Tel: (01365) 327077 / 325301.
CLUB STEWARD: Emlyn Agnew.
Tel: (01365) 327077.
ARCHITECT: Tony Carroll.

The Castle Hume course has been constructed and designed to high standards. In addition to the two water hazards running through the course, there are five man-made hazards and the course has over 6,000 trees, numerous and various shrubs and over 30 bunkers. These obstacles, however, in no way detract from the well drained fairways, the generous tees and the large rolling greens, specifically designed and grown with imported fescue and bent grass.

COURSE INFORMATION

Par 72; SSS 72; Length 5,900 metres.
Visitors: Welcome all day everyday especially weekends.
Opening Hours: Dawn – Dusk.
Ladies: Welcome any day.
Green Fees: Mon – Fri £12; Sat / Sun £18; Juveniles £6.
Juveniles: Welcome.
Clubhouse Dress: Casual.
Clubhouse Facilities: Full catering and bar facilities everyday.
Open Competitions: Lakeland Open – July, plus various other competitions April – December.

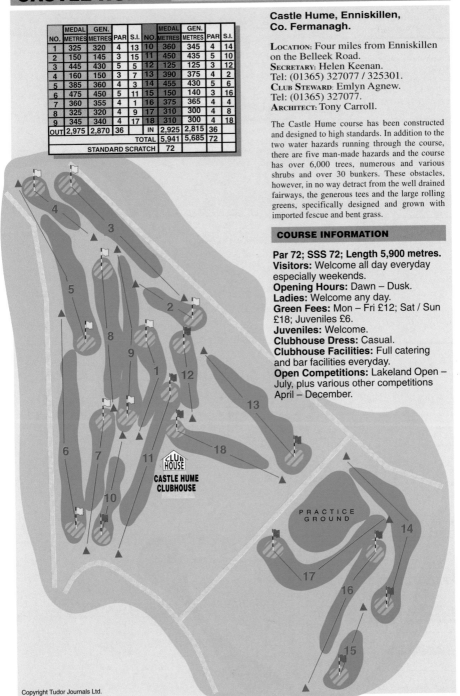

CASTLE HUME CLUBHOUSE

PRACTICE GROUND

ENNISKILLEN

U L S T E R

FERMANAGH

Castlecoole Rd, Enniskillen, Co. Fermanagh.
Tel: (01365) 325250.

Location: Beside Castlecoole Estate.
Secretary: Mr. Raymond Millar.
Tel: (01365) 324562.

The first nine holes of this course are developing well with plenty of new young trees, shrubs and new drainage while the back nine offers a different challenge with a more mature landscape.

COURSE INFORMATION

Par 71; SSS 69; Length 5,588 metres (medal).
Visitors: Welcome to play.
Opening Hours: Daylight hours.
Avoid: Tuesday – all day, and Saturday afternoons.
Ladies Day: Tuesday.
Green Fees: £15 Weekdays; £18 weekends and bank hols. Half price with member, one visitor per member.

Juveniles: Not allowed on course after 5pm, unless accompanied by an adult.
Clubhouse Hours: 9.00am – 11.00pm.
Clubhouse Facilities: All refurbished. Snooker and table-tennis. Snacks and catering available everyday by prior arrangement.
Open Competitions: On a regular basis.

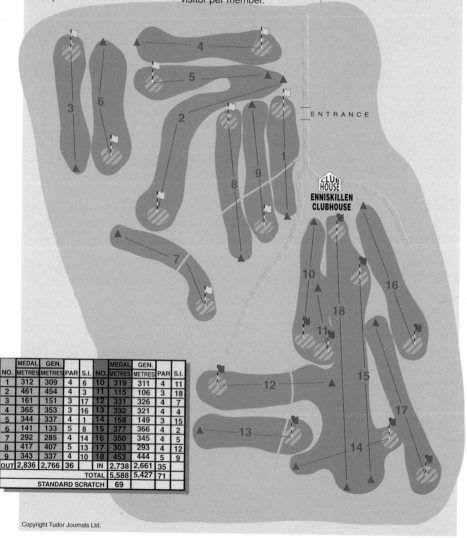

NO.	MEDAL METRES	GEN. METRES	PAR	S.I.	NO.	MEDAL METRES	GEN. METRES	PAR	S.I.
1	312	309	4	6	10	319	311	4	11
2	461	454	4	3	11	115	106	3	18
3	161	151	3	17	12	331	326	4	7
4	365	353	3	16	13	332	321	4	4
5	344	337	4	1	14	158	149	3	15
6	141	133	5	8	15	377	366	4	2
7	292	285	4	14	16	350	345	4	5
8	417	407	5	13	17	303	293	4	12
9	343	337	4	10	18	453	444	5	9
OUT	2,836	2,766	36		IN	2,738	2,661	35	
					TOTAL	5,588	5,427	71	
	STANDARD SCRATCH	69							

**Brown Trout Golf Club,
209 Agivey road,
Aghadowey, Co. L/Derry.**

LOCATION: 7 miles from
Coleraine on A54/B66
intersection.
SECRETARY / MANAGER: Bill
O'Hara.
Tel: (01265) 868209.
PROFESSIONAL: Ken Revie.
ARCHITECT: Bill O'Hara Snr.

A nine hole parkland course which crosses water seven times and is heavily wooded. The feature hole is the 2nd, a 170 yard carry across the Agivey River.

COURSE INFORMATION

Par 70; SSS 68; Length 5,510 yards.
Visitors: Always welcome.
Opening Hours:
7.00am – sunset.
Ladies: No restrictions.
Green Fees: Mon – Fri £10; weekends / holidays £15.
Juveniles: Must be accompanied by an adult on weekends / holidays / Wednesday & Thursday evenings.
Clubhouse Hours: 7.00am – midnight.

Clubhouse Dress: Casual.
Clubhouse Facilities: 17 bedroom hotel, gym and full bar / restaurant.
Open Competitions: 1st Friday of month May – September.

NO.	YARDS	PAR	S.I.	NO.	YARDS	PAR	S.I.
1	466	5	15	10	466	5	16
2	189	3	3	11	189	3	4
3	286	4	9	12	286	4	10
4	155	3	11	13	155	3	12
5	492	5	1	14	492	5	2
6	313	4	7	15	313	4	8
7	345	4	5	16	345	4	6
8	345	4	13	17	345	4	14
9	164	3	17	18	164	3	18
OUT	2,755	35		IN	2,755	35	
				TOTAL	5,510	70	
				STANDARD SCRATCH		68	

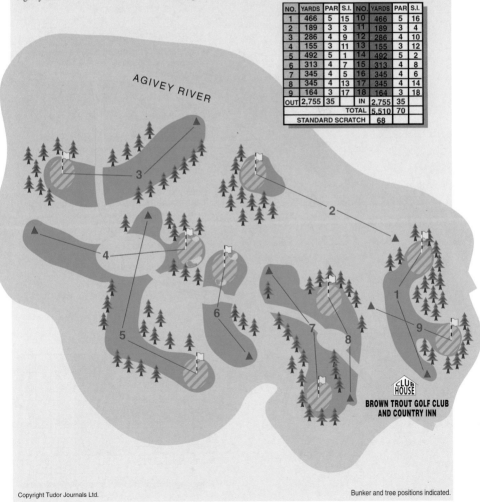

AGIVEY RIVER

CLUB HOUSE

BROWN TROUT GOLF CLUB
AND COUNTRY INN

Bunker and tree positions indicated.

65 Circular Road, Castlerock.
Tel: (01265) 848314.

LOCATION: Six miles north-west of
Coleraine.
SECRETARY: G. McBride.
Tel: (01265) 848314.
PROFESSIONAL: Mr Bobby Kelly.
Tel: (01265) 848314.
ARCHITECT: Ben Sayers.

A true links course, with two courses —
eighteen holes and nine holes. Main feature is
the 4th hole with a burn on left and a railway
on the right! The club claims the best greens
in Ireland twelve months of the year.
Castlerock can sometimes be underestimated,
or not appreciated for the magnificent links
course that it is. There are also superb views
to Donegal and over to Scotland.

COURSE INFORMATION

Par 73; SSS 72; Length 6,499 Yards.
Visitors: Welcome.
Opening Hours: Sunrise – sunset.
Avoid: Weekends.
Ladies Day: Friday. Can play on Sat
afternoons £35.
Green Fees: Mon – Fri £25; Sat / Sun
£35; Juveniles £5.
Juveniles: Cannot play before 4.30pm
or at weekends. Must be accompanied
by an adult. Lessons by prior
arrangements; Club Hire available.
Caddy service available by prior
arrangements.
Clubhouse Hours: 8am – 12 midnight.
Clubhouse Facilities: Full clubhouse
facilities; Snacks; meals by
arrangement.
Clubhouse Dress: Neat (no denims /
trainers) jacket & tie for functions.
Open Competitions: Open Week – July.

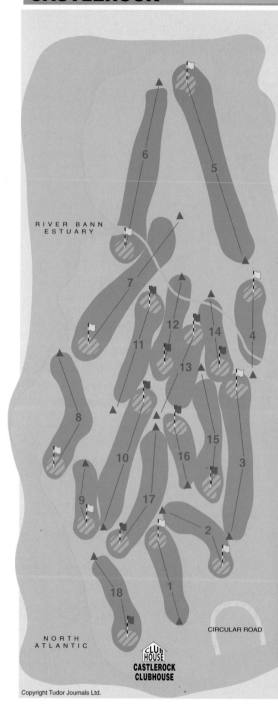

NO.	MEDAL YARDS	COMP YARDS	PAR	S.I.	NO.	MEDAL YARDS	COMP YARDS	PAR	S.I.
1	343	348	4	5	10	386	391	4	4
2	366	375	4	13	11	485	509	5	16
3	493	509	5	11	12	420	430	4	1
4	184	200	3	8	13	363	379	4	14
5	472	477	5	15	14	182	192	3	9
6	336	347	4	7	15	510	518	5	6
7	407	409	4	2	16	145	157	3	18
8	400	411	4	3	17	485	493	5	12
9	193	200	3	17	18	330	342	4	10
OUT	3,194	3,276	36		IN	3,305	3,411	37	
					TOTAL	6,499	6,687	73	
					STANDARD SCRATCH	72	71		

RIVER BANN ESTUARY

NORTH ATLANTIC

CIRCULAR ROAD

CLUB HOUSE
CASTLEROCK
CLUBHOUSE

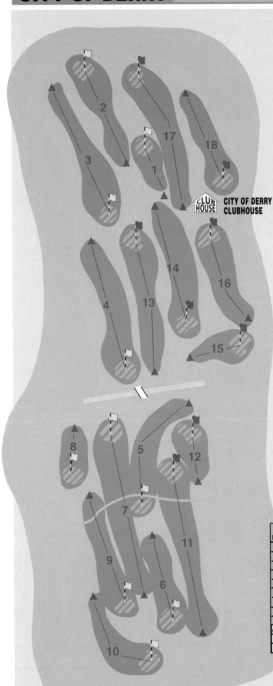

49 Victoria Road, Londonderry, BT47 2PU.
Tel: (01504) 311610.

LOCATION: Three miles from city centre on A5 to Strabane, turn left.
HON. SECRETARY: Mr T. Philips.
PROFESSIONAL: Michael Doherty.
Tel: (01504) 311496.

Parkland course overlooking River Foyle with views towards Donegal. Undulating terrain well lined by plenty of trees. There is also an easy nine hole course which is very suitable for those beginning golf.

COURSE INFORMATION

Par 71; SSS 71; Length 6,429 yards.
Visitors: Welcome anytime. Weekends – please check with the club professional. Contact club for booking.
Opening Hours: Sunrise – sunset.
Avoid: Tuesday (ladies day).
Ladies: Welcome Tuesday.
Green Fees: £20 Monday – Friday; Saturday, Sunday & Bank Holidays £25. 9 hole is £6 daily. Members half price. Handicap certificate required.
Juveniles: Handicap 12 and under anytime, otherwise with adult only. 9 hole course £3. Lessons by prior arrangement. Full clubhouse facilities.
Clubhouse Hours: 8.00am – 12.00 midnight.
Clubhouse Dress: Smart / casual (no jeans).
Clubhouse Facilities: Bar snacks, full meals everyday except Monday. A Handicap Certificate is required for Open competitions.

NO.	MEDAL YARDS	GEN. YARDS	PAR	S.I.	NO.	MEDAL YARDS	GEN. YARDS	PAR	S.I.
1	222	212	3	12	10	362	342	4	13
2	381	374	4	4	11	507	495	5	7
3	540	516	5	8	12	175	166	3	11
4	441	431	4	2	13	412	404	4	3
5	370	362	4	6	14	435	427	4	1
6	338	328	4	16	15	142	130	3	17
7	488	478	5	10	16	299	289	4	15
8	165	154	3	18	17	401	393	44	5
9	379	369	4	14	18	349	341	35	9
OUT	3,324	3,224	36		IN	3,082	2,987	71	
					TOTAL	6,406	6,211		
					STANDARD SCRATCH		71	70	

Foyle International Golf Centre, 12 Alder Road, Londonderry. BT48 8DB.
Tel: (01504) 352222.
Fax: (01504) 353967.

Location: One mile from Foyle Bridge heading for Moville turn left.
Secretary: Margaret Lapsley. Tel: (01504) 352222.
Architect: Frank Ainsworth.
Professional: Kieran McLaughlin.

The Foyle Golf Centre consists of an 18 hole par 72 course, nine hole par three course and a driving range. The parkland course is designed at championship standard with water coming into play on three of the 18 holes. It is well worthy of a visit by the discerning golfer.

COURSE INFORMATION

Par 72; SSS 71; Length 6,678 Yards.
Visitors: Welcome at any time. Guaranteed tee times due to computerised booking system.
Opening Hours: Dawn – Dusk.
Juveniles: Handicap 12 and under anytime, otherwise with an adult.

Green Fees: £11 weekdays, £14 weekends & Bank Holidays.
Clubhouse Hours: 8.00am – midnight.
Clubhouse Dress: Informal.
Clubhouse Facilities: Licensed bar & restaurant with food available every day, a fully stocked golf shop, lockers and changing rooms.

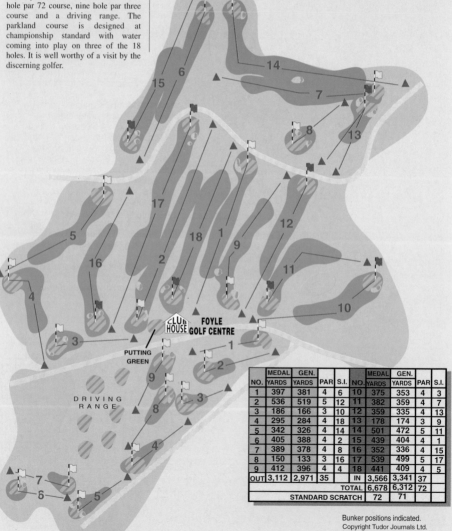

NO.	MEDAL YARDS	GEN. YARDS	PAR	S.I.	NO.	MEDAL YARDS	GEN. YARDS	PAR	S.I.
1	397	381	4	6	10	375	353	4	3
2	536	519	5	12	11	382	359	4	7
3	186	166	3	10	12	359	335	4	13
4	295	284	4	18	13	178	174	3	9
5	342	326	4	14	14	501	472	5	11
6	405	388	4	2	15	439	404	4	1
7	389	378	4	8	16	352	336	4	15
8	150	133	3	16	17	539	499	5	17
9	412	396	4	4	18	441	409	4	5
OUT	3,112	2,971	35		IN	3,566	3,341	37	
					TOTAL	6,678	6,312	72	
					STANDARD SCRATCH	72	71		

Bunker positions indicated.
Copyright Tudor Journals Ltd.

MOYOLA

**Shanemullagh,
Castledawson,
Co. Londonderry.
Tel: (01648) 468468.**

LOCATION: 40 miles north of
Belfast, via M2.
HONORARY SECRETARY: Laurence
Hastings.
Tel: (01648) 468468.
PROFESSIONAL: Vivian Teague.
Tel: (01648) 468830.
Catering Tel: (01648) 468392.
ARCHITECT: Don Patterson.

The course demands long accurate
driving on most holes and the
strategic use of large mature trees
emphasises the need for well placed
approach shots. The 8th hole is a
ninety degree dog-leg which
features a difficult pitch shot to the
green across the Moyola River.

COURSE INFORMATION

**Par 71; SSS 71; Length
6,062 yards.**
Visitors: Welcome mid-week.
Weekends by prior
arrangement.
Opening Hours: Dawn –
Dusk Monday – Saturday.
Avoid: Tuesday and
Wednesday evenings in
Summer; Saturday in Winter.
Ladies: Welcome.
Green Fees: £16 Monday –
Friday (£10 with member);
£25 Saturday / Sunday /
Public Holidays (£17 with
member).
Juveniles: Mon – Fri; after
4.30pm on Sat / Sun. Lessons
by prior arrangement.
Clubhouse Hours: 12am –
11pm. Full clubhouse
facilities.
Clubhouse Facilities: 12am
– 9pm. A la carte by prior
arrangement.
Clubhouse Dress: Casual,
no denims.
Open Competitions: Open
Week – July; usually monthly
in summer (mixed opens).

NO.	YARDS	PAR	S.I.	NO.	YARDS	PAR	S.I.
1	437	4	3	10	352	4	8
2	414	4	7	11	382	4	4
3	347	4	13	12	202	3	14
4	159	3	17	13	493	5	12
5	528	5	15	14	102	3	18
6	430	4	5	15	424	4	2
7	395	4	11	16	315	4	16
8	412	4	1	17	182	3	10
9	379	4	9	18	564	5	6
OUT	3,501	36		IN	3,016	35	
				TOTAL	6,517	71	
	STANDARD SCRATCH	71					

Bunker positions indicated.

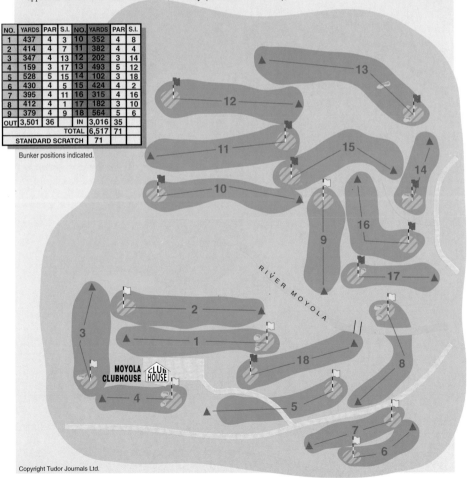

PORTSTEWART

ULSTER L/DERRY

117 Strand Road,
Portstewart, Co. L/Derry.
Tel: (01265) 832015.

LOCATION: Four miles north west
of Coleraine on the north coast.
SECRETARY: Michael Moss.
Tel: (01265) 832015 / 833839.
PROFESSIONAL: Alan Hunter.
Tel: (01265) 832601.
Fax: (01265) 834097.

Difficult, but open links course giving
magnificent views of Donegal Hills,
the rolling Atlantic, Strand Beach and
the River Bann, especially from the
1st, 5th and 12th tees. Greens are fast
and true. The 18th hole links course is
of championship standard with more
than 40 holes on offer.

COURSE INFORMATION

Par 72; SSS 73; Length 6,784
yards (Strand Course).
Par 64; Length 4,730 yards.
(Old Course).
Par 64; Length 5,324 yards.
(Riverside Course).
Visitors: Welcome, booking
necessary.
Avoid: Weekends and Bank
Holidays.
Ladies: Priority on Wednesdays.
Saturdays after 3.00 pm.
Green Fees: Strand Course –
£40 Mon–Fri; £60 Sat / Sun.
Ladies / Juveniles – same fees.
Juveniles: Must be accompanied
by an adult. Lessons by prior

arrangements. Club Hire &
Caddy trolleys available.
Clubhouse Hours: All day
everyday.
Clubhouse Facilities: Full
clubhouse facilities. Oct – March
catering facilities: 12 noon –
2.30pm / 5.00pm – 8.00pm;
April – Sept: 12 noon 2.30pm /
5.00pm – 9.00pm.
Clubhouse Dress: Casual /
Neat.
Open Competitons:
Open Week 11th – 18th July.

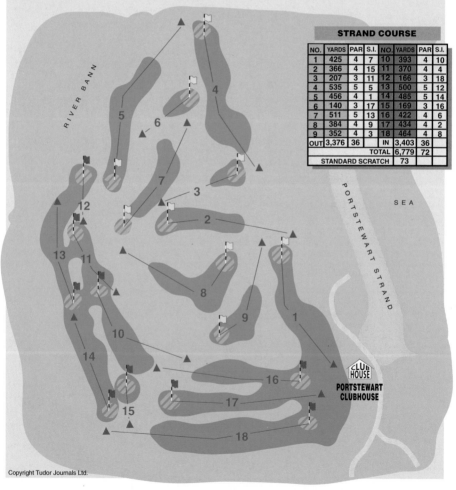

STRAND COURSE

NO.	YARDS	PAR	S.I.	NO.	YARDS	PAR	S.I.
1	425	4	7	10	393	4	10
2	366	4	15	11	370	4	4
3	207	3	11	12	166	3	18
4	535	5	5	13	500	5	12
5	456	4	1	14	485	5	14
6	140	3	17	15	169	3	16
7	511	5	13	16	422	4	6
8	384	4	9	17	434	4	2
9	352	4	3	18	464	4	8
OUT	3,376	36		IN	3,403	36	
				TOTAL	6,779	72	
				STANDARD SCRATCH	73		

PORTSTEWART
CLUBHOUSE

**Radisson Roe Park Hotel and Golf Resort,
Roe Park. Limavady,
Co. Londonderry.
BT49 9LB.
Tel: (015 047) 22222.
Fax: (015 047) 22222.**

LOCATION: In the picturesque Roe Valley, one mile west of Limavady, adjacent to Roe Valley Country Park.
GOLF / LEISURE MANAGER: Ian Ferguson.
Tel: (015 047) 60105.
ARHITECT: Frank Ainsworth.
PROFESSIONAL: Seamus Duffy.
Tel: (015 047) 60105.

The 18 hole parkland course takes full advantage of this beautiful riverside estate setting, with Lough Foyle and the Inishowen Peninsula providing a dramatic backdrop. Water comes into play on five holes, and with a challenging par four 18th to finish, the golfer can enjoy the game to the full.

COURSE INFORMATION

Par 70; SSS 71; Length 6,318 Yards.
Visitors: Welcome.
Opening Hours: 8am – Dusk.
Avoid: No restrictions of prohibited times.
Ladies: Welcome.
Juveniles: Permitted.
Green Fees: £20 daily (£13 with member Mon - Fri), (£16 with member Sat/Sun/Bank hols).
Coach House Hours: Open every day from 10.00am until late.
Coach House Dress: Smart casual.
Coach House Facilities: International menu available all day in the Coach House. Flood-lit and covered Driving Range open to the public.

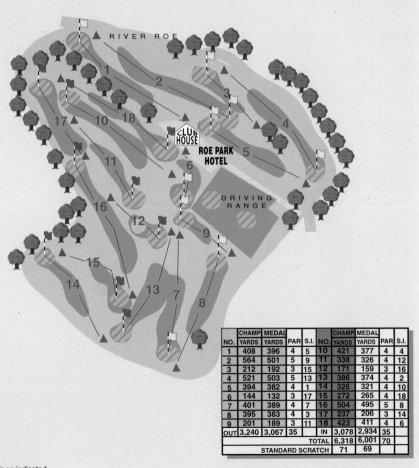

NO.	CHAMP YARDS	MEDAL YARDS	PAR	S.I.	NO.	CHAMP YARDS	MEDAL YARDS	PAR	S.I.
1	408	396	4	5	10	421	377	4	4
2	564	501	5	9	11	338	326	4	12
3	212	192	3	15	12	171	159	3	16
4	521	503	5	13	13	386	374	4	2
5	394	382	4	1	14	326	321	4	10
6	144	132	3	17	15	272	265	4	18
7	401	389	4	7	16	504	495	5	8
8	395	383	4	3	17	237	206	3	14
9	201	189	3	11	18	423	411	4	6
OUT	3,240	3,067	35		IN	3,078	2,934	35	
					TOTAL	6,318	6,001	70	
					STANDARD SCRATCH		71	69	

Tree positions indicated.
Copyright Tudor Journals Ltd.

239

CASTLEBLAYNEY ULSTER MONAGHAN

Onomy, Castleblayney,
Co. Monaghan.

LOCATION: Hope Castle Estate,
Castleblayney.
SECRETARY: Raymond Kiernan.
Tel: (042) 40451.
ARCHITECT: R.J. Browne.

The course enjoys a scenic setting
beside lake and forest. Hilly in
character yet convenient (approx. 500
yards) to town centre the course is
enjoyable for all levels of handicappers.

COURSE INFORMATION

**Par 68; SSS 66; Length
5,378 yards.**
Visitors: Welcome at all times.
Opening Hours: Sunrise –
sunset.
Ladies: Welcome Thursdays.
Green Fees: £8 Mon – Fri; £10
Sat / Sun / all Public Holidays.
Juveniles: Monday, Tuesday,
Thursday, Friday up to 5.00pm;
weekends after 6.00pm.

Clubhouse Hours: Normal.
Full clubhouse facilities.
Clubhouse Dress: Casual
but neat.
Clubhouse Facilities:
Restaurant and bar facilities
everyday all day May –
September (opened mid
1992) in Hope Castle.
Open Competitions: Open
Weekend May ; Open Week
Sat 1st – 8th August.

NO.	YARDS	PAR	S.I.	NO.	YARDS	PAR	S.I.
1	336	4	6	10	356	4	5
2	186	3	10	11	170	3	11
3	302	4	12	12	335	4	7
4	381	4	4	13	381	4	3
5	315	4	14	14	325	4	13
6	389	4	2	15	389	4	1
7	126	3	18	16	126	3	17
8	317	4	16	17	317	4	15
9	311	4	8	18	316	4	9
OUT	2,663	34		IN	2,715	34	
				TOTAL	5,378	68	
			STANDARD SCRATCH	66			

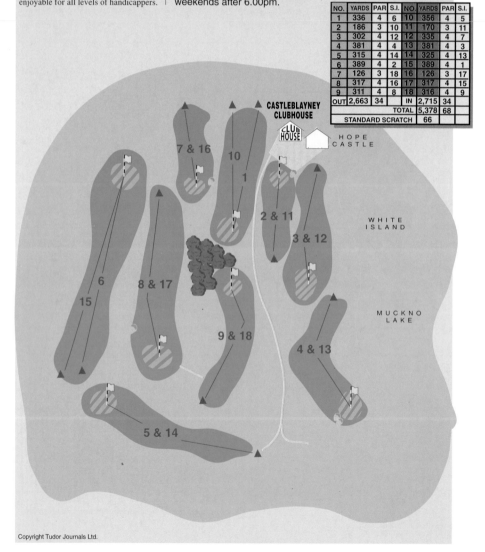

CASTLEBLAYNEY
CLUBHOUSE

CLUB
HOUSE

HOPE
CASTLE

7 & 16
10
1

2 & 11

3 & 12

WHITE
ISLAND

6
8 & 17
15

9 & 18

4 & 13

MUCKNO
LAKE

5 & 14

**Hilton Park, Clones,
Co. Monaghan.
Tel: (047) 56017.**

LOCATION: Scotshouse Road, Clones.
SECRETARY: Peter Mcgrane.

The course is usually playable all year round. It is parkland and set in Hilton Park estate and with its hills, forts, lakes and streams provides a very scenic backdrop for a good test of golf.

NO.	YARDS	PAR	S.I.	NO.	YARDS	PAR	S.I.
1	170	3	13	10	170	3	14
2	447	5	17	11	447	5	18
3	160	3	9	12	160	3	10
4	340	4	3	13	340	4	4
5	420	4	1	14	420	4	2
6	149	3	15	15	149	3	16
7	370	4	11	16	370	4	12
8	357	4	5	17	357	4	6
9	353	4	7	18	353	4	8
OUT	2,766	34		IN	2,766	34	
				TOTAL	5,532	68	
	STANDARD SCRATCH			68			

COURSE INFORMATION

Par 68; SSS 67; Length 5,532 yards.
Visitors: Welcome.
Opening Hours: Sunrise – sunset.
Avoid: Sunday mornings.
Ladies: Thursdays.
Green Fees: £10 Monday – Sunday.
Clubhouse Hours: 2.00pm – 11.30pm.
Clubhouse Dress: Informal.
Clubhouse Facilities: Full clubhouse facilities, evening meals, snacks, etc
Open Competitions: Open Week – early June; Scratch Cups – August; Open Weekend – mid September.

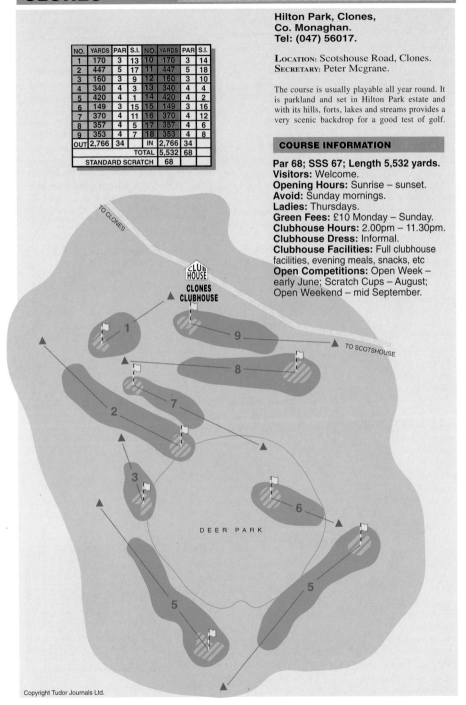

TO CLONES

CLUB HOUSE
**CLONES
CLUBHOUSE**

TO SCOTSHOUSE

DEER PARK

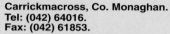

Carrickmacross, Co. Monaghan.
Tel: (042) 64016.
Fax: (042) 61853.

LOCATION: On the Dublin road, one mile from Carrickmacross.
PROFESSIONAL: Maurice Cassidy.

Panoramic views over counties Monaghan, Cavan, Louth, Armagh and Meath. A new eighteen hole championship course opened in August 1991.

COURSE INFORMATION

Par 72; SSS 70; Length 5,900 metres.
Visitors: Welcome everyday.
Opening Hours: Daylight hours.
Avoid: Prior arrangement is preferred.
Green Fees: £18 Weekdays, £22 weekends.
Clubhouse Dress: Casual.
Clubhouse Facilities: Full bar and dining facilities available.
Open Competitions: Open Week – August.

HOTEL

CLUB HOUSE

NUREMORE HOTEL & GOLF COURSE CLUBHOUSE

NO.	METRES	PAR	S.I.	NO.	METRES	PAR	S.I.
1	450	5	11	10	308	4	16
2	443	5	17	11	157	3	12
3	372	4	1	12	329	4	4
4	151	3	15	13	351	4	8
5	369	4	3	14	510	5	6
6	169	3	9	15	446	5	10
7	330	4	5	16	124	3	18
8	328	4	7	17	294	4	14
9	334	4	13	18	435	4	2
OUT	2,946	36		IN	2,954	36	
				TOTAL	5,900	72	
				STANDARD SCRATCH		70	

**Cootehill Road, Monaghan,
Co. Monaghan.
Tel: (047) 81316.**

LOCATION: Two miles south of
Monaghan town on the
Cootehill Road.
SECRETARY: Jimmie McKenna.
ARCHITECT: Des Smith Golf
Design Ltd.

The club has recently undergone an
extensive development from a
shortish nine hole course to a 6,000
yard eighteen hole course, which is
now in operation.

COURSE INFORMATION

**Par 70; SSS 68; Length
5,605 metres.**
Visitors: Welcome – at all
times except on days of major
competitions.
Opening Hours: Sunrise –
sunset.
Ladies: Welcome – have
priority on Wednesdays.
Green Fees: £15 – any day.
(£5 reduction with member).
Juveniles: Welcome any day
except Open Days and Major
Competition days.

Clubhouse Hours: 12.00
noon – 12.00pm Tues – Sun;
6.00pm – 11.00pm Mon; Full
clubhouse facilities.
Clubhouse Dress: Casual.
Clubhouse Facilities: Full
catering availbale from 1.00pm
(except Mondays); large parties
by prior arrangement.
Open Competitions: Open
Week – July; Open
Weekends – April, June &
August.

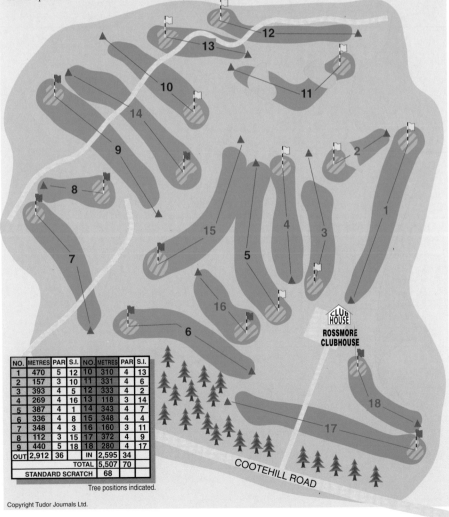

NO.	METRES	PAR	S.I.	NO.	METRES	PAR	S.I.
1	470	5	12	10	310	4	13
2	157	3	10	11	331	4	6
3	393	4	5	12	333	4	2
4	269	4	16	13	118	3	14
5	387	4	1	14	343	4	7
6	336	4	8	15	348	4	15
7	348	4	3	16	160	3	11
8	112	3	15	17	372	4	9
9	440	5	18	18	280	4	17
OUT	2,912	36		IN	2,595	34	
				TOTAL	5,507	70	
				STANDARD SCRATCH		68	

Tree positions indicated.

Aughnacloy Golf Club,
99 Tullyvar Road,
Aughnacloy, Co. Tyrone.

LOCATION: Co. Tyrone.
SECRETARY: S.J. Houston
Tel: (016625) 57050 or
(01365) 327655.

9 hole inland course situated close to the Ballygauley roundabout. Includes a driving range.

COURSE INFORMATION

**Par 68; SSS 67; Length
5,017 metres.**
Visitors: Welcome.
Opening Hours: All day.
Ladies: Welcome, Wednesday afternoons.
Green Fees: Mon – Fri £10; Sat /Sun £12. Special rates for golfing societies.

Juveniles: Welcome.
Clubhouse Hours:
9.00 a.m.– late.
Clubhouse Dress: Casual.
Clubhouse Facilities: Bar, changing room, pool, meals.
Open Competitions: Several. Contact club for details.

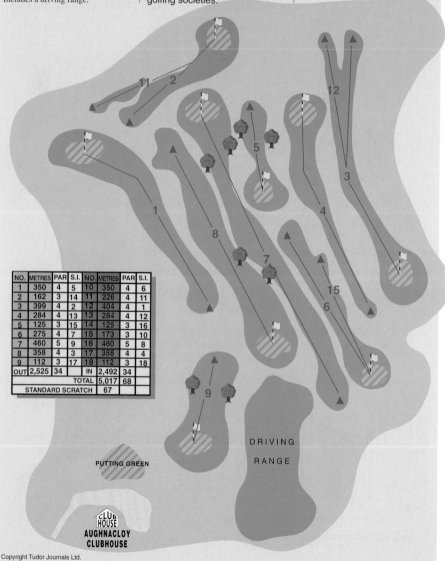

NO.	METRES	PAR	S.I.	NO.	METRES	PAR	S.I.
1	350	4	5	10	350	4	6
2	162	3	14	11	226	4	11
3	399	4	2	12	404	4	1
4	284	4	13	13	284	4	12
5	125	3	15	14	125	3	16
6	275	4	7	15	173	3	10
7	460	5	9	16	460	5	8
8	358	4	3	17	358	4	4
9	112	3	17	18	112	3	18
OUT	2,525	34		IN	2,492	34	
				TOTAL	5,017	68	
				STANDARD SCRATCH		67	

PUTTING GREEN

DRIVING RANGE

AUGHNACLOY CLUBHOUSE

DUNGANNON

ULSTER   TYRONE

**34 Springfield Lane,
Dungannon, Co. Tyrone
BT70 1QX.
Tel: (01868) 722098.**

LOCATION: 40 miles west of
Belfast. 1 mile from
Dungannon off B43
Donaghmore Road.
SECRETARY: Mr L. Agnew.
Tel: (018687) 27338.

The Dungannon Golf Club founded in
1890 is a parkland course with tree –
lined fairways. Here, golf is
flourishing with a membership of
about 600. A challenging and pleasant
course and today the visitor could
reiterate the entry in the old handbook
that the greens are 'very good'.

COURSE INFORMATION

**Par 72; SSS 69; Length
5,433 metres.**
Visitors: Welcome any time.
Opening Hours: 9.00am –
sunset.
Avoid: Saturday.
Ladies: Tuesday.
Green Fees: £15 Mon – Fri;
£18 Sat / Sun / all public
holidays. Ladies £12 Mon –
Fri; £15 Sat / Sun / all public
holidays. £3 Juveniles.
Juveniles: Mon – Fri before
5.00pm. Sat / Sun play after
4.00pm. Lessons by prior
arrangement.

Clubhouse Dress: Casual.
Clubhouse Facilities: By
arrangment. Mon, Tues, Thurs.
7.00pm – 11.00pm; Wed / Fri
4.00pm – 11pm. Sat / Sun
12.00noon – 11.00pm.
Open Competitions: May –
Aughnacloy putter; July -
Mixed foursomes; Aug –
Ladies & Gents open day;
Ladies – Aug; Open Week
23rd – 30th August.

NO.	METRES	PAR	S.I.	NO.	METRES	PAR	S.I.
1	477	5	11	10	347	4	12
2	161	3	15	11	183	3	8
3	558	5	1	12	492	5	16
4	341	4	7	13	338	4	2
5	332	4	13	14	379	4	6
6	129	3	5	15	283	4	14
7	488	5	17	16	90	3	18
8	390	4	3	17	554	5	4
9	146	3	9	18	358	4	10
OUT	3,022	36		IN	3,024	36	
				TOTAL	6,046	72	
				STANDARD SCRATCH		69	

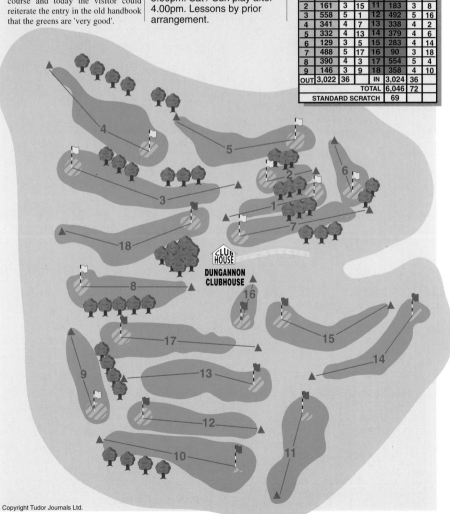

DUNGANNON
CLUBHOUSE

FINTONA

1 Kiln Street, Ecclesville Demesne, Fintona, Co. Tyrone.
Tel: (01662) 841480.
Fax: (01662) 841480.

LOCATION: 8 miles from Omagh.
HON. SECRETARY: Damian Montague.
Tel: (01662) 841480.

An attractive parkland course, its main feature being a trout stream which meanders through the course causing many problems for badly executed shots. Rated one of the top nine hole courses in the province.

COURSE INFORMATION

Par 72; SSS 70; Length 5,766 metres.
Visitors: Welcome Mon – Fri. Sat by arrangement.
Opening Hours: Daylight.
Ladies: Welcome Mondays.

Green Fees: £12 Mon – Fri; £15 weekends.
Juveniles: Welcome. Saturday by prior arrangement.
Clubhouse Dress: Casual.
Clubhouse Facilities: Full clubhouse facilities. Bar snacks available. Meals on request.
Open Competitions: Telephone club for details.

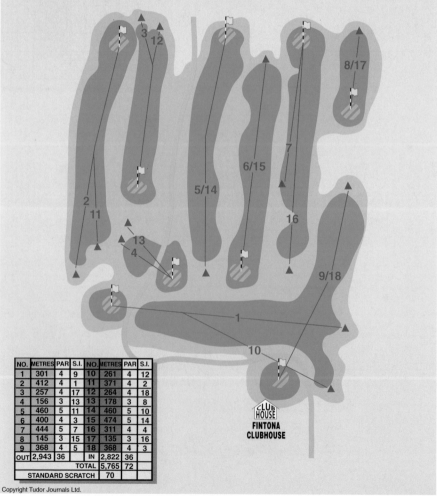

FINTONA CLUBHOUSE

NO.	METRES	PAR	S.I.	NO.	METRES	PAR	S.I.
1	301	4	9	10	261	4	12
2	412	4	1	11	371	4	2
3	257	4	17	12	264	4	18
4	156	3	13	13	178	3	8
5	460	5	11	14	460	5	10
6	400	4	3	15	474	5	14
7	444	5	7	16	311	4	4
8	145	3	15	17	135	3	16
9	368	4	5	18	368	4	3
OUT	2,943	36		IN	2,822	36	
				TOTAL	5,765	72	
	STANDARD SCRATCH		70				

246

KILLYMOON

**200 Killymoon road,
Cookstown, Co. Tyrone
BT80 8TW.
Tel: (016487) 62254.**

LOCATION: South end of
Cookstown, 1 mile from
Dungannon roundabout.
HON. SECRETARY: Brian Rouse.
Tel: (016487) 63762 / 62976
GOLF SHOP: (016487) 63460.

A parkland course set on high
ground with the soil being a sandy
consistency. The 1st is the most
picturesque hole, which is a dog
leg skirting the woods of
Killymoon Castle.

COURSE INFORMATION

**Par 70; SSS 69; Length
5,488 metres.
Visitors:** Welcome Monday,
Tuesday, Wednesday, Friday,
Sunday. Must have current
handicap. Members only
Thursday and Saturday.
Ladies: Have priority on
Thursdays.
Green Fees: £15 Monday –
Friday; £18 Sat (after 5pm) &
Sun.
Juveniles: Monday – Friday.
Handicap Certificate required
for open competitions.

**Clubhouse Hours:
Clubhouse Dress:** Smart and
casual.
Clubhouse Facilities: Full
catering and bar facilities
available.

NO.	MEDAL METRES	GEN. METRES	PAR	S.I.	NO.	MEDAL METRES	GEN. METRES	PAR	S.I.
1	469	462	5	8	10	327	317	4	9
2	151	139	3	14	11	176	158	3	5
3	454	436	5	6	12	390	382	4	1
4	332	323	4	12	13	157	143	3	17
5	304	292	4	16	14	446	435	5	15
6	276	268	4	18	15	479	470	5	11
7	181	172	3	4	16	175	163	3	13
8	151	139	3	10	17	359	345	4	3
9	336	314	4	2	18	325	300	4	7
OUT	2,654	2,545	35		IN	2,834	2,713	35	
					TOTAL	5,488	5,258	70	
					STANDARD SCRATCH	69	68		

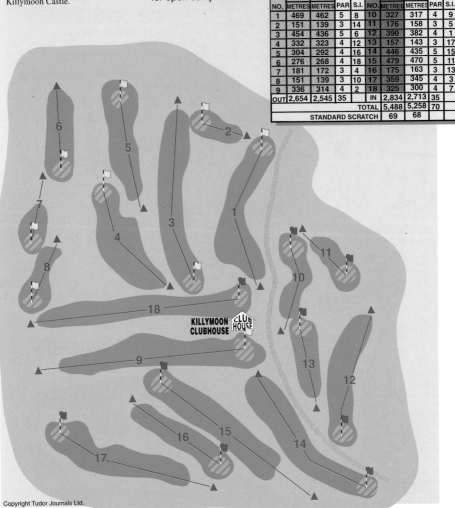

KILLYMOON
CLUBHOUSE

Copyright Tudor Journals Ltd.

**38 Golf Course Road,
Newtownstewart, Omagh, Co.
Tyrone BT78 4HU.
Tel: (016626) 61466 / 6661829.
Fax: (016626) 62506.**

LOCATION: 2 miles west of
Newtownstewart.
SECRETARY / MANAGER: Diane Cooke.
Tel: (016626) 61466.

Newtownstewart, although only an hour and a
half from Belfast lies in a different world in
the west of Tyrone. The course is positioned
at the confluence of the Strule and the
Glenelly rivers and at the foot of the Sperrin
Mountains.

COURSE INFORMATION

**Par 70; SSS 69; Length
5,341 metres.
Visitors:** Welcome any day
(telephone first).
Opening Hours: 8.30am – 8.30pm.
Avoid: Saturday and Sunday.
Ladies: Welcome Thursdays.
Green Fees: £10 Mon – Fri (with
member £5); £15 Sat / Sun / all
public holidays (with member £7.50).
£50 weekly; £90 monthly.
Juveniles: Welcome.
Clubhouse Dress: Casual except
on competition evenings.
Clubhouse Facilities: By prior
arrangements. Bar & Restaurant.
Open Competitions: Open week –
July. Visitors welcome with Handicap
Certificate from home club.
Competitions throughout the season,
ie. May–Sept.

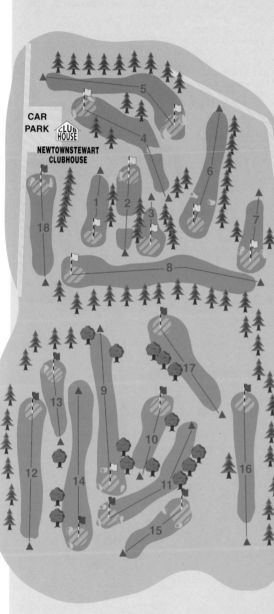

CAR PARK

CLUB HOUSE

NEWTOWNSTEWART CLUBHOUSE

NO.	METRES	PAR	S.I.	NO.	METRES	PAR	S.I.
1	277	4	17	10	132	3	18
2	279	4	16	11	321	4	3
3	127	3	12	12	349	4	2
4	347	4	6	13	178	3	13
5	270	4	10	14	460	5	5
6	354	4	1	15	142	3	15
7	194	3	8	16	454	5	11
8	343	4	4	17	332	4	9
9	421	5	14	18	361	4	7
OUT	2,612	35		IN	2,729	35	
				TOTAL	5,341	70	
STANDARD SCRATCH					69		

Bunker and tree positions indicated.

NO.	MEDAL METRES	GEN. METRES	PAR	S.I.	NO.	MEDAL METRES	GEN. METRES	PAR	S.I.
1	321	313	4	5	10	147	137	3	14
2	276	287	4	15	11	260	250	4	17
3	199	189	3	9	12	356	305	4	4
4	460	443	5	13	13	125	116	3	18
5	380	350	4	1	14	390	385	4	2
6	500	480	5	7	15	485	476	5	10
7	333	320	4	6	16	305	296	4	8
8	380	354	4	3	17	164	155	3	12
9	308	255	4	11	18	285	271	4	16
OUT	3,157	2,991	37		IN	2,517	2,391	34	
					TOTAL	5,674	5,382	71	
	STANDARD SCRATCH					70	68		

83a Dublin Road, Omagh, Co. Tyrone, BT78 1HQ. Tel: (01662) 243160 / 241442.

LOCATION: 1 mile from town centre on main Omagh – Dublin Road.
HON. SECRETARY: Joseph A. McElholm. Tel: (01662) 244140 (work) or (01662) 243749 (home).
SECRETARY: Florence Caldwell.
ARCHITECT: Don Patterson.

Attractive course with four of the holes bordering the River Drumragh. The course is split on either side by the Dublin road.

COURSE INFORMATION

Par 71; SSS 70; Length 5,674 metres.
Visitors: Individuals or societies welcome.
Avoid: Tuesdays and Saturdays
Ladies have priority on the 1st Tee all day Tuesday.
Green Fees: £10 Mon – Fri; £15 Sat / Sun (£2 reduction if playing with a member). O.A.P & students £5 (weekdays) & £7.50 (weekends). Reduced rates for societies.
Clubhouse Hours: 11.30am – 1.30pm and 4.30pm – 11.00pm.
Clubhouse Dress: Casual / neat.
Clubhouse Facilities: Bar snacks available. Full catering by arrangement with caterer.
Open Competitions: Open Week – July, plus various other Open Days, (telephone for details).

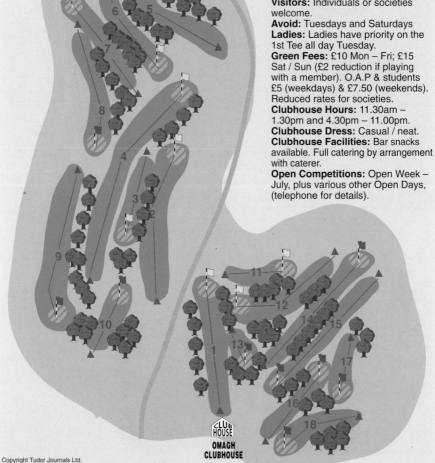

OMAGH
CLUBHOUSE

STRABANE

33 Ballycolman Road,
Strabane, Co. Tyrone,
BT82 9PH.
Tel: (01504) 382271.

LOCATION: 1 mile from Strabane on the Dublin Road.
SECRETARY / MANAGER: Eamon Kennedy.
Tel: (01504) 883109.
ARCHITECT: Desmond Hackett.

Rolling parkland intersected by the River Mourne, which runs alongside the 9th fairway, making the 9th one of the most picturesque and feared holes. The course is at the foothills of the Sperrin Mountains which provide an attractive back-drop to the river falls. Agreed by professionals and low handicapped players as an excellent test of golf.

COURSE INFORMATION

Par 69; SSS 69; Length 5,458 metres.
Visitors: Welcome. Telephone appointment advisable.
Opening Hours: 8.00am – dusk.
Avoid: Saturday.
Ladies: Tuesday.
Green Fees: £12 Monday – Friday; (£10 with member); £14 Saturday / Sunday / all public holidays (£12 with member). £8 Societies (by arrangement).
Juveniles: Welcome. Lessons available by prior arrangements. Caddy service available by prior

arrangements. Under 18's not allowed in clubhouse.
Handicap Certificate required for competition. Prior arrangement required at times.
Clubhouse Hours: 2.00pm – 11.00pm Mon – Fri; 12.00 – 11.00pm Sat; 12.00 – 1.30pm, 5.00pm – 7.00pm and 8.00pm – 10.00pm Sundays.
Clubhouse Dress: Informal but respectable.
Clubhouse Facilities: Cateing by arrangement only. Full bar.
Open Competitions: One Saturday per month; Open Week, 28th July – 5th August.

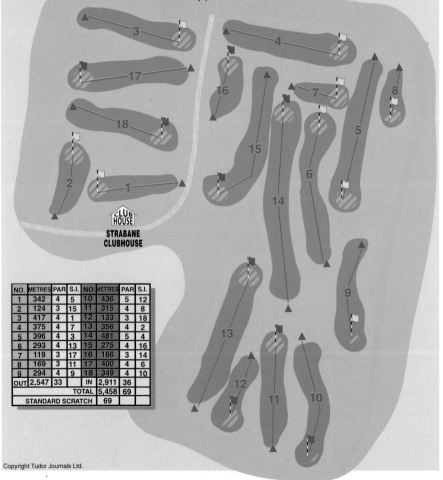

STRABANE CLUBHOUSE

NO.	METRES	PAR	S.I.	NO.	METRES	PAR	S.I.
1	342	4	5	10	436	5	12
2	124	3	15	11	315	4	8
3	417	4	1	12	133	3	18
4	375	4	7	13	356	4	2
5	396	4	3	14	481	5	4
6	293	4	13	15	275	4	16
7	119	3	17	16	166	3	14
8	169	3	11	17	400	4	6
9	294	4	9	18	349	4	10
OUT	2,547	33		IN	2,911	36	
				TOTAL	5,458	69	
STANDARD SCRATCH		69					

MUNSTER

BY JACK MAGOWAN

If ever there was a name that sounded Irish, it's Ballybunion. And if ever there was a no-frills, absolutely true test of links golf, it is to be found on both Ballybunion courses lapped by the Atlantic winds of an exposed, sometimes inhospitable Shannon Estuary.

Asked to choose one course on which he would be happy to play for the rest of his life, Bob Sommers, a former editor of the U.S. *Golf Journal,* didn't hesitate.

"I'm still working on it," he declared. "But there are two in Ireland high up on my list – Ballybunion and Royal Co. Down. Both are rare jewels (and)

Ballybunion's natural terrain makes it one of the top three courses in Ireland and top ten in the world.

difficult to seperate. Ballybunion may be the more spectacular test, but County Down is the more relentlessly demanding. It never stops asking for first-class shot-making."

Sommers then agreed with me on one score. To play golf at Ballybunion is to slide into a blissful vacuum happy in the knowledge that if you hear the phone ring, you'll know the call will be for somebody else!. Waterville, Killarney, Lahinch, Tralee, Shannon, Adare and Ballybunion ... they string out like green pearls on a jeweller's tray as the loveliest, most inviting part of Munster welcomes more and more

254

Waterside tranquility at Kenmare Golf Club.

golfers every season.

Today, Ireland's South-West is as closely linked to the Royal and Ancient game as The Curragh is to horses, or Blarney to the Stone. Like O'Connell Street at rush-hour, I once said of the first tee at Killarney, and nothing has changed. The Killeen and Mahony's Point courses now host 40,000 visitors a year, a record for any European club and worth a staggering £1 million-plus in green fees alone. Small wonder some less glamorous neighbours must be green with envy.

Irish golf has a liberating sense of space and freedom, never more so than on the first course Arnold Palmer built outside America – Tralee. It's new, it's scenic, it's tough, and the wind is as fresh as tomorrow's milk. Banna Strand, where *Ryan's Daughter* was filmed, is only a nine-iron shot away from the third green, an elusive target on what is the classiest of short holes. Tralee's wind-swept dunes are impressive, yet no bigger than a mole hill compared to those at Ballybunion. Here, as Golf World once said, "you're driving over them, into them, up them, and on to them," which might have

prompted King Christy's famous remark: "Anybody who breaks 70 on either of these courses on a windy day is playing better than he knows how!".

Full marks, then, to a couple of amateurs called Mulcare and McGimpsey. Record-holder Pat Mulcare (66) was the only man ever to better McGimpsey's gale-lashed round of 67 in the Irish Championship of 1979, the day on which Garth shot five birdies on his way to a flawless outward half of 31. Freak stuff.

Tom Watson fell in love with Ballybunion the first time he ever saw it, and so did the late, great Jimmy

Bruen. A burly, overweight Bruen was only 17 and still at school 12 months before playing in Britain's winning Walker Cup side of 1938. Like Mulcare he lost a brave fight against cancer and died at the age of 50.

Nobody ever swung a golf club the way Bruen did, or with such stunning effect.

"Hogan and Cotton could stir the imagination and command attention," wrote Pat Ward-Thomas in Masters Of Golf. "And Thomson and Snead could create an awareness of beauty ...... but the golf of none of these mortals had a greater dramatic appeal for me than that of James Bruen, citizen of Cork."

Ballesteros, Nicklaus, Norman, John Daly—Bruen would have matched them all for magnetism and power-play. Jimmy hit the ball like he had a grudge against it, and in a style that was entirely his own. The 'Bruen loop' was his copyright, clubhead drawn back so much outside the line of flight that at the top of the swing it would be pointed in the direction of the tee-box. The club was then whipped inside and down into the hitting area with animal ferocity.

It's no exaggeration to say there must have been a foot or more between Bruen's arcs. Anybody who didn't know who he was would have been inclined to scoff, Ward-Thomas used to say, but not for long. The action of his hands was identical to that of cracking a whip and was the source of tremendous power.

Henry Cotton once asked Bruen to try swinging normally, and Jimmy hit the ball as well as any scratch player

Continued on Page 261

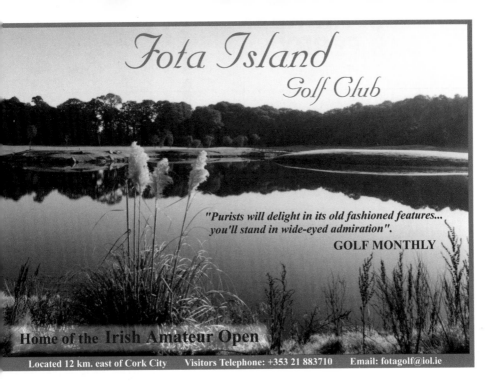

KILLIMER / TARBERT CAR FERRY

M.V. "Shannon Willow" (44 cars) loading at Killimer.

From Killimer, Co. Clare DEPARTURE ON THE HOUR		FIRST SAILING	LAST SAILING
APRIL / SEPTEMBER.	Weekdays	7.00 a.m.	9.00 p.m.
	Sundays	9.00 a.m.	9.00 p.m.
OCTOBER / MARCH	Weekdays	7.00 a.m.	7.00 p.m.
	Sundays	10.00 a.m.	7.00 p.m.

From Tarbert, Co. Kerry DEPARTURE ON THE HALF HOUR		FIRST SAILING	LAST SAILING
APRIL / SEPTEMBER.	Weekdays	7.30 a.m.	9.30 p.m.
	Sundays	9.30 a.m.	9.30 p.m.
OCTOBER / MARCH	Weekdays	7.30 a.m.	7.30 p.m.
	Sundays	10.30 a.m.	7.30 p.m.

SAILINGS
Every day of the year except Christmas Day.

TWO FERRY SERVICE
During the peak holiday period both Ferry Boats operate to give half-hourly sailings each side.

m.v."Shannon Willow" (44Cars)
m.v."Shannon Dolphin" (52 Cars)

SHANNON FERRY LTD.
KILLIMER, KILRUSH, CO,CLARE
Telephone   Fax
065-53124   065-53125

Breathtaking stuff at Tralee.

Great Southern Hotels

SHANNON

115 En-Suite Bedrooms with all modern facilities for your comfort
Restaurant & Bar
Residents Car Park

Because of the Hotel's convenient location to the passenger terminal
at Shannon Airport, this luxurious Hotel offers an ideal base for golf
enthusiasts visiting the Shannon region:

Within walking distance of Shannon Golf Club
Six miles from Dromoland Golf Club
Thirty miles from Lahinch Golf Club

Tel: (061) 471122 Fax: (061) 471982 E-Mail: res@shannon.gsh.ie

TORC KILLARNEY

96 En-Suite Bedrooms with all modern facilities for your comfort
Restaurant & Bar
Residents Car Park
Swimming Pool, Steam Room & Jacuzzi

This elegant and modern Hotel is just a five minute walk from the
bustling town of Killarney and is the perfect base for your golfing
holiday. The Hotel is located:

Two miles from Killarney Golf Club
(Green fee concessions available Monday - Friday)
Seven miles from Beaufort Golf Club
Forty miles from Ballybunion Golf Club
Forty miles from Waterville Golf Club

Tel: (064) 31611 Fax: (064) 31824 E-Mail: res@torc.gsh.ie

KILLARNEY

180 En-Suite Bedrooms with all modern facilities for your comfort
Restaurant & Bar
Residents Car Park
Leisure Centre

Built in 1854 this elegant and old world Hotel is located in the heart
of Killarney town. The Hotel is located:

Two miles from Killarney Golf Club
(Green fee concessions available Monday - Friday)
Seven miles from Beaufort Golf Club
Forty miles from Ballybunion Golf Club
Forty miles from Waterville Golf Club

Tel: (064) 31262 Fax: (064) 31642 E-Mail: res@killarney.gsh.ie

The Killarney Club enjoys two excellent courses sharing the majestic MacGillycuddy's Reeks and Lough Leane.

would. Not with the same clubhead speed, however, the key to his great length, especially off the tee.

No rough or hazard was ever tough enough to bold Bruen, yet you could never have said he was erratic.

"There was an almost hypnotic quality about his play," wrote Ward-Thomas. "It's very strangeness was compelling; its power and unusual beauty fascinating. No course, however long or difficult, was safe from destruction when Bruen teed it up. There will never be another like him!"

It was soon after winning the Amateur Championshipin 1946 at Royal Birkdale that Jimmy felt a sudden pain in his right wrist while lifting tiles in his garden at home. The explosive violence of a unique but

gifted swing had taken its toll. He was never the same player again, and quit tournament golf on the day he lost to Joe Carr in the semi-finals of the Irish Amateur at Killarney. The year: 1963.

All great golf courses are remorseless in the face of sloppy play. Hit the ball badly and the likes of Ballybunion, Lahinch, Waterville or Adare will devour you. Hit it well, and you'll be rewarded.

Nobody talks of Waterville without mentioning John Mulcahy, the Irish American visionary who gave the course, and resort, a new dimension nearly 30 years ago.

There are so many good holes at Waterville that it's impossible to think of a weak hole. Liam Higgins, the professional there and another prodigious hitter of the ball, once

262

Famous and challenging test of golf — Lahinch, Co. Clare.

holed out at the 350-yard 16th on his way to a round of 65, but Liam, now 50- plus and playing the Seniors' Tour, almost stands alone among those who can boast of breaking 70. Raymond Floyd still thinks Waterville deserves a top-ten world rating, so who are we to disagree.

The eleventh there might be the best par-5 hole in Ireland!

Adare, too, is special, not only for its length (7000 yards plus) but superb hotel. There's water and wood everywhere on this Robert Trent Jones' creation, which has aleady been ranked

among Britain's top 10 new courses, a timely bonus.

American styled Shannon is so close to the aiport that you can almost count the rivets on a 'jumbo' coming in to land, but the trees here also grow tall and are magnificent, as indeed they are at Fota Island, host to the '97 Irish PGA championship.

Harbour Point, Muskerry, Douglas and Fota Island how lucky Cork golfers are to have four courses of such quality right on their doorstep!

Golf is a passion, somebody said, that doesn't make a lot of sense, and in Ireland it's completely mad. Was he thinking of Lahinch, I wonder, and the goats there?. For Lahinch is where the barometer on the wall has no hands; just a note saying 'See Goats'. If they are grazing close to the clubhouse, that's a weather warning — wind and rain is on the horizon. Away from the clubhouse, and it'll be a bright and clear day, no rain gear needed.

Don't bank on it. Once a visiting golfer, happy that the goats were nicely placed, set off in short sleeves and summer slacks for a round that was soon washed out by a thunder shower.

"What happened?", he frowned. "How could the goats have got it so badly wrong?"

"Sorry," said the barman "We've just had a delivery of new goats!" Which sums up the laid-back charm of Irish golf very nicely.

Newmarket-on-Fergus, Co. Clare.
Tel: (061) 368144 or 368444.

LOCATION: Six miles North of Shannon Airport. Eight miles South of Ennis.
SECRETARY: John O'Halloran. Tel: (061) 368144.
PROFESSIONAL: Philip Murphy. Tel: (061) 368144.
ARCHITECT: Robert Trent Jones.

This course became affiliated to the Golfing Union of Ireland although it has been in use for some considerable time. It is a course of character with natural lakes and streams, which come into play on a number of holes. Set in the grounds of Dromoland Castle Hotel the course is particularly wooded and very attractive.

COURSE INFORMATION

Par 71; SSS 71; Length 5719 metres.
Visitors: Welcome at all times.
Opening Hours: 9am – 9pm.
Avoid: Special event days.
Ladies: Welcome.

Green Fees: £25 Mon – Fri; Sat, Sun & Bank Hols £30. For societies £27.50, including four course meal.
Juveniles: Welcome.
Lessons available; Club Hire available; Caddy Service available.
Clubhouse Hours: 9.00am – 10.00pm.
Clubhouse Dress: Smart / casual.
Clubhouse Facilities: At Dromoland Castle Hotel (full catering and bar, plus gymnasium and leisure facilities).
Open Competitions: Open Day – 17th August.

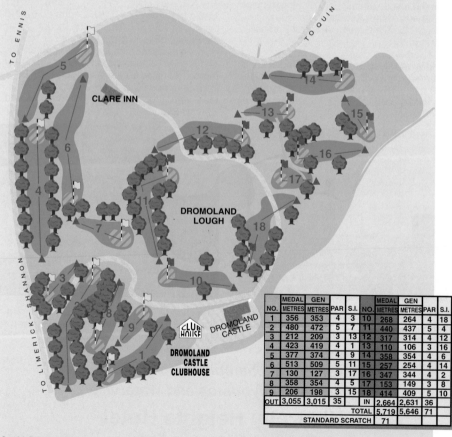

NO.	MEDAL METRES	GEN METRES	PAR	S.I.	NO.	MEDAL METRES	GEN METRES	PAR	S.I.
1	356	353	4	3	10	268	264	4	18
2	480	472	5	7	11	440	437	5	4
3	212	209	3	13	12	317	314	4	12
4	423	419	4	1	13	110	106	3	16
5	377	374	4	9	14	358	354	4	6
6	513	509	5	11	15	257	254	4	14
7	130	127	3	17	16	347	344	4	2
8	358	354	4	5	17	153	149	3	8
9	206	198	3	15	18	414	409	5	10
OUT	3,055	3,015	35		IN	2,664	2,631	36	
					TOTAL	5,719	5,646	71	
					STANDARD SCRATCH	71			

**East Clare Golf Club,
Coolreagh, Bodyke.
Co. Clare.
Tel: (061) 921322.
Fax: (061) 921388.**

Bodyke

LOCATION: One and a half
miles from Bodyke Village,
situated among the rolling
hills and lakes of East Clare.
SECRETARY: Paul Nesbitt.
Tel: (061) 921322.
ARHITECT: Arthur Spring.

All weather challenging parkland
18-hole course with special water
features, designed with the players
satisfaction, comfort and safety in
mind.

COURSE INFORMATION

**Par 71; SSS 71; Length
5,922 metres.
Visitors:** Pay as you play.
Opening Hours: As
clubhouse.

Ladies: Welcome.
Juveniles: Permitted.
Green Fees: Weekdays £12;
weekends £15.
Clubhouse Hours: Winter
9am – 4.30pm; summer
7.30am – 10pm.
Clubhouse Dress: Informal.
Clubhouse Facilities: Light
snacks always available, full
catering by arrangement.
Open Competitions:
Golf/Angling competition, May.

NO.	YARDS	PAR	S.I.	NO.	YARDS	PAR	S.I.
1	396	4		10	365	4	
2	204	3		11	398	4	
3	398	4		12	515	5	
4	189	3		13	197	3	
5	525	5		14	358	4	
6	510	5		15	432	4	
7	415	4		16	521	5	
8	175	3		17	191	3	
9	440	4		18	435	4	
OUT	3,252	35		IN	3,412	36	
				TOTAL	6,664	71	
STANDARD SCRATCH							

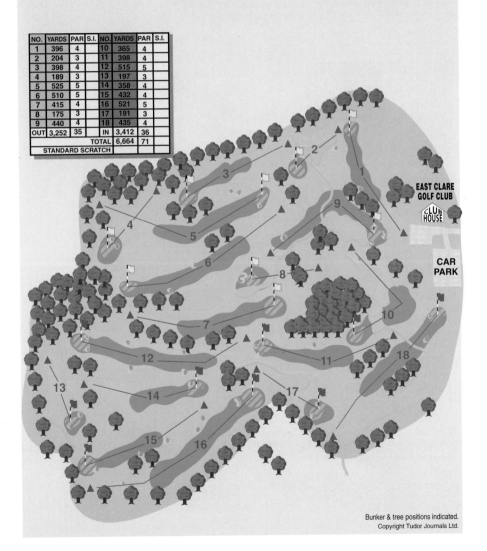

EAST CLARE
GOLF CLUB

CLUB
HOUSE

CAR
PARK

Bunker & tree positions indicated.
Copyright Tudor Journals Ltd.

**Drumbiggle, Ennis,
Co. Clare.
Tel: (065) 24074.**

LOCATION: One mile west of town.
SECRETARY: John Normoyle.
Tel: (065) 24074.
PROFESSIONAL: Martin Ward.
Tel: (065) 20690.

Rolling parkland course with tree-lined narrow fairways. The course overlooks the town of Ennis to the east and the green cliffs of Clare to the west.

COURSE INFORMATION

Par 69; SSS 68; Length 5,275 metres.
Visitors: Welcome Mon – Fri.
Opening Hours: 9.00am – sunset.
Avoid: Tuesday after 2.00pm.
Ladies: Welcome.
Green Fees: £18.
Juveniles: Welcome (half green fee is playing with an adult). Lessons available; Club Hire available; Caddy service available by prior arrangements. Telephone

appointment required.
Clubhouse Hours: 9.00am – 11.00pm.
Clubhouse Dress: Casual.
Clubhouse Facilities: Snacks and a la carte.
Open Competitions: Open Week August. Handicap Certificate required for Open Competitions.

NO.	METRES	PAR	S.I.	NO.	METRES	PAR	S.I.
1	328	4	5	10	160	3	12
2	114	3	18	11	308	4	11
3	296	4	13	12	365	4	2
4	246	4	15	13	158	3	16
5	320	4	7	14	377	4	3
6	417	4	1	15	299	4	6
7	141	3	17	16	180	3	14
8	345	4	4	17	294	4	8
9	468	5	9	18	459	5	10
OUT	2,675	35		IN	2,600	34	
				TOTAL	5,275	69	
				STANDARD SCRATCH	68		

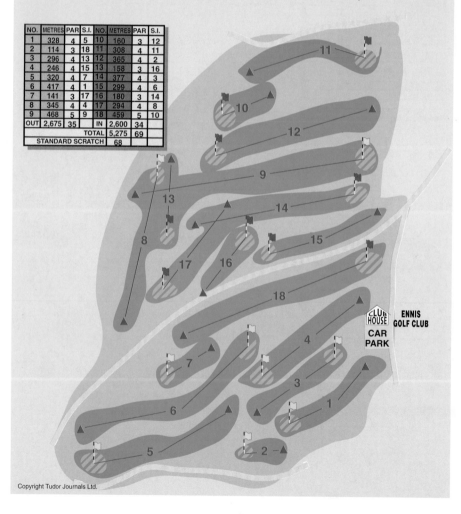

ENNIS GOLF CLUB
CLUB HOUSE
CAR PARK

**Kilkee Golf Club,
East End,
Kilkee, Co. Clare.
Tel: (065) 56048.
Fax: (065) 56977.**

LOCATION: Kilkee.
SECRETARY: Mary Haugh.
Tel: (065) 56048
ARCHITECT: Eddie Hackett.

Kilkee Golf Club is proud of its new-look 18 hole Links. Situated on the edge of the Atlantic Ocean in a most spectacular setting overlooking Moore Bay and its famous horse-shoe beach.

COURSE INFORMATION

**Par 71; SSS 71; Length 5,928 metres.
Visitors:** Welcome.
Opening Hours: Sunrise – sunset.
Avoid: Competition dates.
Green Fees: £20 daily; £12 with member; societies (12+) £12.
Juveniles: Welcome.
Lessons available by prior arrangement; Clubs and

trolleys for hire; Caddy service available.
Clubhouse Hours: 9.00am – closing.
Clubhouse Dress: Casual.
Clubhouse Facilities:
Comfortable bar / snack bar, Restaurant with view over Kilkee Bay and Golf shop.
Open Competitions: During June, July and August. Handicap Certificate required for Open Competitions.

NO.	CHAMP METRES	PAR	S.I.	NO.	CHAMP METRES	PAR	S.I.
1	341	4	9	10	313	4	14
2	443	5	11	11	279	4	18
3	297	4	17	12	468	5	10
4	390	4	5	13	366	4	8
5	292	4	15	14	425	4	4
6	165	3	7	15	387	4	2
7	402	4	1	16	125	3	16
8	374	4	3	17	365	4	6
9	153	3	13	18	343	4	12
OUT	2,857	35		IN	3,071	36	
				TOTAL	5,928	71	
STANDARD SCRATCH		71					

BAY

ATLANTIC OCEAN

CLUB HOUSE

KILKEE GOLF CLUB

PITCH & PUTT

KILRUSH

Parknamoney,Ennis Road, Kilrush, Co. Clare.
Tel: (065) 51138

LOCATION: One mile on Kilrush – Ennis Road.
SECRETARY: Gerry Kelly.
Tel: (065) 59005.

Course with scenic view overlooking Shannon Estuary. Particularly challenging Par 3 especially the 9th hole. The Par 5's will prove very demanding to any golfer. Further developments to both clubhouse and course recently completed.Also, an eighteen hole course was opened in July 1994.

COURSE INFORMATION

Par 68; SSS 70; Length 4,850 metres.
Visitors: Welcome.
Ladies: Welcome Thursdays.
Green Fees: £16 Mon – Fri; £18 weekends.
Juveniles: Welcome if accompanied by an adult. Club Hire available; Caddy service available by prior arrangements.
Clubhouse Hours: 11.00am – 11.30pm; Clubhouse facilities.
Clubhouse Dress: Casual.
Clubhouse Facilities: Lunches & evening meals available everyday May – September.

Open Competitions:
Intermediate Scratch Cup; 3rd May: Open Fourballs; 30th & 31st May – 1st June / 20th & 21st June / 29th & 30th July: Open Week; 26th June – 5th July: Bank Holiday Opens (sponsored by 'Super-Value') –1st, 2nd & 3rd August. Team of 4; 11th,12th & 13th April: 3rd of May; Inter Scratch Cup: 20th & 21st June / 18th & 19th July; four ball: 28th – 30th August; Open Weekend.

NO.	CHAMP YARDS	MEDAL YARDS	PAR	S.I.	NO.	CHAMP YARDS	MEDAL YARDS	PAR	S.I.
1	324	313	4	4	10	285	263	4	17
2	348	324	4	16	11	421	416	4	1
3	442	438	4	2	12	338	327	4	11
4	136	127	3	18	13	504	450	5	15
5	402	391	4	6	14	176	161	3	13
6	349	338	4	10	15	505	490	5	7
7	490	483	5	14	16	398	388	4	3
8	166	158	3	12	17	196	184	3	9
9	168	159	3	8	18	338	326	4	5
OUT	2,825	2,731	34		IN	3,161	3,005	36	
					TOTAL	5,986	5,736	70	
					STANDARD SCRATCH	70	68		

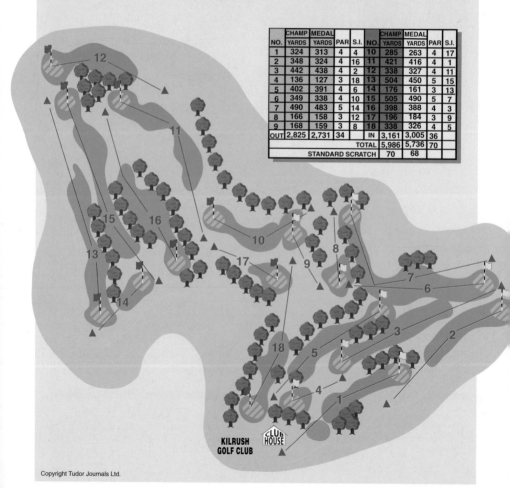

KILRUSH GOLF CLUB

Lahinch, Co Clare.
Tel: (065) 81003.
Fax: (065) 81592.

LOCATION: 35 Miles North West of Shannon Airport.
SECRETARY: Alan Riordan.
Tel: (065) 81003.
PROFESSIONAL: Robert McCavery.
Tel: (065) 81408.
ARCHITECT: Dr Alastair MacKenzie.

Lahinch is steeped in history and has such famous holes as 'Dell' and 'Klondyke'. The features of this famous course are carved out of natural terrain. The Old Course is the permanent home of the South of Ireland Open Amateur Championship, first played in 1895 and which annually attracts the cream of Ireland's amateur golfers to play for this most coveted title and the magnificent trophy which goes with it.

COURSE INFORMATION

Par 72; SSS 73; Length 6123 metres (Old Course).
Visitors: Welcome most days – booking is advisable.
Opening Hours: Sunrise – sunset.

Ladies: Welcome.
Green Fees: £45 per round, £55 per day.
Juveniles: Welcome.
Clubhouse Hours: 8am – 11pm approx. summertime.
Clubhouse Dress: Casual.
Clubhouse Facilities: Full clubhouse facilities; lessons available by prior arrangements; club hire available; caddy service, while available, cannot be guaranteed.
Open Competitions: South of Ireland Amateur Open Championship – July.

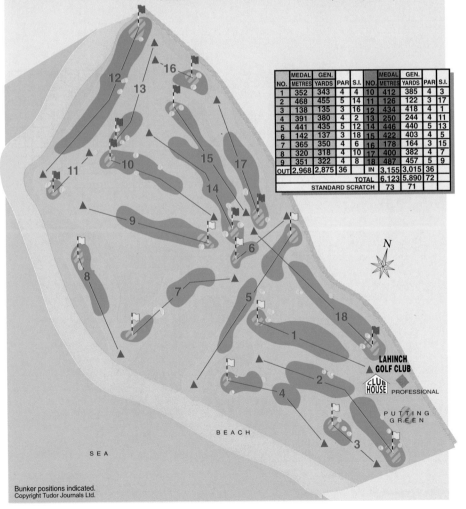

NO.	MEDAL METRES	GEN. YARDS	PAR	S.I.	NO.	MEDAL METRES	GEN. YARDS	PAR	S.I.
1	352	343	4	4	10	412	385	4	3
2	468	455	5	14	11	126	122	3	17
3	138	135	3	16	12	434	418	4	1
4	391	380	4	2	13	250	244	4	11
5	441	435	5	12	14	446	440	5	13
6	142	137	3	18	15	422	403	4	5
7	365	350	4	6	16	178	164	3	15
8	320	318	4	10	17	400	382	4	7
9	351	322	4	8	18	487	457	5	9
OUT	2,968	2,875	36		IN	3,155	3,015	36	
					TOTAL	6,123	5,890	72	
					STANDARD SCRATCH	73	71		

N

LAHINCH GOLF CLUB

CLUB HOUSE PROFESSIONAL

PUTTING GREEN

BEACH

SEA

Lahinch, Co Clare.
Tel: (065) 81003.
Fax: (065) 81592.

LOCATION: 300yds from
Lahinch village.
SECRETARY: Alan Reardon.
Tel: (065) 81003.
PROFESSIONAL: Robert
McCavery.
Tel: (065) 81408.

The Castle course at the
famous Lahinch club has
been upgraded dramatically
and has hosted several
championships. It is a links
course and, although less daunting than
the Old Course, still provides an
excellent challenge to your game.

COURSE INFORMATION

**Par 70; SSS 69/70; Length
5,115 mtrs.**
Visitors: Welcome.
Opening Hours: Dawn – Dusk.
Ladies: Welcome.
Green Fees: £25 daily (Apr –
Oct); £20 daily at all other times;
£9 with members.
Juveniles: Welcome. Lessons
available; Club Hire available;
Caddy service available.
Clubhouse Hours: 8.00am –
11.00pm summertime.
Clubhouse Facilities:
Lunches, dinners and snacks.
Full clubhouse facilities.
Open Competitions:
Intermediate Scratch Trophy –
May.

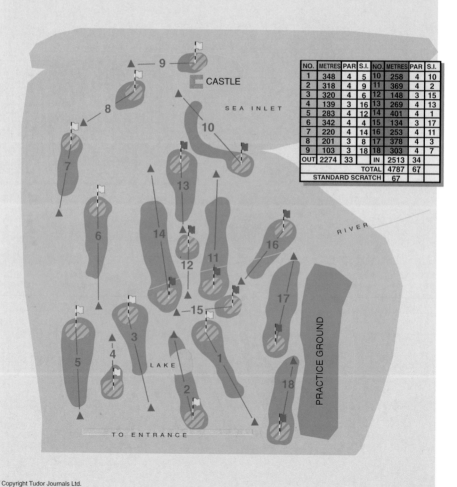

NO.	METRES	PAR	S.I.	NO.	METRES	PAR	S.I.
1	348	4	5	10	258	4	10
2	318	4	9	11	369	4	2
3	320	4	6	12	148	3	15
4	139	3	16	13	269	4	13
5	283	4	12	14	401	4	1
6	342	4	4	15	134	3	17
7	220	4	14	16	253	4	11
8	201	3	8	17	378	4	3
9	103	3	18	18	303	4	7
OUT	2274	33		IN	2513	34	
				TOTAL	4787	67	
STANDARD SCRATCH				67			

Shannon Airport, Shannon, Co. Clare.
Tel: (061) 471849 or 471020/471551

LOCATION: Two Hundred yds beyond Airport terminal building.
PROFESSIONAL: Michael Corry Tel: (061) 471551.
Fax: (061) 471507
ARCHITECT: John D. Harris

American styled golf course with plenty of water hazards and bunkers. Tree lined fairways demand accurate tee shots. The greens are largely by protected by mounds and bunkers. Course is flat and presents a superb challenge for every category of golfer. The par 3, 17th hole is the signature hole with a carry of 185 yds over the Shannon estuary.

COURSE INFORMATION

Par 72; SSS 72: Length 6,874 yards.
Visitors: Welcome at all times, subject to availability.
Opening Hours: Dawn to dusk.
Avoid: Sunday.
Ladies: Welcome Tuesdays.
Green Fees: £22 midweek; £27 weekends.
Juveniles: Must be accompanied by an adult. Lessons by prior arrangement. Club Hire available. Caddy . service available by prior arrangement; telephone appointment required.

Clubhouse Hours: Summer; 11.00am – 10.00pm Mon – Fri. 10.00am – 10.00pm weekends. Winter; 11.00am – 6.00pm Mon – Fri. 10.00am – 6.00pm weekends.
Clubhouse Dress: Casual. No shorts.
Clubhouse Facilities: Full bar and catering facilities available throughout the year. Advisable to book for 4 or more people.
Open Competitions: Handicap certificate required for Open Competitions. Open Week, July. Most Bank Hol. weekends are Open Weekends (exc. May).

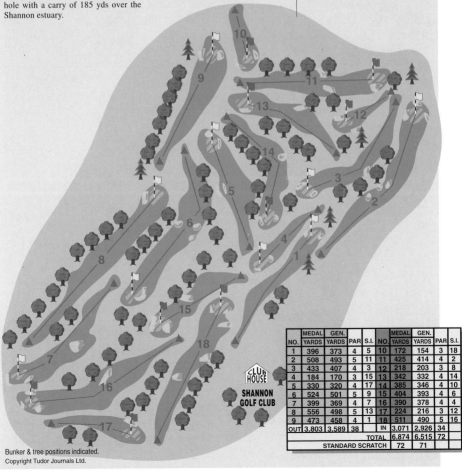

SHANNON GOLF CLUB

NO.	MEDAL YARDS	GEN. YARDS	PAR	S.I.	NO.	MEDAL YARDS	GEN. YARDS	PAR	S.I.
1	396	373	4	5	10	172	154	3	18
2	508	493	5	11	11	425	414	4	2
3	433	407	4	3	12	218	203	3	8
4	184	170	3	15	13	342	332	4	14
5	330	320	4	17	14	385	346	4	10
6	524	501	5	9	15	404	393	4	6
7	399	369	4	7	16	390	378	4	4
8	556	498	5	13	17	224	216	3	12
9	473	458	4	1	18	511	490	5	16
OUT	3,803	3,589	38		IN	3,071	2,926	34	
					TOTAL	6,874	6,515	72	
					STANDARD SCRATCH		72	71	

Bunker & tree positions indicated.

Spanish Point, Miltown Malbay, Co. Clare.
Tel: (065) 84198.

LOCATION: Two miles from Miltown Malbay.
SECRETARY: Dave Fitzgerald.
Tel: (065) 84219.

This links course overlooks the picturesque golden beach at Spanish Point. Playable all year it is renowned for its unique six Par 3's and three Par 4's. The strong Atlantic winds can make life difficult, but it is both fun to play and a challenge for any golf enthusiast.

COURSE INFORMATION
Par 64; SSS 63; Length 4624 metres.
Visitors: Welcome (restrictions on Sundays).
Opening Hours: Sunrise – Sunset.
Ladies: Welcome.
Green Fees: £10 per day (Sept – June). £15 (July – Aug). £8 with a member anytime.
Juveniles: Welcome if accompanied by adult. Juveniles under 14 are not allowed after 5pm or on Sat / Sun.

Clubhouse Hours: 10.00am – 11.00pm (summer); full clubhouse facilities.
Clubhouse Dress: Casual.
Clubhouse Facilities: Sandwiches and light snacks available in bar everyday during the summer.
Open Competitions: Open Week in June; Open Weekend – May. Intermediate Scratch Cup in September. Handicap certificate required for Open Competitions.

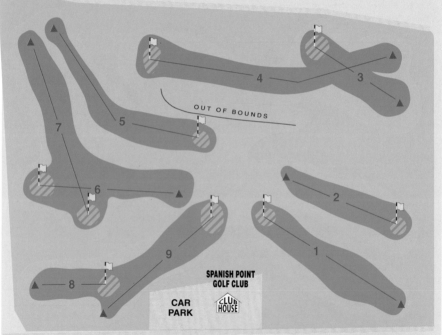

NO.	METRES	PAR	S.I.	NO.	METRES	PAR	S.I.
1	201	3	7	10	201	3	8
2	196	3	11	11	196	3	12
3	176	3	5	12	176	3	6
4	325	4	3	13	325	4	4
5	225	4	17	14	225	4	18
6	180	3	9	15	180	3	10
7	260	4	15	16	260	4	16
8	75	3	13	17	75	3	14
9	202	3	1	18	202	3	2
OUT	1,787	30		IN	1,787	30	
				TOTAL	3,754	60	
			STANDARD SCRATCH		58		

Woodstock Golf & Country Club, Shanaway Road. Ennis, Co. Clare.
Tel: (065) 29463.
Fax: (065) 20304.

LOCATION: Approx 2 miles from the centre of Ennis off the Lahinch Road.
SECRETARY: Anne Marie Russell. Tel: (065) 29463.
ARCHITECT: Dr. Arthur Spring.

The course is championship standard with green built to the highest standard. It is built on 155 acres of free draining soil and is playable all year round. The course is challenging, yet is built so that it may be enjoyed by all categories of golfers. All who visit Woodstock will be sure of a warm welcome.

COURSE INFORMATION

Par 71; SSS 71; Length 6429 yards, 5879 metres.
Visitors: Visitors are welcome all days including weekends, but are advised to avoid members time at weekend (check with secretary).
Opening Hours: 8.00am until dusk.
Ladies: No restrictions. Have priority on Tuesdays.
Green Fees: £20 Mon – Fri; £25 Sat / Sun (£15 with member).
Juveniles: Welcome, although must be accompanied by an adult.
Clubhouse Hours: 9.00am until closing time.
Clubhouse Dress: Informal but neat.
Clubhouse Facilities: Club shop. Caddy cars and caddies on request. Full bar and Four Seasons Restaurant all day everyday.
Open Competitions: Mainly Bank Holiday Weekends.

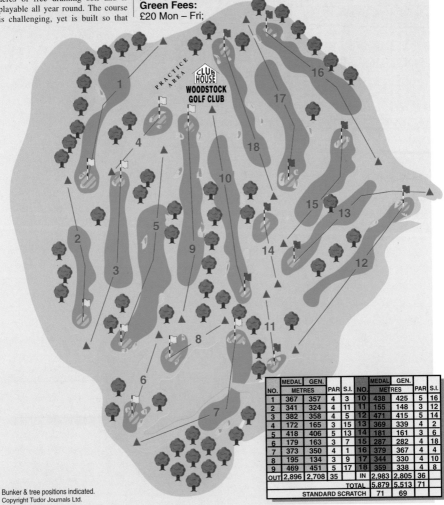

NO.	MEDAL METRES	GEN. METRES	PAR	S.I.	NO.	MEDAL METRES	GEN. METRES	PAR	S.I.
1	367	357	4	3	10	438	425	5	16
2	341	324	4	11	11	155	148	3	12
3	382	358	4	5	12	471	415	5	14
4	172	165	3	15	13	369	339	4	2
5	418	406	5	13	14	181	161	3	6
6	179	163	3	7	15	287	282	4	18
7	373	350	4	1	16	379	367	4	4
8	195	134	3	9	17	344	330	4	10
9	469	451	5	17	18	359	338	4	8
OUT	2,896	2,708	35		IN	2,983	2,805	36	
					TOTAL	5,879	5,513	71	
					STANDARD SCRATCH	71	69		

Bunker & tree positions indicated.

Castlebernard, Bandon, Co. Cork.
Tel: (023) 41111 / 42224 / 44690.

LOCATION: Two miles west of Bandon Town.
SECRETARY: P. Kehoe.
Tel: (023) 41111.
PROFESSIONAL: Paddy O'Boyle.
Tel: (023) 42224.

Beautiful parkland course which some consider difficult due to the sloping fairways. It is one of a few eighteen hole course in West Cork.

COURSE INFORMATION

Par 70; SSS 69; Length 6,193 yards, 5,663 metres.
Visitors: Welcome Mon – Fri excluding Wednesday.
Opening Hours: Sunrise – sunset.
Ladies: Welcome.
Ladies Day: Wednesday.
Green Fees: Mon – Fri £12; Sat / Sun £15.
Juveniles: Welcome. Competition every Tuesday, otherwise must be accompanied by an adult.

Lessons and Caddy service available by prior arrangements; Club Hire available.
Clubhouse Hours: 10.30am; Full clubhouse facilities; Full catering facilities everyday.
Clubhouse Dress: Casual.
Open Competitions: Open Fourball – Fri 27th June, plus variuos other competitions; telephone for details. Handicap certificate required for Open Competitions.

	MEDAL	GEN.				MEDAL	GEN.		
NO.	METRES	METRES	PAR	S.I.	NO.	METRES	METRES	PAR	S.I.
1	271	260	4	16	10	320	320	4	11
2	337	319	4	8	11	380	372	4	1
3	457	447	5	14	12	179	169	3	7
4	326	316	4	6	13	454	444	5	13
5	155	155	3	12	14	402	392	4	3
6	105	105	3	18	15	348	338	4	5
7	405	395	4	2	16	315	305	4	15
8	363	353	4	4	17	302	292	4	17
9	348	348	4	10	18	176	166	3	9
OUT	2,767	2,698	35		IN	2,896	2,798	35	
					TOTAL	5,663	5,496	70	
					STANDARD SCRATCH	69	68		

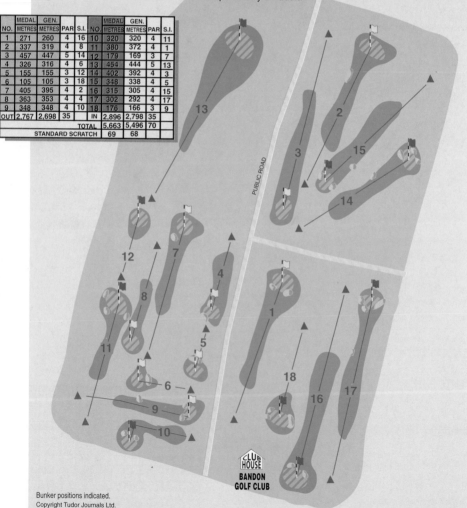

PUBLIC ROAD

CLUB HOUSE

BANDON GOLF CLUB

Bunker positions indicated.
Copyright Tudor Journals Ltd.

Bantry, West Cork
Tel: (027) 50579.

LOCATION: Two miles from Bantry on Glengarriff Road.
SECRETARY: Mr. Enda Lonergan.
Tel: (027) 50372.

Bantry Park is considered an interesting and difficult course. Several plantations are steadily coming into play, and are making the recently built 18 hole course more intriguing.

COURSE INFORMATION

Par 71; SSS 72; Length 6,432 yards; 5,946 metres.
Visitors: Welcome 10.00am –12.30pm & 2.00 – 5.00pm Mon – Fri. 11.30am – 1.30pm and 3.00 – 4.30pm Sat / Sun.
Opening Hours: 9.00am – sunset.
Avoid: Days of major competitions. Prior arrangement for societies.
Ladies: Welcome.
Green Fees: £18 Mon–Fri, £20 Sat & Sun.

Juveniles: Welcome. Club Hire available; Caddy service (restricted at weekends) available by prior arrangements; telephone appointment required.
Clubhouse Hours: 9.00am – sunset during summer months.
Clubhouse Dress: Casual.
Clubhouse Facilities: Bar snacks everyday all day during summer months.
Open Competions: Team Classic (Team of 4) 16th-19th July.

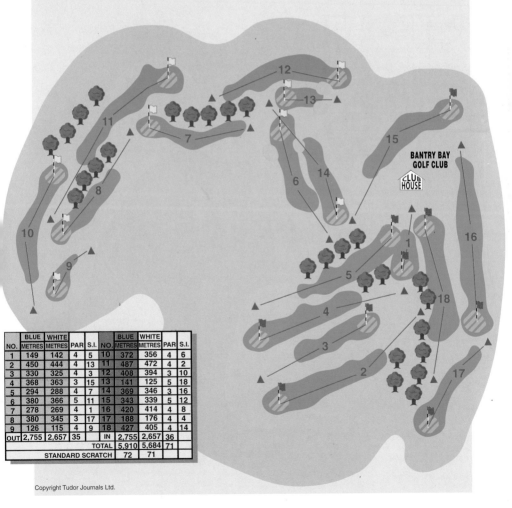

BANTRY BAY GOLF CLUB

	BLUE	WHITE				BLUE	WHITE		
NO.	METRES	METRES	PAR	S.I.	NO.	METRES	METRES	PAR	S.I.
1	149	142	4	5	10	372	356	4	6
2	450	444	4	13	11	487	472	4	2
3	330	325	4	3	12	408	394	3	10
4	368	363	3	15	13	141	125	5	18
5	294	288	4	7	14	369	346	3	16
6	380	366	5	11	15	343	339	5	12
7	278	269	4	1	16	420	414	4	8
8	380	345	3	17	17	188	176	4	4
9	126	115	4	9	18	427	405	4	14
OUT	2,755	2,657	35		IN	2,755	2,657	36	
					TOTAL	5,910	5,684	71	
					STANDARD SCRATCH		72	71	

**Filane, Castletownbere,
Co. Cork.
Tel: (027) 70700.**

LOCATION: 3 miles from
Castletownbere on the
Glengarriff road.
HON. SECRETARY:
Barry Harrington.

A scenic sea-side links set on the
edge of West Cork in a beautiful and
quiet location. Water is a feature of
the course both visually and in play.
The latter features three holes where
water comes into play, particularly
on the Par 3 9th which requires a tee
shot over the water. A new
clubhouse was completed in 1994

which has other tourist facilities
such as a caravan park, picnic area
tennis courts and shingle beach.

COURSE INFORMATION

**Par 68; SSS 64; Length
2,566 yards; 2,346 metres.
Visitors:** Welcome at
anytime.
Opening Hours: 8am – Dark.
Avoid: 2nd weekend Sep and
3rd weekend Aug (Major
competitions).
Ladies: Welcome (no
restrictions).
Green Fees: £10 per day.

Juveniles: Welcome; £5; If
busy must be accompanied
by adult. Club Hire available.
Clubhouse Hours: 11.00 –
11.30pm in season, otherwise
at weekends 12.00 noon –
11.00pm.
Clubhouse Dress: Casual.
Clubhouse Facilities: Full
facilities from June including
showers, saunas and pool.
Open Competitions: Paddy
Crowley Memorial – July;
Open Week – July / August.

NO.	METRES	PAR	S.I.	NO.	METRES	PAR	S.I.
1	288	4	11	10	291	4	14
2	428	5	7	11	391	4	1
3	240	4	17	12	241	4	18
4	366	4	2	13	408	5	8
5	310	4	15	14	300	4	16
6	156	3	15	15	156	3	6
7	255	4	13	16	260	4	12
8	166	3	9	17	166	3	10
9	160	3	5	18	177	3	3
OUT	2369	34		IN	2390	34	
				TOTAL	4759	68	
		STANDARD SCRATCH			64		

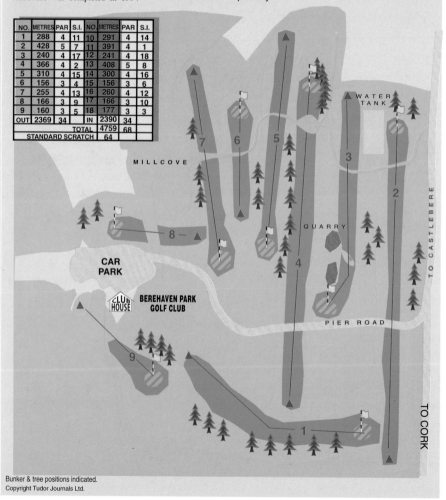

**Charleville Golf Club,
Charleville, Co. Cork.
Tel: (063) 81257.
Fax: (063) 81274.**

LOCATION: On main road from
Cork to Limerick.
SECRETARY: Matt Keane.
Tel: (063) 81257.
HON. SECRETARY: Tony Murphy.

Both of Charleville's attractive and well
maintained parkland courses are located
in the foothills of the scenic Ballyhoura
Mountains, in the heart of Ireland's
Golden Vale. This 18 hole championship
course, renowned for its lush fairways
and excellent greens,

offers relaxed and uncrowded golf in,
peaceful surroundings. The
introduction of a new, fully qualified
instructor in April – David Keating.

COURSE INFORMATION

**Par 71; SSS 69; Length
6,244 yards.**
Visitors: Welcome.
Opening Hours:
9.00am – sunset.
Avoid: Weekends telephone
in advance. Avoid major
competitions.
Ladies: Welcome.
Green Fees: £15 Mon – Fri;
£17 weekends.
Juveniles: Welcome.

Clubhouse Hours:
9.00am – 12.00 midnight.
Clubhouse Dress: Casual.
Clubhouse Facilities:
Full bar and catering facilities
available.
Open Competitions: Ladies
Open – May, July &
September; Senior Scratch –
10th May. Intermediate &
Minor – 24th May. Handicap
Certificate required for Open
Competitions. Telephone for
details.

NO.	YARDS	PAR	S.I.	NO.	YARDS	PAR	S.I.
1	335	4	13	10	370	4	8
2	155	3	18	11	362	4	4
3	369	4	1	12	303	4	15
4	379	4	9	13	533	5	10
5	344	4	5	14	350	4	14
6	373	4	11	15	376	4	6
7	374	4	3	16	158	3	17
8	383	4	7	17	481	5	12
9	162	3	16	18	437	4	2
OUT	2,874	34		IN	3,370	37	
				TOTAL	6,244	71	
		STANDARD SCRATCH			69		

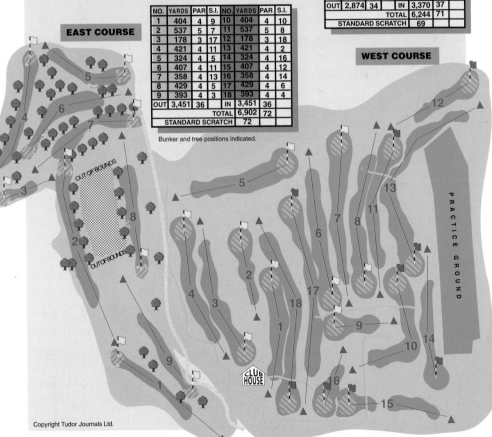

EAST COURSE

NO.	YARDS	PAR	S.I.	NO.	YARDS	PAR	S.I.
1	404	4	9	10	404	4	10
2	537	5	7	11	537	5	8
3	178	3	17	12	178	3	18
4	421	4	11	13	421	4	2
5	324	4	5	14	324	4	16
6	407	4	11	15	407	4	12
7	358	4	13	16	358	4	14
8	429	4	5	17	429	4	6
9	393	4	3	18	393	4	4
OUT	3,451	36		IN	3,451	36	
				TOTAL	6,902	72	
		STANDARD SCRATCH			72		

Bunker and tree positions indicated.

WEST COURSE

COBH

CORK

Cobh, Co. Cork.
Tel: (021) 812399.

LOCATION:
One mile from Cobh Town.
SECRETARY: Diarmuid Kilcullen.
Tel: (021) 271361.
MANAGER: Henry Cunningham.
ARCHITECT: E. Hackett.
Tel: (021) 812399.

A pleasant course on the outskirts of Cobh, noted for the short 2nd hole which is a real card wrecker, with the out-of-bounds only feet away from the back of the green and all down along the right-hand side.

COURSE INFORMATION

Par 67; SSS 64; Length 4796 yards; 4386 metres.
Visitors: Welcome. Telephone appointment required for weekend play.
Opening Hours: 9.00am – sunset.
Avoid: Tuesday.
Ladies: Welcome Tuesdays.
Green Fees: £8 Mon – Fri, £9 weekends.
Juveniles: Welcome.
Clubhouse Hours: 12.00 noon – 11.30pm.

Clubhouse Dress: Smart / casual.
Clubhouse Facilites: Full catering and bar facilities. Club Hire and Caddy trolleys available.
Open Competitions: Open Week – August: Junior and Intermediate Scratch Cups.

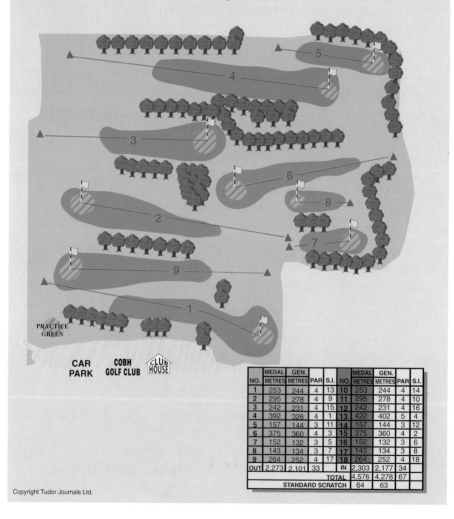

NO.	MEDAL METRES	GEN. METRES	PAR	S.I.	NO.	MEDAL METRES	GEN. METRES	PAR	S.I.
1	253	244	4	13	10	253	244	4	14
2	295	278	4	9	11	295	278	4	10
3	242	231	4	15	12	242	231	4	16
4	392	326	4	1	13	422	402	5	4
5	157	144	3	11	14	157	144	3	12
6	375	360	4	3	15	375	360	4	2
7	152	132	3	5	16	152	132	3	6
8	143	134	3	7	17	143	134	3	8
9	264	252	4	17	18	264	252	4	18
OUT	2,273	2,101	33		IN	2,303	2,177	34	
					TOTAL	4,576	4,278	67	
					STANDARD SCRATCH	64	63		

**Coosheen, Schull,
Co. Cork.
Tel: (028) 28182.**

LOCATION: One and a half miles
East of Schull.
SECRETARY: Linda Morgan.
Tel: (028) 28182.
OWNER: Daniel Morgan.
ARHITECT: Daniel Morgan.

A nine hole course overlooking
beautiful Schull Harbour. The faiways
are tight and testing in windy
conditions, especially the Par 3's, 8th
and 9th holes over water. Renowned for
its Par 3's.

COURSE INFORMATION

**Par 60; SSS 61; Length 4,018
yards.**

Visitors: (Restrictions on Sun).
Opening Hours: 8am – sunset.
Ladies: (Restrictions on Sun).
Juveniles: (Restricted at weekends).
Green Fees: £10 at all times.
Clubhouse Hours: 9am – 10pm.
Clubhouse Dress: Casual.
Clubhouse Facilities: Bar
food/Restaurant (see clubhouse
notice board for opening times). Bar
open to the Public. Golf shop.
Open Competitions: July / Aug.
Handicap Certificates required for
Open Competitions.

NO.	YARDS	PAR	S.I.	NO.	YARDS	PAR	S.I.
1	120	3	13	10	120	3	14
2	240	3	3	11	240	3	4
3	100	3	17	12	100	3	18
4	417	4	1	13	417	4	2
5	320	4	11	14	320	4	12
6	130	3	9	15	130	3	10
7	217	3	5	16	217	3	6
8	200	3	15	17	200	3	16
9	265	4	7	18	265	4	8
OUT	2,009	30		IN	2,009	30	
				TOTAL	4,018	60	
			STANDARD SCRATCH		61		

SCHULL HARBOUR

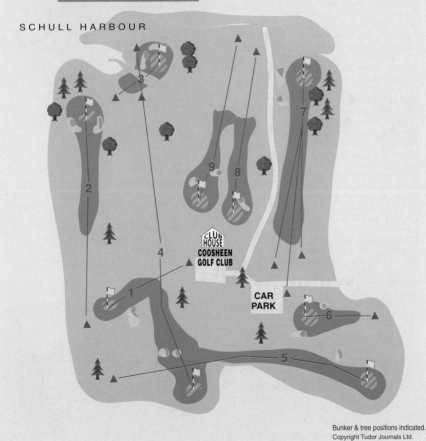

Bunker & tree positions indicated.
Copyright Tudor Journals Ltd.

Little Island, Co. Cork.
Tel: (021) 353451/353037
353263.

LOCATION: Five miles East of
Cork City on N25
Rosslare Road.
GENERAL MANAGER: Matt Sands.
Tel: (021) 353451
Fax: (021) 353410.
ARCHITECT: A. McKenzie.

NO.	MEDAL METRES	GEN. METRES	PAR	S.I.	NO.	MEDAL METRES	GEN. METRES	PAR	S.I.
1	340	335	4	8	10	374	358	4	2
2	460	442	5	16	11	454	450	5	15
3	244	244	4	18	12	289	286	4	11
4	411	402	4	1	13	157	149	3	13
5	510	504	5	6	14	397	380	4	4
6	300	272	4	14	15	383	366	4	7
7	169	158	3	10	16	323	315	4	17
8	379	374	4	3	17	360	335	4	9
9	178	170	3	12	18	387	370	4	5
OUT	2,991	2,901	36		IN	3,124	3,009	36	
					TOTAL	6,115	5,910	72	
					STANDARD SCRATCH	72	70		

Not many clubs have such an
attractive setting for a golf course
with parkland running down to a
rocky outcrop of land reaching out
into Lough Mahon. An excellent
championship test and one of the most
attractive courses in Ireland.

COURSE INFORMATION

**Par 72; SSS 72; Length 6632
yards; 6,115 metres.**
Visitors: Welcome Mon / Tues /
Wed / Fri except from 12.30pm
– 2.00pm or after 4pm.
Opening Hours: Sunrise
– sunset.
Avoid: Thursday Ladies Day.
Telephone appointment required
for wekends.
Ladies: Welcome.
Lessons available by prior
arrangements; Club Hire
available, Caddy service
available.
Green Fees: £35 Mon – Fri;
£40 Sat / Sun.
Juveniles: Welcome. Lessons
available by prior arrangements;
Club Hire available, Caddy
service available.
Clubhouse Hours: Sunrise –
sunset.
Clubhouse Dress: Smart /
casual except after 6.00pm from
1/4 – 31/10 when jacket and tie
must be worn.
Clubhouse Facilities:
11.00am – 9.00pm.

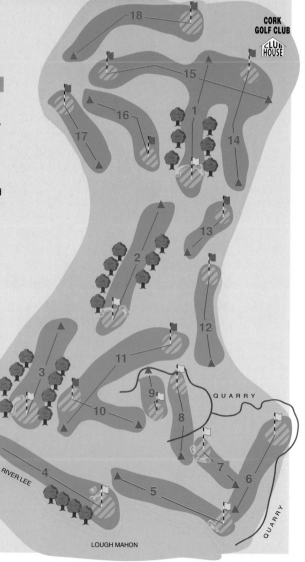

CORK
GOLF CLUB

**Doneraile Golf Club,
Co. Cork.
Tel: (022) 24137.**

LOCATION: Less than one mile from Doneraile town.
SECRETARY: Pat Lennox.
Tel: (079) 62594.

Attractive parkland course with many old oak, lime and beech trees. Deep and wide river valley which must be crossed twice in each nine holes. The Par 3 8th hole is a real gem. It is one of the nicest nine hole courses in the country.

COURSE INFORMATION

**Par 68; SSS 66; Length 5,768 yards, 5,274 metres.
Visitors:** Welcome Mon – Fri.
Opening Hours:
9.00am – Sunset.
Avoid: Saturday mornings and Sunday afternoons.
Ladies: Welcome.
Green Fees: £10.

Juveniles: Welcome.
Clubhouse Hours: Evenings only.
Clubhouse Dress: Casual.
Clubhouse Facilities: By prior arrangement only.

NO.	METRES	PAR	S.I.	NO.	METRES	PAR	S.I.
1	405	4	3	10	405	4	4
2	313	4	17	11	313	4	18
3	370	4	7	12	370	4	8
4	185	3	5	13	185	3	6
5	343	4	9	14	343	4	10
6	364	4	13	15	364	4	14
7	311	4	15	16	311	4	16
8	164	3	11	17	164	3	12
9	429	4	1	18	429	4	2
OUT	2,884	34		IN	2,884	34	
					TOTAL	5,768	68	
				STANDARD SCRATCH		66	

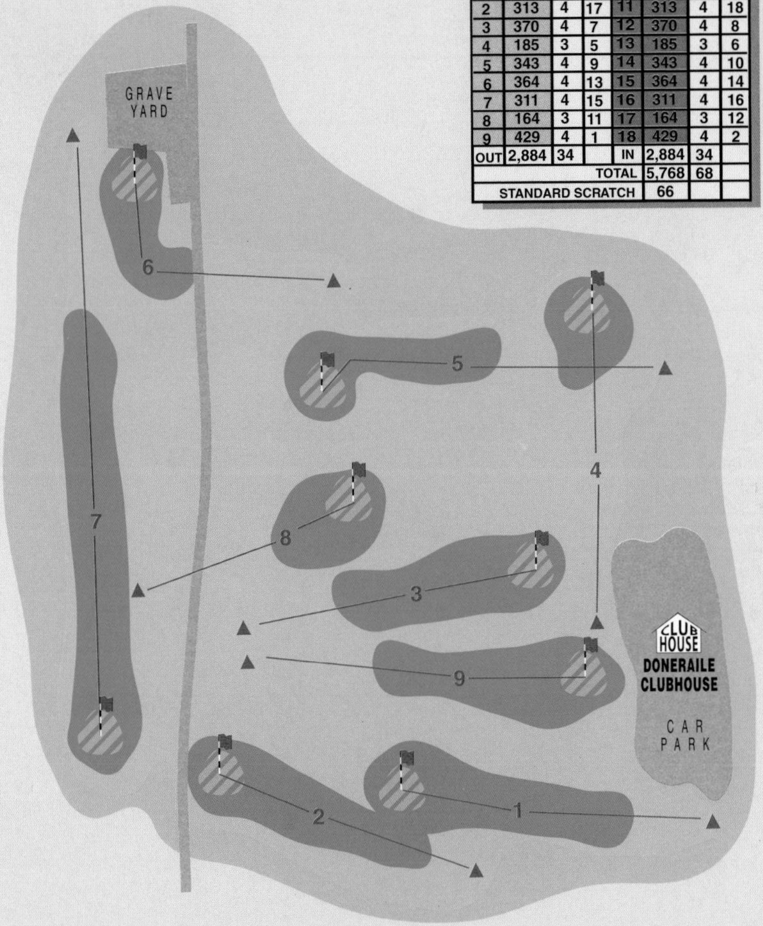

GRAVE YARD

6

5

4

7

8

3

9

CLUB HOUSE

DONERAILE CLUBHOUSE

CAR PARK

2

1

DUNMORE

CORK

Dunmore, Clonakilty, West Cork.
Tel: (023) 34644.

LOCATION: Three miles south of Clonakilty.
SECRETARY: Ger O'Sullivan.
Tel: (023) 33959.

A short, tight course. Accurate driving is called for as out-of-bounds prevails in six of the nine holes.

COURSE INFORMATION

Par 64; SSS 61; Length 4,464 yards, 4,080 metres.
Visitors: Welcome avoid Sundays.
Opening Hours: Sunrise – sunset.
Avoid: Saturday mornings up to noon.
Ladies: Welcome every day.
Green Fees: £38 June – Sept; £35 Off Season (Mon – Sun).

Juveniles: Welcome every day – must be accompanied by an adult after 6.00pm in summer. Handicap Certificate required in competitions.
Clubhouse Hours: 9.00am – 11.00pm.
Clubhouse Dress: Casual.
Clubhouse Facilities: In Hotel attached to course – usual trading hours.
Open Competitions: Beginning of July and Aug.

NO.	YARDS	PAR	S.I.	NO.	YARDS	PAR	S.I.
1	270	4	9	10	270	4	10
2	346	4	3	11	346	4	4
3	159	3	13	12	159	3	14
4	440	4	1	13	440	4	2
5	109	3	17	14	109	3	18
6	303	4	11	15	303	4	12
7	275	4	15	16	275	4	16
8	160	3	7	17	160	3	8
9	170	3	5	18	170	3	6
OUT	2,241	32		IN	2,241	32	
				TOTAL	4,482	64	
				STANDARD SCRATCH	61		

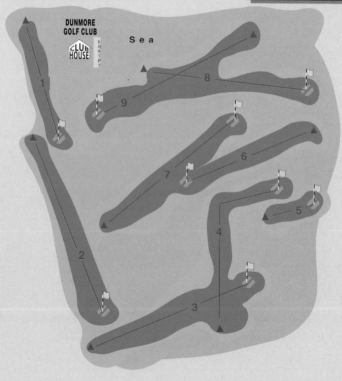

DUNMORE GOLF CLUB

CLUB HOUSE

Sea

**Gortacrue, Midleton,
Co. Cork.
Tel: (021) 631687.**

LOCATION: Two miles outside town
of Midleton.
SECRETARY: Mr Maurice Moloney.
Tel: (021) 631687.
ARCHITECT: E. Hackett.

A fine eighteen hole course, very tight as
many trees planted in past years, are now
coming into play. A new clubhouse opened
in May 1992.

COURSE INFORMATION

**Par 69; SSS 67; Length 5,774
metres.
Visitors:** Welcome.
Opening Hours: 6.00am – 9.00pm.
Avoid: Saturday afternoon; Sunday
morning.
Ladies: Welcome.
Green Fees: £15.00.
Juveniles: Welcome.
Clubhouse Hours: 6am – 11pm.
Clubhouse Dress: Casual.
Clubhouse Facilities: Hot food,
soup, sandwiches, tea and coffee.
Additional Facilities: Pro Shop.
Driving Range
Open Competitions: 4 per year from
April – Oct: Friday night open
Fourball, Tues night Invitation Mixed
Foursomes.

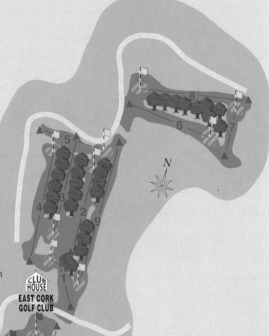

NO.	MEDAL METRES	GEN.	PAR	S.I.	NO.	MEDAL METRES	GEN.	PAR	S.I.
1	176	153	3	3	10	261	251	4	14
2	329	309	4	5	11	325	289	4	8
3	333	313	4	9	12	336	316	4	2
4	343	313	4	1	13	328	300	4	4
5	160	150	3	7	14	142	127	3	10
6	302	287	4	17	15	441	411	5	16
7	130	120	3	15	16	128	128	3	18
8	316	290	4	11	17	480	450	5	12
9	496	470	5	13	18	181	161	3	6
OUT	2,585	2,405	34		IN	2,622	2,433	35	
					TOTAL	5,774	4,838	69	
					STANDARD SCRATCH	67	65		

**Corrin, Fermoy,
Co. Cork.
Tel: (025) 31472.**

LOCATION: Two miles south west of Fermoy.
SECRETARY: Siun Hallihan.
ARCHITECT: Commander Harris.

Heathland course with undulating terrain approximately 700ft above sea level so wind is a major factor. Plenty of scope with wide fairways. There are two distinct nine holes bisected by a road and the average width of fairways is 25 yards.

COURSE INFORMATION

Par 70; SSS 70; Length 5825 metres.
Visitors: Welcome.
Opening Hours: 8.30am – sunset.
Green Fees: £16 Sat / Sun; £13 Mon – Fri.
Juveniles: Welcome before 5.00pm. Must be accompanied by an adult.
Clubhouse Hours: 10.00am – 11.30pm.
Clubhouse Dress: Casual.
Clubhouse Facilities: 11.00am – 9.00pm.
Open Competitions: Various throughout the year telephone for details.

FERMOY
GOLF CLUB

CLUB
HOUSE

NO.	MEDAL METRES	GEN. METRES	PAR	S.I.	NO.	MEDAL METRES	GEN. METRES	PAR	S.I.
1	183	161	3	18	10	458	439	5	15
2	479	479	5	16	11	159	159	3	17
3	305	305	4	8	12	380	380	4	5
4	181	152	3	9	13	339	339	4	3
5	388	348	4	2	14	366	328	4	10
6	320	320	4	14	15	328	310	4	11
7	161	156	3	12	16	158	158	3	13
8	349	308	4	6	17	349	349	4	4
9	395	395	4	1	18	527	464	5	7
OUT	2,761	2,624	34		IN	3,064	2,926	36	
					TOTAL	5,825	69	70	
					STANDARD SCRATCH	70			

286

FOTA ISLAND
M U N S T E R — CORK

Fota Island, Carrigtwohill, Co. Cork.
Tel: 353 21 883700.

LOCATION: 9 miles from Cork.

MANAGER: Kevin Mulcahy.
Tel: (021) 883700.

PROFESSIONAL: Kevin Morris.
Tel: (021) 883710.

Fota Island Golf Club is located in the heart of 780 acres of landscape. The woodlands are woven into a 72 par championship course which is a natural compliment to the other fine clubs in south west Ireland. Venue for the 1997 Irish Amateur Open Championship. "Pursuits will delight at the old fashioned features......you'll stand in wide-eyed admiration." (Golf Monthly).

COURSE INFORMATION

Par 72; SSS 74; Length 6,886 yards.
Visitors: Welcome.
Opening Hours: 8.30am – 5.00pm.

Ladies: Welcome Tuesdays (members).
Green Fees: £38 weekdays. £37 weekends.
Juveniles: Welcome - student rate Mon – Fri.
Clubhouse Hours: 8.30am – 7.30pm.
Clubhouse Dress: Smart / Casual.
Clubhouse Facilities: Full restaurant and bar.

NO.	MEDAL YARDS	GEN. YARDS	PAR	S.I.	NO.	MEDAL YARDS	GEN. YARDS	PAR	S.I.
1	428	412	4	3	10	502	475	5	6
2	435	411	4	9	11	201	142	3	14
3	182	148	3	15	12	425	373	4	4
4	501	486	5	11	13	183	151	3	10
5	577	546	5	5	14	440	404	4	2
6	375	362	4	17	15	445	385	4	12
7	170	146	3	7	16	417	387	4	8
8	484	477	5	13	17	204	139	3	18
9	425	397	4	1	18	492	475	5	16
OUT	3,577	3,385	37		IN	3,309	2,931	35	
					TOTAL	6,886	6,200	72	
					STANDARD SCRATCH	74	70		

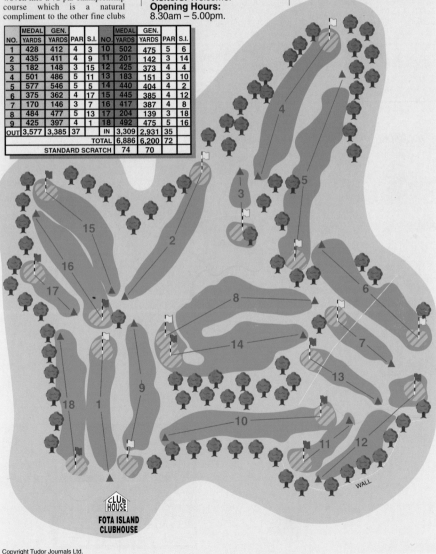

FOTA ISLAND CLUBHOUSE

Frankfield,
Cork
Tel: (021) 361199.

LOCATION: Two miles from Cork Airport; Three miles from Cork City.
SECRETARY: George Towmey. Tel: (021) 361199.
PROFESSIONAL: David Whyte. Tel: (021) 363656.
OWNER: Michael Ryan. Tel: (021) 363124.
ARCHITECT: M. Ryan.

Short, pleasant nine hole course on a hillside overlooking Cork City. Has a 30 bay driving range, one of the best in Muster and is a training centre used by the Irish Naitonal Coach in the Muster area.

COURSE INFORMATION

Par 68; SSS 65; Length 5137 yards; 4697 metres.
Visitors: Welcome.
Opening Hours: 9.00am – Dusk.
Avoid: Sat / Sun morning, after 2.00pm Thursdays & major competitions.
Ladies: Welcome.
Green Fees: £5
Juveniles: Welcome. Under 16's must be accompanied by an adult.

Clubhouse Hours: 10.30am – 11.00pm.
Clubhouse Dress: Casual.
Clubhouse Facilities: Lunches and snacks available at all times. Lunches Mon – Fri.·
Open Competitions: Guinness Open Singles; 28th March: Lostos Open Singles; 2nd – 5th May: Tom Heggarty's Open Singles; 30th June: Intermediate Scratch; 13th Sep: Minor Scratch; 20th Sep: Junoir Scratch; 27th Sep.

NO.	YARDS	PAR	S.I.	NO.	YARDS	PAR	S.I.
1	336	4	6	10	341	4	5
2	302	4	14	11	302	4	15
3	135	3	17	12	135	3	18
4	179	3	12	13	179	3	13
5	344	4	3	14	344	4	4
6	325	4	10	15	325	4	9
7	355	4	1	16	355	4	2
8	315	4	7	17	315	4	8
9	260	4	16	18	290	4	11
OUT	2,551	34		IN	2,586	34	
					TOTAL	5,137	68	
				STANDARD SCRATCH		65	

**Drumgarriff,
Glengarriff, Co. Cork.
Tel: (027) 63150.**

LOCATION: One mile from
Glengarriff Village.
SECRETARY: Noreen Deasy.
Tel: (027) 63134.

This is a course in a particularly
beautiful part of Ireland. There are
many breath-taking views of
mountains, forestry and sea as most of
the holes overlook Glengarriff
Harbour and Bantry Bay.

NO.	METRES	PAR	S.I.	NO.	METRES	PAR	S.I.
1	270	4	9	10	270	4	10
2	270	4	5	11	270	4	6
3	149	3	13	12	149	3	14
4	245	4	11	13	245	4	12
5	122	3	17	14	122	3	18
6	259	4	7	15	259	4	8
7	257	4	3	16	257	4	4
8	144	3	15	17	144	3	16
9	331	4	1	18	331	4	2
OUT	2,047	33		IN	2,047	33	
				TOTAL	4,094	66	
STANDARD SCRATCH		62					

COURSE INFORMATION

**Par 66; SSS 62; Length 4477
yards; 4094 metres.**
Visitors: Welcome at all times.
Opening Hours: 9.00am –
sunset.
Ladies: Welcome.
Green Fees: £12 weekdays &
weekends.
Juveniles: Welcome. Club Hire
available; Caddy service and
cars available by prior
arrangement.
Clubhouse Hours: 10.30am –
11.30pm.
Clubhouse Dress: Casual.
Clubhouse Facilities: Bar
snacks available all week. Full
catering available by prior
arrangement.
Open Competitions: Maurine
O'Hara Classic (mixed); 25th –
29th May: Blair Classic; June.
Open Scrambles every
Wednesday & Friday evening:
Mixed Foursomes.

CAR
PARK

GLENGARRIFF
GOLF CLUB

Clash, Little Island, Co. Cork.
Tel: (021) 353094.
Fax: (021) 354408.

LOCATION: Seven km from City Centre.
SECRETARY: Niamh O'Connell Tel: (021) 353094.
PROPRIETOR: Sean O'Connell.

Little Island on the banks of the River Lee has a particular rustic charm. Little Island by it topography and setting has all the natural gifts required for a great golf course. In fact it is more than a championship golf course with each fairway tree lined and each green

intricately contoured. It is a complex with an in-built 21 bay, all weather and flood-lit driving range positioned in acres of ground between the fifth and ninth holes.

COURSE INFORMATION

Par 72; SSS 69; Length 5733 metres.
Visitors: Always welcome. Telephone appointment required.
Opening Hours: 8am – 5pm.
Avoid: Sunday before 11am.
Green Fees: £20 Mon – Thurs; £12.50 before 11.00am (Early Bird Special);

£22 Fri/Sat/Sun. For group rates please telephone for information.
Juveniles: Welcome.
Clubhouse Hours: 8am – 12 midnight.
Clubhouse Dress: Neat.
Clubhouse Facilities: Full Restaurant and Bar. Catering hours: 10.30am – 6.00pm (winter). 10.30am – 9.00pm (summer).
Open Competitions: Open weekend, July.

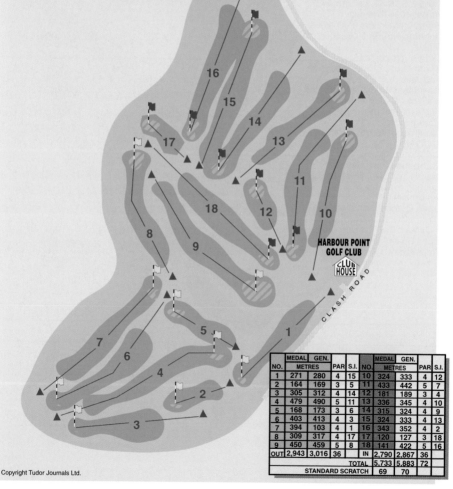

HARBOUR POINT
GOLF CLUB

	MEDAL	GEN.				MEDAL	GEN.		
NO.	METRES		PAR	S.I.	NO.	METRES		PAR	S.I.
1	271	280	4	15	10	324	333	4	12
2	164	169	3	5	11	433	442	5	7
3	305	312	4	14	12	181	189	3	4
4	479	490	5	11	13	336	345	4	10
5	168	173	3	6	14	315	324	4	9
6	403	413	4	3	15	324	333	4	13
7	394	103	4	1	16	343	352	4	2
8	309	317	4	17	17	120	127	3	18
9	450	459	5	8	18	141	422	5	16
OUT	2,943	3,016	36		IN	2,790	2,867	36	
					TOTAL	5,733	5,883	72	
					STANDARD SCRATCH	69	70		

Fairy Hill Golf Club, Kanturk, Boyle, Co. Cork.
Tel: (029) 50534.

LOCATION: Location Fairyhill, Kanturk.
SECRETARY: John Pigott.
Tel: (029) 50588.

Lots of plantations and out-of-bounds on several parts of the course. A friendly atmosphere prevails at this club whose course overlooks the Bogeresh Mountains. 18th hole opening soon.

COURSE INFORMATION

Par 70; SSS 69; Length 5,527 metres.
Visitors: Welcome.
Opening Hours:
Sunrise – sunset.
Ladies: Welcome. Ladies day Wednesday.
Green Fees: £10 per round. Special rate for families £12; Gentleman & lady £10; Juvenile £2.
Juveniles: Welcome.

Clubhouse Hours:
After Club Competitions.
Clubhouse Dress: Casual.
Clubhouse Facilities: By prior arrangement. (Mrs. Clery 50587).
Open Competitions: One open event per month.

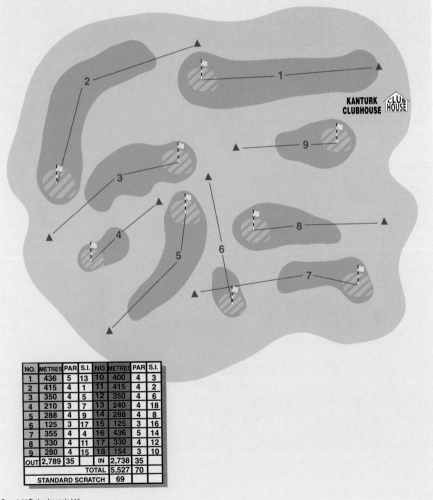

NO.	METRES	PAR	S.I.	NO.	METRES	PAR	S.I.
1	436	5	13	10	400	4	3
2	415	4	1	11	415	4	2
3	350	4	5	12	350	4	6
4	210	3	7	13	240	4	18
5	288	4	9	14	288	4	8
6	125	3	17	15	125	3	16
7	355	4	4	16	436	5	14
8	330	4	11	17	330	4	12
9	280	4	15	18	154	3	10
OUT	2,789	35		IN	2,738	35	
				TOTAL	5,527	70	
	STANDARD SCRATCH				69		

Copyright Tudor Journals Ltd.

**Kinsale Golf Club,
Farrangalway, Kinsale,
Co. Cork.
Tel: (021) 774722.**

LOCATION: 3 miles from Kinsale, turn right at Blue Haven Hotel.
SECRETARY: Deirdre O'Sullivan.
Tel: (021) 774722.

An 18 hole parkland course, the first holes maximise the roll of the land. The back nine incorporate natural waterways which makes for a pleasant and testing fold of play.

COURSE INFORMATION

Par 71; SSS 71; Length; 6,609 metres.
Visitors: Welcome, book at weekends..
Opening Hours: 7.00am – dusk.
Ladies: Welcome.
Green Fees: Weekdays £20; weekends £25. Early bird 7-10am £12.50.
Juveniles: Welcome.
Clubhouse Hours: 9.00am – 11.30pm.

Clubhouse facilities: Bar and restaurant.
Clubhouse Dress: Smart / casual.
Clubhouse Facilities: Catering facilities all day.

NO.	MEDAL YARDS	GEN. YARDS	PAR	S.I.	NO.	MEDAL YARDS	GEN. YARDS	PAR	S.I.
1	372	365	4	13	10	405	398	4	8
2	123	118	3	17	11	216	206	3	7
3	415	407	4	2	12	438	431	4	5
4	280	274	4	16	13	395	387	4	4
5	368	358	4	11	14	421	401	4	14
6	175	163	3	18	15	183	168	3	9
7	431	419	4	3	16	368	361	4	10
8	556	548	5	12	17	411	404	4	1
9	560	550	5	6	18	492	482	5	15
OUT	3,280	3,202	36		IN	3,329	3,238	35	
					TOTAL	6,609	6,440	71	
					STANDARD SCRATCH		72	71	

CLUB HOUSE
KINSALE GOLF CLUB

NO.	MTRS.	PAR	S.I.	NO.	MTRS.	PAR	S.I.
1	439	5	12	10	452	5	11
2	115	3	15	11	140	3	13
3	358	4	1	12	302	4	3
4	296	4	18	13	169	3	7
5	308	4	8	14	315	4	5
6	183	3	6	15	250	4	16
7	444	5	10	16	282	4	17
8	339	4	14	17	460	5	9
9	372	4	4	18	350	4	2
OUT	2,854	36		IN	2,720	36	
				TOTAL	5,574	72	
		STANDARD SCRATCH			70		

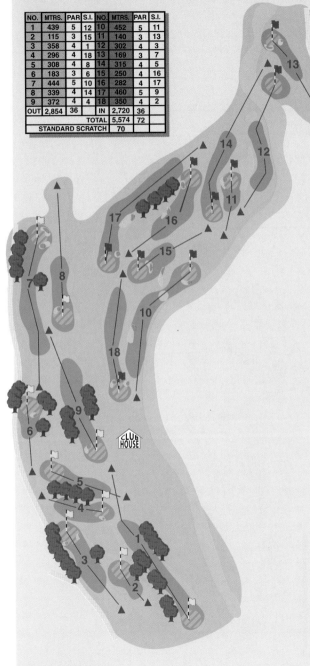

**Lackaduve, Macroom,
Co. Cork.
Tel: (026) 41072.
Fax: (026) 41391.**

LOCATION: On grounds of
Castle Demesne in centre
of town.
SECRETARY: Leo Goold.

An undulating scenic 18 hole
parkland course, within the town
and constructed around the River
Sullane, natural water hazards being
a major feature of the course.
Situated on the main Cork /
Killarney Road with entrance
through castle gates.

COURSE INFORMATION

**Par 72; SSS 70; Length
5574 metres.**
Visitors: Welcome Mon – Fri
all day – check for weekends.
Opening Hours: Sunrise –
sunset.
Avoid: Days of major
competitions.
Ladies: Ladies day Wed.
Ladies full membership.
Green Fees: £13 Mon – Fri;
£16 at weekends.
Juveniles: Cannot play after
6.00pm or at weekends.
Caddy service available by
prior arrangement; telephone
appointment required.
Clubhouse Hours: 11.00am
– 11.30pm from Easter to Nov;
weekend service from Nov –
April. Full catering facilities.
Clubhouse Dress: Casual.
Open Competitions: About
six in the year as advertised in
newspapers – dates vary due
sometimes to sponsorship.
Open Week, August.

Bunker & tree positions indicated.
Copyright Tudor Journals Ltd.

Skehard Road, Cork.
Tel: (021) 362480.

LOCATION: Skehard Road
(Three miles from city).
HONORARY SECRETARY: Ashley
Hennessy
Tel: (021) 362727.
SECRETARY: Tim O'Connor.

Mahon is a municipal course and is
administered by Cork Corporation. It
is built on the very edge of the River
Douglas Estuary and because of this
has many interesting holes, the 9th
especially is not a place for the
faint-hearted, with a tee shot over
water.

COURSE INFORMATION

**Par 68; SSS 66; Length 4818
mtrs.**
Visitors: Welcome. Should
ring in advance.
Opening Hours: Sunrise -
Sunset.
Avoid: Friday mornings.
Ladies: Welcome.
Green Fees: £8.50 Mon - Fri;
£9.50 Weekends/Bank
Holidays; Pensioners £3.50;
Students £3.00 Mon - Fri.
Juveniles: £3.00 Mon - Fri. All
clubhouse facilities. Club hire
available.
Clubhouse Dress: Casual.
Clubhouse Facilities: Bar and
catering facilities available at
the Cloverhill House.
Tel: 358311
Open Competitions:
Throughout the year.

DOUGLAS
RIVER

GOAT
ISLAND

NO.	METRES	PAR	S.I.	NO.	METRES	PAR	S.I.
1	339	4	4	10	437	5	11
2	134	3	18	11	279	4	15
3	324	4	8	12	341	4	3
4	192	3	2	13	274	4	13
5	252	4	12	14	180	3	5
6	99	3	16	15	248	4	17
7	166	3	6	16	145	3	9
8	282	4	14	17	334	4	1
9	444	5	10	18	348	4	7
OUT	2,232	33		IN	2,586	35	
				TOTAL	4,818	68	
	STANDARD SCRATCH				66		

**Ballyellis, Mallow,
Co Cork.
Tel: (022) 21145.
Fax: (022) 42501.**

LOCATION: One mile from centre of
Mallow town on the Kilavullen
Road.
SECRETARY / MANAGER:
Vincent Devlin. Tel: (022) 21145 .
PROFESSIONAL: Sean Conway.
Tel: (022) 43424.
ARCHITECT:
Commander John D. Harris.

This majestic parkland course, with
exceptional views of both the Mushera
and the distant Galtee mountains, boasts
an idyllic rural setting. Set in the heart
of the Blackwater Valley, Mallow's
undulating treelined fairways transport
the golfer from tee to green, and provide
an enjoyable testing round of golf.

COURSE INFORMATION

**Par 72; SSS 72; Length 5,960
metres.
Visitors:** Welcome to play on
weekdays but pre-booking is
essential.
Opening Hours: 8am to late
evening.
Avoid: Saturday and Sunday.
Prior arrangement is essential.
Green Fees: £20 per day; £25
weekends. Caddy car hire
available by prior arrangment.
Clubhouse Hours: 9.00am –
11.00pm.
Clubhouse Dress: Casual, no
denim jeans.
Clubhouse Facilities: 3 tennis
courts, 2 squash courts,
snooker room, television lounge
and sauna. Snacks at all times.
Full bar and catering facilities.
Open Competitions: Open
week, July.

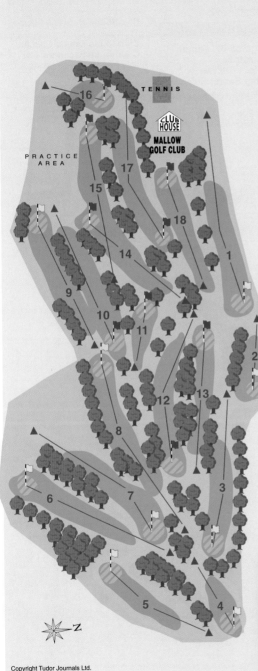

TENNIS

CLUB HOUSE

MALLOW
GOLF CLUB

PRACTICE
AREA

NO.	MEDAL METRES	GEN. METRES	PAR	S.I.	NO.	MEDAL METRES	GEN. METRES	PAR	S.I.
1	367	359	4	7	10	393	381	4	6
2	174	166	3	9	11	155	145	3	12
3	448	439	5	11	12	496	490	5	8
4	172	167	3	15	13	379	356	4	2
5	347	339	4	3	14	287	273	4	16
6	462	440	5	13	15	351	345	4	4
7	413	388	4	1	16	116	107	3	18
8	435	428	5	17	17	446	435	5	14
9	339	333	4	5	18	180	173	3	10
OUT	3,157	3,059	37		IN	2,803	2,710	35	
					TOTAL	5,960	5,769	72	
					STANDARD SCRATCH	72	71		

MITCHELSTOWN M U N S T E R

Gurrane, Mitchelstown, Co. Cork.
Tel: (025) 24072.

LOCATION: One mile on Limerick road from Mitchelstown.
SECRETARY: J. Mullins.
Tel: (025) 24519.

A level course which appears easy, but should not be under estimated. The main attraction to visitors are the nearby Galtee Mountains. Additional holes opening soon.

COURSE INFORMATION

Par 67; SSS 67; Length 5,148 metres.
Visitors: Welcome.
Opening Hours: Sunrise – sunset.
Avoid: Sunday.
Green Fees: £10.00
Juveniles: Welcome. Must be accompanied by an adult after 6.00pm.
Clubhouse Hours: 9.00am – 11.30pm.
Clubhouse Dress: Casual.
Clubhouse Facilities: Bar only in evenings. Snacks available in evenings.
Open Competitions: Open week June. Various open weekends throughout the year, generally on Bank Holidays.

NO.	MEDAL METRES	GEN. METRES	PAR	S.I.	NO.	MEDAL METRES	GEN. METRES	PAR	S.I.
1	384	375	4	3	10	164	145	3	10
2	192	182	3	9	11	359	349	4	2
3	348	348	4	11	12	353	333	4	4
4	325	314	4	13	13	143	128	3	12
5	175	175	3	7	14	272	258	4	6
6	328	328	4	15	15	322	308	4	8
7	137	126	3	17	16	451	434	5	16
8	357	340	4	1	17	109	107	3	18
9	376	258	4	5	18	353	353	4	14
OUT	2,622	2,546	33		IN	2,526	2,415	34	
					TOTAL	5,148	4,961	67	
					STANDARD SCRATCH	67	66		

MITCHELSTOWN
GOLF CLUB

CLUB HOUSE

10
11
9
12
13
14
4
5
6
3&18
15
7
17
8
2
1
16

296

Parkgariffe, Monkstown, Co. Cork.
Tel: (021) 841225.

LOCATION: Seven miles from City.
HON. SECRETARY: Philip O'Dwyer.
PROFESSIONAL: Mr B. Murphy.
Tel: (021) 841686.
ARCHITECTS: Peter O'Hare and Tom Carey.

A testing parkland course where, because of many trees and bunkers, accuracy is at a premium. All greens are well protected. From the first nine there are many scenic views of Cork Harbour, and on the back nine, water features on four holes. 85 bunkers were constructed and remodelled offering a great golfing challenge.

COURSE INFORMATION

Par 70; SSS 69; Length 6,199 yards; 5,669 metres.
Visitors: Welcome. Telephone bookings in advance advisable.
Opening Hours: 8.00am – sunset.
Avoid: Tues (Ladies Day); Wed afternoon; Sat / Sun mornings.
Ladies: Welcome Tuesdays and at quiet times.
Green Fees: £23 Mon – Thurs; £26 Fri / Sun. Reductions for societies.
Juveniles: Must be accompanied by an adult. Lessons available by prior arrangements; Club Hire and Caddy cars available; telephone appointment advisable.
Clubhouse Hours: 8.00am – 11.30pm.
Clubhouse Dress: Casual. No denims or sneakers.
Clubhouse Facilities: Breakfast, Lunch, Dinner, a la carte. Last orders 9.00pm; tel: 841098. Bar open 12.00 noon – 11.30pm.
Open Competitions: Intermediate, Junior and Senior Scratch Cups.

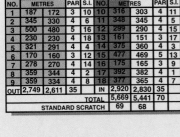

NO.	MEDAL METRES	GEN.	PAR	S.I.	NO.	MEDAL METRES	GEN.	PAR	S.I.
1	187	172	3	10	10	316	303	4	11
2	345	330	4	6	11	348	345	4	5
3	500	480	5	16	12	299	290	4	15
4	230	230	4	18	13	161	151	3	17
5	321	291	4	4	14	375	360	4	3
6	170	160	3	12	15	477	469	5	13
7	278	270	4	14	16	175	165	3	9
8	359	344	4	2	17	392	382	4	1
9	359	334	4	8	18	377	365	4	7
OUT	2,749	2,611	35		IN	2,920	2,830	35	
					TOTAL	5,669	5,441	70	
					STANDARD SCRATCH	69	68		

Bunker positions indicated.
Copyright Tudor Journals Ltd.

Carrigrohane, Co. Cork.
Tel: (021) 385297.
Fax: (021) 385297.

Location: Eight miles north west of Cork City; Two miles west of Blarney.
Secretary: J. J. Moynihan.
Tel: (021) 385297.
Professional: M. Lehane.
Tel: (021) 381445.

Undulating on three levels. The 6th hole could be described as good a Par 3 as will be found anywhere. Last four holes provide a most challenging finish, the last two crossing a river. Precise clubbing and accuracy are demanded on this course.

COURSE INFORMATION

Par 71; SSS 70; Length 6,327 yards; 5,786 metres.
Visitors: Welcome: Mon & Tue all day; Wed up to 11.00am; Fri up to 4.00pm; Sat / Sun enquire. Telephone in advance each day.
Opening Hours: 9.00am – sunset.

Green Fees: £22.00 midweek. £23.00 Sat / Sun (if available).
Juveniles: Welcome. Lessons available by prior arrangement; Club Hire available; telephone in advance at all times.
Clubhouse Hours: 9.00am - 11.30pm.
Clubhouse Dress: Neat / casual.
Clubhouse Facilities: Full catering and bar.
Open Competitions: Senior, Junior and Intermediate Scratch Cups.

NO.	MEDAL METRES	GEN. METRES	PAR	S.I.	NO.	MEDAL METRES	GEN. METRES	PAR	S.I.
1	385	372	4	2	2	294	294	4	15
2	243	241	4	18	18	361	339	4	11
3	349	343	4	10	8	156	143	3	13
4	448	435	5	12	10	373	347	4	5
5	339	329	4	4	6	437	430	5	17
6	192	182	3	6	4	155	147	3	9
7	432	423	5	14	16	391	375	4	3
8	162	148	3	16	12	405	377	4	1
9	309	285	4	8	14	354	349	4	7
OUT	2,859	2,758	36		IN	2,926	2,801	35	
					TOTAL	5,785	5,559	71	
		STANDARD SCRATCH				71	70		

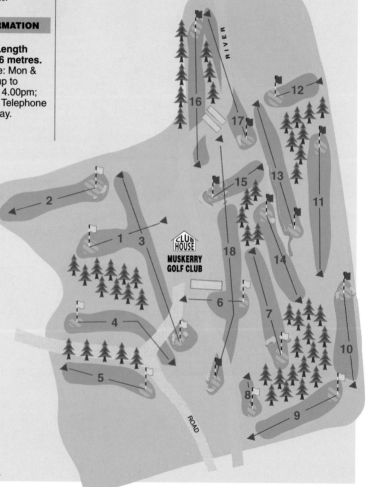

MUSKERRY GOLF CLUB

OLD HEAD

Old Head Golf Links, Kinsale, Co. Cork. Tel: (021) 778444.

LOCATION: 7 miles south of Kinsale town.
DIRECTOR OF GOLF: Jim O'Brien.
Tel: (021) 778444.

The links is situated on an Atlantic promontory rising hundreds of feet high above dramatic cliffs, surrounded by the ocean on all sides and commanding the most spectacular views.
During 1998 fourteen new tees were added, extending the course length to 7,200 yards.

COURSE INFORMATION

Par 72; SSS 72; Length 6,756 yards.
Visitors: Welcome at all times.
Opening Hours: 8am – 10pm.
Ladies: Welcome.
Green Fees: £50 weekdays; £60 weekends.
Juveniles: Welcome

Clubhouse Hours: 8am – 10pm.
Clubhouse Dress: Smart/casual, denim jeans and sneakers prohibited.
Clubhouse Facilities: Bar/Restaurant and Golf Shop.

NO.	MEDAL YARDS	GEN YARDS	PAR	S.I.	NO.	MEDAL YARDS	GEN YARDS	PAR	S.I.
1	420	392	4	7	10	493	456	5	16
2	387	376	4	5	11	180	158	3	12
3	153	135	3	15	12	498	466	5	14
4	407	396	4	3	13	222	208	3	8
5	405	362	4	9	14	429	412	4	2
6	488	475	5	13	15	340	292	4	18
7	164	138	3	11	16	186	162	3	10
8	496	466	5	17	17	628	597	5	4
9	449	428	4	1	18	411	366	4	6
OUT	3369	3168	36		IN	3387	3117	36	
					TOTAL	6756	6285	72	
					STANDARD SCRATCH	72	70		

Bunker/hedge and tree positions indicated.
Copyright Tudor Journals Ltd.

OLD HEAD CLUBHOUSE

Ringaskiddy, Co. Cork.
Tel: (021) 378430.

LOCATION: Ten miles from Cork.
MANAGER: David Harrington.
TREASURER: Derry Murphy.
ARCHITECT: E. Hackett.

A scenic course whose special features are tough over-water shots. Straight, accurate play will get best results. The 8th and 9th are two fearsome holes with the Lake coming into play.

COURSE INFORMATION

Par 70; SSS 68; Length 5,575 yards, 5,098 metres.
Visitors: Welcome.
Opening Hours: Sunrise – sunset.
Avoid: Competition times; Sat / Sun mornings.
Ladies: Welcome Mon – Fri.

Green Fees: £12 Mon – Fri; £14 Sat / Sun; £9 early morning Mon – Friday.
Juveniles: Welcome Tues-Fri up to 6.00pm. Telephone appointment required.
Clubhouse Hours: 9.00am – 11.30pm.
Clubhouse Dress: Casual.
Clubhouse Facilities: Snacks available, full meals by prior arrangement.

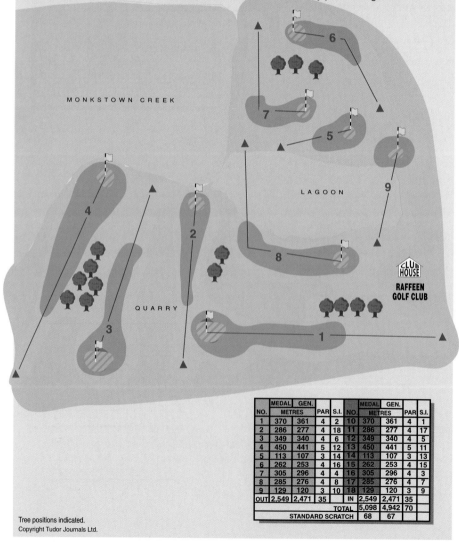

NO.	MEDAL METRES	GEN. METRES	PAR	S.I.	NO.	MEDAL METRES	GEN. METRES	PAR	S.I.
1	370	361	4	2	10	370	361	4	1
2	286	277	4	18	11	286	277	4	17
3	349	340	4	6	12	349	340	4	5
4	450	441	5	12	13	450	441	5	11
5	113	107	3	14	14	113	107	3	13
6	262	253	4	16	15	262	253	4	15
7	305	296	4	4	16	305	296	4	3
8	285	276	4	8	17	285	276	4	7
9	129	120	3	10	18	129	120	3	9
OUT	2,549	2,471	35		IN	2,549	2,471	35	
					TOTAL	5,098	4,942	70	
					STANDARD SCRATCH	68	67		

Tree positions indicated.
Copyright Tudor Journals Ltd.

Licknavar, Skibbereen.
Co. Cork.
Tel: (028) 21227.

LOCATION: Approx. two miles Skibbereen.
SECRETARY: Mr. Brit.
Tel: (028) 21227.
CAPTAIN: John McNamara.
Tel: (028) 21700.

A course with very few hazards and wide open fairways, excellent for the high handicapper. Extra nine holes opened in late 1993.

COURSE INFORMATION

Par 71; SSS 68; Length 5,967 yards; 5,279 metres.
Visitors: Welcome.
Opening Hours: Sunrise – sunset.

Avoid: Thursday afternoons (Men's Competition); Friday (Ladies Day).
Ladies: Welcome Fridays.
Green Fees: £18 for 18 holes. £10 for 9 holes. Club Hire and Caddy trolleys available.
Clubhouse Hours: 8.00am – 10.00pm (summer); irregular hours in winter.

Clubhouse Dress: Casual.
Clubhouse Facilities: All day, drinks, soups, sandwiches (summer). Full restaurant & bar food everyday.
Open Competitions: At fixed dates during summer and at Bank Holiday weekends.

SKIBBEREEN &
WEST CARBERY
GOLF CLUB

NO.	YARDS	PAR	S.I.	NO.	YARDS	PAR	S.I.
1	418	4	1	10	450	5	14
2	159	3	16	11	349	4	6
3	424	4	5	12	182	3	8
4	276	4	17	13	301	4	13
5	494	5	10	14	330	4	12
6	358	4	9	15	305	4	18
7	319	4	15	16	347	4	3
8	528	5	4	17	200	3	7
9	143	3	11	18	384	4	2
OUT	3,119	36		IN	2,848	35	
				TOTAL	5,967	71	
			STANDARD SCRATCH		68		

**Knockaveryy, Youghal,
Co. Cork.
Tel: (024) 92787.
Fax: (024) 92641.**

LOCATION: Knockaverry, Youghal.
SECRETARY: Margaret O'Sullivan.
Tel: (024) 92787.
PROFESSIONAL: Liam Burns.
ARCHITECT: Commander Harris.

Meadowland course offering
panoramic views of Youghal Bay and
Blackwater estuary. It is enjoyable for
high handicap golfers while still
offering a good test for the low
handicap golfer.

COURSE INFORMATION

**Par 70; SSS 69; Length
5,646 metres.
Visitors:** Welcome every day
except Wednesday; telephone
appointment required for
weekends.
Opening Hours:
9.00am – sunset.
Green Fees: £18 Mon – Fri;
£20 Sat / Sun.
Clubhouse Hours: 9.30am –
11.30pm. Variable in winter
months; full clubhouse facilities.
Clubhouse Dress: Casual.
Clubhouse Facilities: Snacks
available at all times; full meals
served from 10.30am –
9.00pm.
Open Competitions: One
week in July and first two
weeks in August and weekends
during summer.

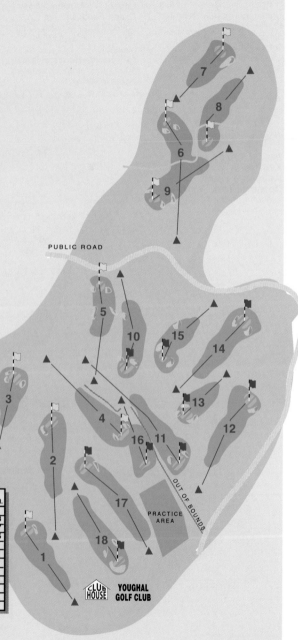

NO.	CHAMP METRES	MED. METRES	PAR	S.I.	NO.	CHAMP METRES	MED. METRES	PAR	S.I.
1	275	252	4	14	10	370	359	4	4
2	451	438	5	10	11	329	320	4	13
3	142	142	3	16	12	302	289	4	17
4	371	358	4	3	13	151	140	3	15
5	401	390	4	5	14	381	369	4	2
6	320	309	4	7	15	335	322	4	11
7	281	268	4	12	16	183	174	3	9
8	381	362	4	1	17	349	340	4	8
9	243	240	4	18	18	381	373	4	6
OUT	2865	2759	36		IN	2781	2686	34	
					TOTAL	5646	5445	70	
					STANDARD SCRATCH	69	68		

Bunker positions indicated.
Copyright Tudor Journals Ltd.

YOUGHAL
GOLF CLUB

CLUB HOUSE

302

ARDFERT

KERRY

Ardfert Golf Club, Sackville, Ardfert, Tralee, Co. Kerry.
Tel: (066) 34744.
Fax: (066) 34744.

LOCATION: Six miles from Tralee.
SECRETARY: Sinead Mansell.
Tel: (066) 34744.
PROFESSIONAL: Noel Cassidy and Brian Higgins.

A nine hole parkland course greatly compliments the scenic countryside with a river and lake featured in its design. It has 12 all weather driving range bays lessons available by appointment. Club hire is also available.

COURSE INFORMATION

Par 70; SSS 67; Length 5,118 Yards.
Visitors: Welcome.
Opening Hours: 9am – sunset.
Ladies: Welcome.

Juveniles: Welcome, lessons available.
Green Fees: £9 for 9 holes. £14 for 18 holes.
Clubhouse Hours: 9.00am – 9.30pm.
Clubhouse Dress: Casual.
Clubhouse Facilities: Tea, coffee & light snacks available everyday.

NO.	YARDS	PAR	S.I.	NO.	YARDS	PAR	S.I.
1	180	3	10	10	188	3	9
2	338	4	14	11	362	4	13
3	511	5	2	12	542	5	1
4	352	4	6	13	360	4	5
5	306	4	16	14	320	4	15
6	328	4	4	15	340	4	3
7	452	5	18	16	465	5	17
8	163	3	12	17	180	3	11
9	130	3	8	18	155	3	7
OUT	2,760	35		IN	2,912	35	
				TOTAL	5,672	70	
				STANDARD SCRATCH	67		

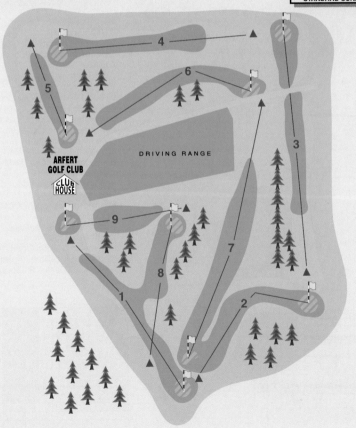

Copyright Tudor Journals Ltd.

303

Ballybunion Co Kerry.
Tel: (068) 27146.

LOCATION: Ballybunion.
SECRETARY: Jim McKenna.
Tel: (068) 27146.
PROFESSIONAL: Brian O'Callaghan.
Tel: (068) 27146.

The 'Old Course' at Ballybunion is world famous and is consistently rated amonst the top ten courses in the world. A magnificent course with several holes right on the shore and towering sandhills coming into play on all. One of Ireland's greatest golfing challenges it regularly receives golfing accolades from all over the world. (The Cashen Course was designed by Robert Treant Jones and is every bit as demanding (if not more) as the Old Course).

COURSE INFORMATION

Par 71; SSS 72; Length 6,542 yards.
Visitors: Welcome.
Opening Hours: 7.00am – 4.30pm.
Avoid: Weekends.
Ladies: Welcome
Green Fees: £55 (Old Course); £65 (Both Courses).
Juveniles: Welcome. Lessons available by prior arrangement; Club Hire available by prior arrangement; Caddy service available; Handicap Certificate required; telephone appointment required for green fees times.
Clubhouse Hours: 7.00am – 11.00pm;
Clubhouse Dress: Neat.
Clubhouse facilities:
Professional Shop Open; full clubhouse facilities; full catering facilities 9.00am – 9.00pm.

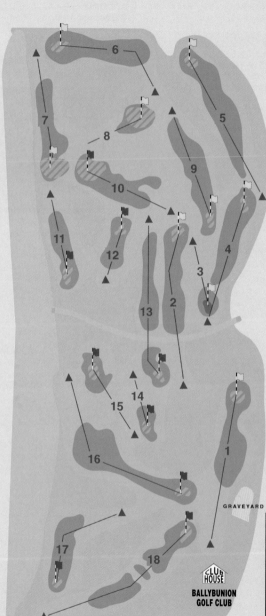

GRAVEYARD

CLUB HOUSE

BALLYBUNION GOLF CLUB

NO.	MEDAL YARDS	GEN. YARDS	PAR	S.I.	NO.	MEDAL YARDS	GEN. YARDS	PAR	S.I.
1	392	366	4	9	10	359	336	4	10
2	445	394	4	1	11	449	400	4	2
3	220	211	3	11	12	192	179	3	16
4	498	490	5	15	13	484	480	5	8
5	508	489	5	13	14	131	125	3	18
6	364	344	4	7	15	216	207	3	4
7	423	400	4	5	16	490	482	5	14
8	153	134	3	17	17	385	368	4	12
9	454	430	4	3	18	379	366	4	6
OUT	3,457	3,258	36		IN	3,085	2,943	35	
					TOTAL	6,542	6,201	71	
					STANDARD SCRATCH	72	70		

Ballybunion, Co Kerry.
Tel: (068) 27146.

LOCATION: Ballybunion.
SECRETARY: Jim McKenna.
Tel: (068) 27146.
PROFESSIONAL: Brian
O'Callaghan.
Tel: (068) 27146.

The 'Cashen Course' at Ballybunion
was designed by Robert Trent
Jones and is every bit as
demanding - if not more - than the
'Old Course'. Both courses enjoy
the benefit of the Atlantic coastline.
The remote location of the course
is instrumental in reducing the
number of casual players leaving
those on 'pilgrimage' with more
solitude.

COURSE INFORMATION

**Par 72; SSS 73; Length
6,278 yards.**
Visitors: Welcome.
Opening Hours: 7.00am –
5.30pm.
Avoid: Weekends.
Ladies: Welcome.
Green Fees: £30 (Cashen
Course); £72 (Both Courses).
Juveniles: Welcome. Lessons
available by prior
arrangement; Club Hire
available by prior
arrangement; Caddy service
available; Handicap Certificate
required; telephone
appointment required for green
fee times.
Clubhouse Hours: 7.00am –
11.00pm.
Clubhouse Dress: Neat.
Clubhouse Facilities:
Professional Shop open; full
clubhouse facilities; full
catering facilities 9.00am -
9.00pm.

BALLYBUNION
GOLF CLUB

NO.	MEDAL YARDS	GEN. YARDS	PAR	S.I.	NO.	MEDAL YARDS	GEN. YARDS	PAR	S.I.
1	324	312	4	11	10	432	399	4	2
2	146	140	3	17	11	377	359	4	8
3	237	223	4	13	12	154	141	3	18
4	395	374	4	1	13	350	325	4	10
5	400	355	4	7	14	378	373	4	6
6	487	476	5	3	15	155	143	3	16
7	199	145	3	15	16	314	303	4	12
8	479	476	5	9	17	605	585	5	4
9	368	361	4	5	18	478	451	5	14
OUT	3,035	2,826	36		IN	3,243	3,079	36	
					TOTAL	6,278	5,941	72	
					STANDARD SCRATCH	73	72		

305

Beaufort Golf Course, Churchtown, Beaufort, Killarney. Co. Kerry.
Tel: (064) 44440.
Fax: (064) 44752.

LOCATION: Seven miles west of Killarney, just off the N72.
SECRETARY: Colin Kelly.
Tel: (064) 44440.
ARHITECT: Arthur Spring.

Parkland, 6,605 Yds. Par 71. Situated in the centre of South West Ireland's golfing mecca. Just five miles from the world famous Killarney Golf Club. Course is surrounded by Kerry mountains and the back nine is dominated by the ruins of Castle Core.

COURSE INFORMATION

Par 71; SSS 72; Length 6,605 yards.
Visitors: Avoid 1.00pm –

2.00pm (members only).
Opening Hours: 7.30am until darkness.
Ladies: Welcome.
Juveniles: Permitted.
Green Fees: £25 weekdays, £30 weekends.
Clubhouse Hours: 7.30am until 11.00pm.
Clubhouse Dress: Informal but neat.
Clubhouse Facilities: Bar & bar food.

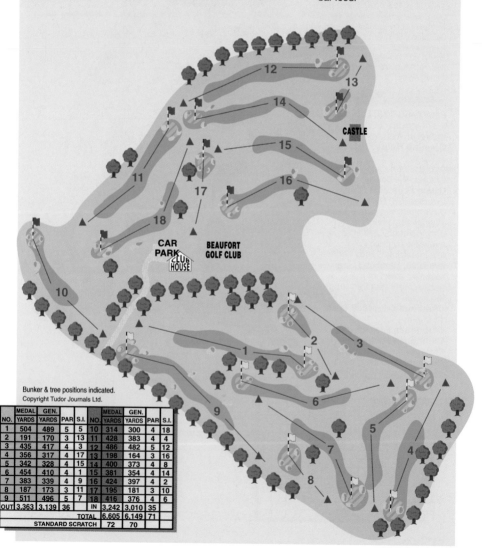

Bunker & tree positions indicated.
Copyright Tudor Journals Ltd.

NO.	MEDAL YARDS	GEN. YARDS	PAR	S.I.	NO.	MEDAL YARDS	GEN. YARDS	PAR	S.I.
1	504	489	5	5	10	314	300	4	18
2	191	170	3	13	11	428	383	4	4
3	435	417	4	3	12	486	482	5	12
4	356	317	4	17	13	198	164	3	16
5	342	328	4	15	14	400	373	4	8
6	454	410	4	1	15	381	354	4	14
7	383	339	4	9	16	424	397	4	2
8	187	173	3	11	17	195	181	3	10
9	511	496	5	7	18	416	376	4	6
OUT	3,363	3,139	36		IN	3,242	3,010	35	
					TOTAL	6,605	6,149	71	
					STANDARD SCRATCH		72	70	

Castlegregory Golf & Fishing Club, Stradbally, Castlegregory, Co. Kerry.
Tel: (066) 39444.

LOCATION: 2 miles west of Castlegregory.
SECRETARY: Matt Moloney.
Tel: (066) 39444.
ARCHITECT: Arthur Spring.

9 hole links course, 1 par 5 and 3 par 3's. Scenically situated between a fresh water lake and the sea.

COURSE INFORMATION

Par 68; SSS 68; Length 5,880 yards.
Visitors: Welcome.
Opening Hours: Early mornings – late evenings.
Avoid: Club competitions.
Ladies: Welcome.
Green Fees: £12.
Juveniles: Welcome.
Clubhouse Hours: 9.00am – 9.00pm.
Clubhouse Dress: Casual.

Clubhouse Facilities:
Catering facilities available.
Open Competitions:
All summer, Mens' and Ladies' clubs.

NO.	METRES	PAR	S.I.	NO.	METRES	PAR	S.I.
1	497	5	11	10	497	5	12
2	186	3	7	11	186	3	8
3	242	4	17	12	242	4	18
4	374	4	3	13	374	4	4
5	183	3	9	14	183	3	10
6	286	4	15	15	286	4	16
7	397	4	1	16	397	4	2
8	365	4	5	17	365	4	6
9	145	3	13	18	145	3	14
OUT	2,675	34		IN	2,675	34	
				TOTAL	5,350	68	
		STANDARD SCRATCH			68		

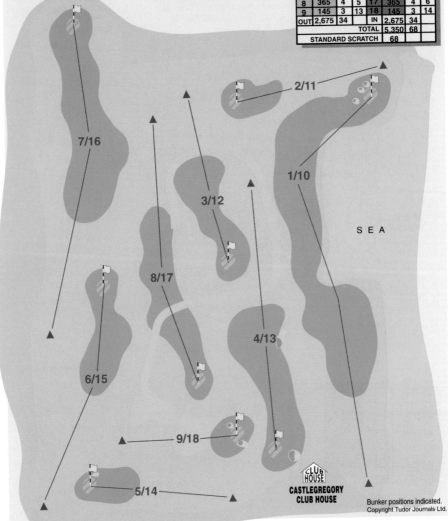

7/16

2/11

1/10

3/12

SEA

8/17

4/13

6/15

9/18

5/14

CLUB HOUSE
CASTLEGREGORY CLUB HOUSE

Bunker positions indicated.
Copyright Tudor Journals Ltd.

**Ballyoughterach,
Ballyferriter, Co. Kerry.
Tel: (066) 56255/56408.
Fax: (066) 56409.**

LOCATION: Dingle Penisula.
HON. SECRETARY: Tomás Ó Sé.
MANAGER: Steve Fahy.
PROFESSIONAL: Dermot
O'Connor.
Tel: (066) 56255/56408.
ARCHITECT: E. Hackett /
Christy O'Connor Jnr.

A links course with wind proving a big factor as it sweeps in from the Atlantic Ocean. The design of the course uses the natural terrain and has the advantage of the area's marvellous turf. A setting for traditional golf with panoramic surroundings.

COURSE INFORMATION

**Par 72; SSS 71; Length
6,690 yards; 6,074 metres.
Visitors:** Welcome at all times.
Opening Hours: Sunrise – sunset.
Avoid: Sunday afternoons.
Ladies: Welcome.
Green Fees: £21 per round & £27 per day Sat, Sun & Bank Hols.

Lessons available by prior arrangements; Club Hire available, Caddy service available by prior arrangements.
Juveniles: Welcome (accompanied by adult June – Aug).
Clubhouse Hours: 8.00am – 9.00pm; Professional Shop open.
Clubhouse Dress: Casual.
Clubhouse Facilities: Full clubhouse facilities everyday.
Open Competitions: Easter Sunday; Toyota Open 4th – 6th September.

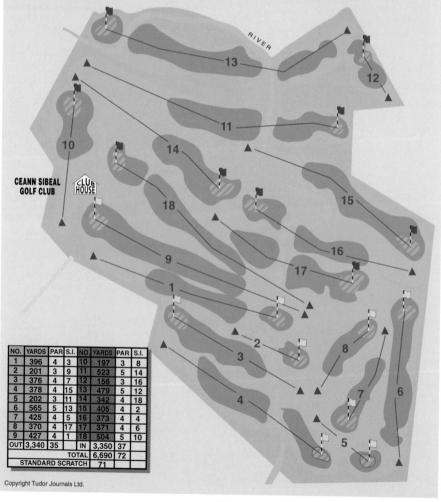

NO.	YARDS	PAR	S.I.	NO.	YARDS	PAR	S.I.
1	396	4	3	10	197	3	8
2	201	3	9	11	523	5	14
3	376	4	7	12	156	3	16
4	378	4	15	13	479	5	12
5	202	3	11	14	342	4	18
6	565	5	13	15	405	4	2
7	425	4	5	16	373	4	4
8	370	4	17	17	371	4	6
9	427	4	1	18	504	5	10
OUT	3,340	35		IN	3,350	37	
				TOTAL	6,690	72	
		STANDARD SCRATCH		71			

**Dooks, Glenbeigh,
Co. Kerry.
Tel: (066) 68205/68200.
Fax: (066) 68476.**

LOCATION: Four miles from
Killorglin.
SECRETARY: M. Shanahan.
Tel: (066) 67370.

Dooks-a word derived from Gaelic
'drumhac' meaning sand-bank - is a
testing 18 hole links situated in one
of the most picturesque corners of
the Ring of Kerry. The golf course

is laid out on one of three stretches
of sand-dunes at the head of
picturesque Dingle Bay.

COURSE INFORMATION

**Par 70; SSS 68; Length
6,572 yards; 6,010 metres.
Visitors:** Welcome.
Opening Hours: Sunrise -
sunset.
Avoid: Weekends.
Ladies: Welcome. Caddy
service available; Handicap

Certificate required.
Green Fees: £20 per round
any day.
Clubhouse Hours: 9.00am –
11.00pm.
Clubhouse Dress: Casual.
Clubhouse Facilities:
11.00am – 7.00pm.
Open Competitions: By
invitation.

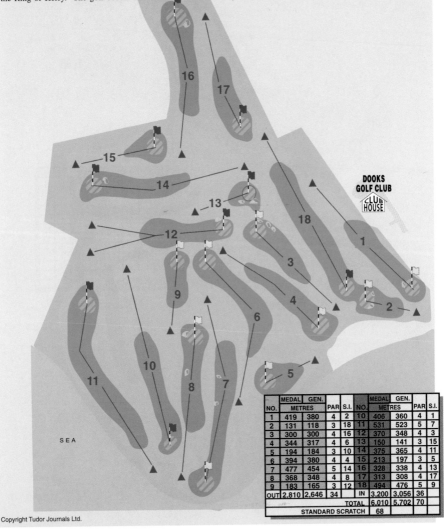

DOOKS
GOLF CLUB
CLUB
HOUSE

SEA

NO.	MEDAL METRES	GEN. METRES	PAR	S.I.	NO.	MEDAL METRES	GEN. METRES	PAR	S.I.
1	419	380	4	2	10	406	360	4	1
2	131	118	3	18	11	531	523	5	7
3	300	300	4	16	12	370	348	4	3
4	344	317	4	6	13	150	141	3	15
5	194	184	3	10	14	375	365	4	11
6	394	380	4	4	15	213	197	3	5
7	477	454	5	14	16	328	338	4	13
8	368	348	4	8	17	313	308	4	17
9	183	165	3	12	18	494	476	5	9
OUT	2,810	2,646	34		IN	3,200	3,056	36	
					TOTAL	6,010	5,702	70	
					STANDARD SCRATCH		68		

Kenmare, Co. Kerry.
Tel: (064) 41291.

LOCATION: Turn left at top of town.
SECRETARY / MANAGER:
M. MacGearailt.
Tel: (064) 41291 or 41636.
SECRETARY (for bookings):
Siobhan O'Callaghan.

The course was increased recently from nine to eighteen holes. It is picturesque and mainly very sheltered which leaves it playable in all kinds of weather. It also has the advantage of being sited in one of Ireland's areas of outstanding scenery.

COURSE INFORMATION

Par 71/70; SSS 69/68;
Length 6,003 yards.
Visitors: Welcome at any time. Booking in advance is advisable (especially weekends).
Opening Hours: Everyday, peak time May – Sept 6am – 7pm. Off peak time 9am – 6pm.
Ladies: Welcome.
Juveniles: Welcome, to be accompanied by adult.
Green Fees: £16 everyday

societies £13; Club Hire £5; Caddy trolley £1.
Clubhouse Hours: 7.00am – sunset.
Clubhouse Dress: Casual.
Clubhouse Facilities: Tea, coffee & snacks 8.00am – sunset.
Open Competitions: Ladies Open April; Ladies Scratch Cup July; Mitsubishi fourball June; Kenmare open day July; Scratch Cups July; GAA Classic July / Aug; The Brothers Classic Sept.

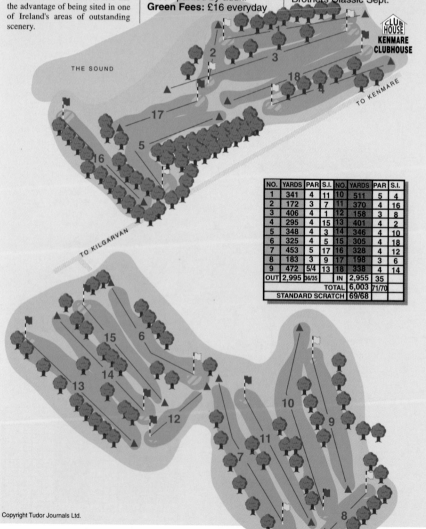

NO.	YARDS	PAR	S.I.	NO.	YARDS	PAR	S.I.
1	341	4	11	10	511	5	4
2	172	3	7	11	370	4	16
3	406	4	1	12	158	3	8
4	295	4	15	13	401	4	2
5	348	4	3	14	346	4	10
6	325	4	5	15	305	4	18
7	453	5	17	16	328	4	12
8	183	3	9	17	198	3	6
9	472	5/4	13	18	338	4	14
OUT	2,995	36/35		IN	2,955	35	
				TOTAL	6,003	71/70	
				STANDARD SCRATCH	69/68		

The Kerries,
Tralee, Co.Kerry.
Tel: (066) 22112.

LOCATION: 1 mile west of Tralee Town.
SECRETARY: Helen Barrett.
Tel: (066) 22112.
ARCHITECT: Dr. Arthur Spring.

9 hole Parklands course in an attractive setting overlooking Tralee Bay and the Dingle Peninsula.

COURSE INFORMATION

Par 70; SSS 68; Length 5,720 yards. Competition yds; 5,944.
Visitors: Welcome.
Opening Hours: Daylight hours.
Avoid: Saturday (10am – noon) & Sunday (8am –noon).
Ladies: Welcome.
Green Fees: 18 holes £15; 9 holes £9.
Juveniles: Welcome.

Clubhouse Hours:
8.00am – 9.00pm (summer); 9.30am – 4.00pm (winter).
Clubhouse Dress: Casual.
Clubhouse Facilities:
Changing room & showers; Snack & Bar facilities. New Clubhouse opened April 1998.

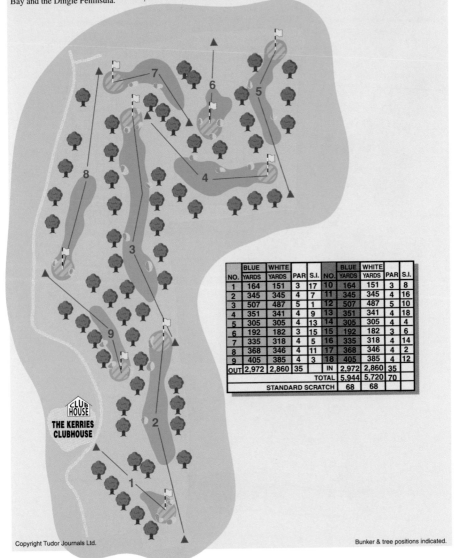

NO.	BLUE YARDS	WHITE YARDS	PAR	S.I.	NO.	BLUE YARDS	WHITE YARDS	PAR	S.I.
1	164	151	3	17	10	164	151	3	8
2	345	345	4	7	11	345	345	4	16
3	507	487	5	1	12	507	487	5	10
4	351	341	4	9	13	351	341	4	18
5	305	305	4	13	14	305	305	4	4
6	192	182	3	15	15	192	182	3	6
7	335	318	4	5	16	335	318	4	14
8	368	346	4	11	17	368	346	4	2
9	405	385	4	3	18	405	385	4	12
OUT	2,972	2,860	35		IN	2,972	2,860	35	
					TOTAL	5,944	5,720	70	
					STANDARD SCRATCH	68	68		

THE KERRIES CLUBHOUSE

Bunker & tree positions indicated.

Mahony's Point, Killarney, Co. Kerry.
Tel: (064) 31034 / 31242 / 33899.

LOCATION: Two miles west of Killarney.
SECRETARY: Tom Prendergast. Tel: (064) 31034 Fax: (064) 33065.
PROFESSIONAL: Tony Coveney. Tel: (064) 31615.
ARCHITECT: Sir Guy Campbell. (Mahony's Point).

Two excellent parkland courses occupying a site of great natural beauty, both courses adjacent to Lough Leane, with the mountains of Kerry rising on the other side of the lake. The additional eighteen holes were completed in 1971 and the new holes were mixed with the old to form the two courses – 'Killeen' and Mahony's Point'

COURSE INFORMATION

Par 72; SSS 72; Length 6,164 metres (Mahony's Point).
Visitors: Welcome..
Opening Hours: 7.30am – 6.00pm.
Avoid: Sunday.
Ladies: Welcome to play every day.
Green Fees: £38 per round. Certificate of Handicap required.
Juveniles: Welcome to play every day.
Clubhouse Hours: 7.30am – 11.30pm.
Clubhouse Dress: Casual.
Clubhouse Facilities: Professional shop. Lunches and dinners all day.

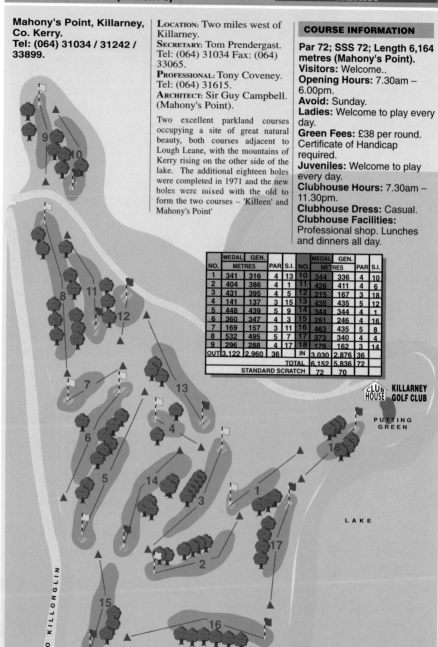

NO.	MEDAL METRES	GEN. METRES	PAR	S.I.	NO.	MEDAL METRES	GEN. METRES	PAR	S.I.
1	341	316	4	13	10	344	336	4	10
2	404	386	4	1	11	426	411	4	6
3	431	395	4	5	12	215	167	3	18
4	141	137	3	15	13	435	435	5	12
5	448	439	5	9	14	344	344	4	1
6	360	347	4	3	15	251	246	4	16
7	169	157	3	11	16	463	435	5	8
8	532	495	5	7	17	373	340	4	4
9	296	288	4	17	18	179	162	3	14
OUT	3,122	2,960	36		IN	3,030	2,876	36	
					TOTAL	6,152	5,836	72	
					STANDARD SCRATCH	72	70		

CLUB HOUSE   KILLARNEY GOLF CLUB

PUTTING GREEN

LAKE

TO KILLORGLIN

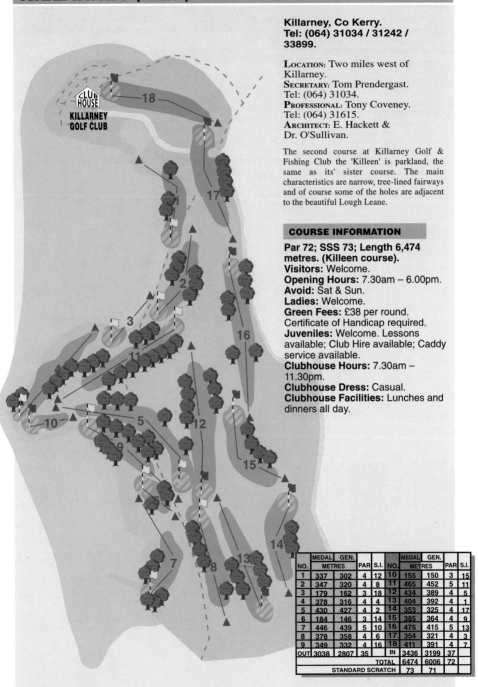

Killarney, Co Kerry.
Tel: (064) 31034 / 31242 / 33899.

Location: Two miles west of Killarney.
Secretary: Tom Prendergast.
Tel: (064) 31034.
Professional: Tony Coveney.
Tel: (064) 31615.
Architect: E. Hackett & Dr. O'Sullivan.

The second course at Killarney Golf & Fishing Club the 'Killeen' is parkland, the same as its' sister course. The main characteristics are narrow, tree-lined fairways and of course some of the holes are adjacent to the beautiful Lough Leane.

COURSE INFORMATION

Par 72; SSS 73; Length 6,474 metres. (Killeen course).
Visitors: Welcome.
Opening Hours: 7.30am – 6.00pm.
Avoid: Sat & Sun.
Ladies: Welcome.
Green Fees: £38 per round.
Certificate of Handicap required.
Juveniles: Welcome. Lessons available; Club Hire available; Caddy service available.
Clubhouse Hours: 7.30am – 11.30pm.
Clubhouse Dress: Casual.
Clubhouse Facilities: Lunches and dinners all day.

NO.	MEDAL METRES	GEN.	PAR	S.I.	NO.	MEDAL METRES	GEN.	PAR	S.I.
1	337	302	4	12	10	155	150	3	15
2	347	320	4	8	11	465	452	5	11
3	179	162	3	18	12	434	389	4	5
4	378	316	4	4	13	404	392	4	1
5	430	427	4	2	14	353	325	4	17
6	184	146	3	14	15	385	364	4	9
7	446	439	4	10	16	475	415	5	13
8	378	358	4	6	17	354	321	4	3
9	349	332	4	16	18	411	391	4	7
OUT	3038	2807	35		IN	3436	3199	37	
					TOTAL	6474	6006	72	
					STANDARD SCRATCH	73	71		

**Killorglin Golf Club,
Steelrue,
Killorglin. Co. Kerry.
Tel: (066) 61979/62078.
Fax. (066) 61437.**

Location: Two miles from
Killorglin, on Tralee Road, 14
miles from Kilarney.
Secretary: Billy Dodd.
Tel: (066) 61979.
Architect: Eddie Hackett.

Eddie Hackett has made marvellous
use of the dramatic physical features
of the lands in providing golf shots

that are delightful & challenging
territory in Ireland. It offers a new &
exciting challenge to visiting golfers.

COURSE INFORMATION

**Par 73; SSS 71; Length
6,497 yards.
Visitors:** Welcome at all
times.
Opening Hours: Sunrise -
sunset.
Ladies: Welcome at
all times.
Green Fees: Mon - Fri £14;
Sat, Sun & Bank Hols £16.

Juveniles: Welcome if
accompanied by an adult.
Lessons by prior
arrangement.
Clubhouse Hours: 8.30am –
11.30pm.
Clubhouse Dress: Smart /
casual.
Clubhouse Facilites:
Pro-shop, Bar and food all
day everyday. Caddies
available by prior
arrangement. For reservations
tel: Eileen or Billy.

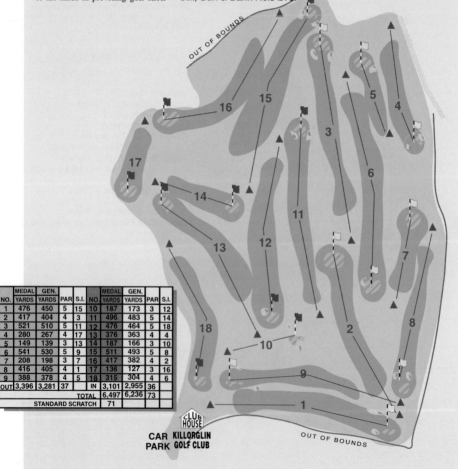

	MEDAL	GEN.				MEDAL	GEN.		
NO.	YARDS	YARDS	PAR	S.I.	NO.	YARDS	YARDS	PAR	S.I.
1	476	450	5	15	10	187	173	3	12
2	417	404	4	3	11	496	483	5	14
3	521	510	5	11	12	476	464	5	18
4	280	267	4	17	13	376	363	4	4
5	149	139	3	13	14	187	166	3	10
6	541	530	5	9	15	511	493	5	8
7	208	198	3	7	16	417	382	4	2
8	416	405	4	1	17	136	127	3	16
9	388	378	4	5	18	315	304	4	6
OUT	3,396	3,281	37		IN	3,101	2,955	36	
					TOTAL	6,497	6,236	73	
					STANDARD SCRATCH	71			

CAR **KILLORGLIN**
PARK **GOLF CLUB**

Bunker positions indicated.
Copyright Tudor Journals Ltd.

314

Parknasilla Great Southern Hotel, Sneem, Co. Kerry.
Tel: (064) 45122.

LOCATION: Parknasilla.
SECRETARY: Mr. J. Feeney.
Tel: (064) 45122.
PROFESSIONAL: Charles McCarthy.
Tel: (064) 45172.

Well laid out course in beautiful scenery overlooking Kenmare Bay. The course is part of the Parknasilla Great Southern Hotel and golfers have the added advantage of having these facilities available to them.

COURSE INFORMATION

Par 69; SSS 64; Length 4,886 yards; 4,467 metres.
Visitors: Welcome.
Opening Hours: 8.00am – 7.00pm.
Ladies: Welcome.
Green Fees: £10 – 9 holes; £15 – 18 holes.

Juveniles: Welcome. Lessons available by prior arrangement; Club Hire available; Caddy service available by prior arrangment; telephone appointment required.
Clubhouse Dress: Casual.
Clubhouse Facilities: Full catering facilities at hotel, a half mile away.
Open Competitions: Small competitions throughout the year.

NO.	YARDS	PAR	S.I.	NO.	YARDS	PAR	S.I.
1	314	4	7	10	269	4	10
2	116	3	17	11	116	3	18
3	432	4	3	12	477	5	6
4	279	4	13	13	278	4	14
5	275	4	11	14	275	4	12
6	251	4	5	15	255	4	4
7	96	3	15	16	101	3	16
8	383	4	1	17	392	4	2
9	283	4	9	18	294	4	8
OUT	2,429	34		IN	2,457	35	
				TOTAL	4,886	69	
				STANDARD SCRATCH	64		

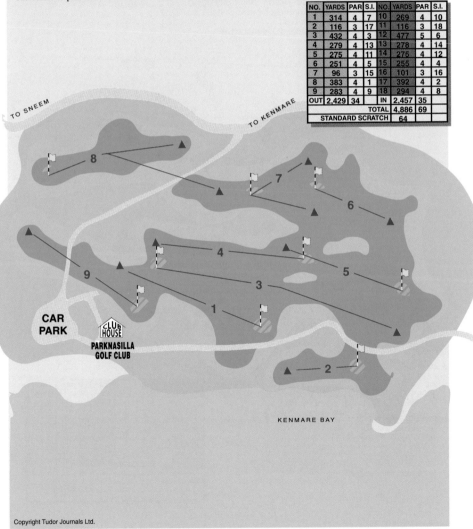

TO SNEEM

TO KENMARE

CAR PARK

CLUB HOUSE
PARKNASILLA GOLF CLUB

KENMARE BAY

**Ring of Kerry Golf Club,
Templenoe, Kenmare,
Co. Kerry.
Tel: (064) 42000.**

LOCATION: 4 miles from
Kenmare, Co. Kerry.
ARCHITECT: Roger Jones Golf
Associates, Killarney.
CONCEPT DESIGNER: Eddie Hacket.

One of the newest additions to the
Co. Kerry circuit, with panoramic
views of Kenmare Bay from every
hole. Described as 'world class' in
Ireland to have its fairways newly
built from sand. Full drainage and
irrigation will ensure a year round
facility. Situated just 25 miles from
Killarney and 4 miles from Kenmare,
this will be a popular course in the
Kingdom of Kerry. It will test serious
golfers from the back tees and provide
equal enjoyment for all from the more
forward ones.

COURSE INFORMATION

**Par 72; SSS TBA; Length
6,420 yards.
Visitors:** All day every day.
Opening Hours: Sunrise to
sunset.
Ladies: No restrictions.

Green Fees: £27 Mon – Fri.
£30 Sat/Sun.
Juveniles: Welcome. Must be
accompanied by an adult.
Clubhouse Hours:
Sunrise – sunset.
Clubhouse Dress:
Casual but smart.
Clubhouse Facilities:
Temporary Clubhouse until
December 1998. Full facilities
thereafter.

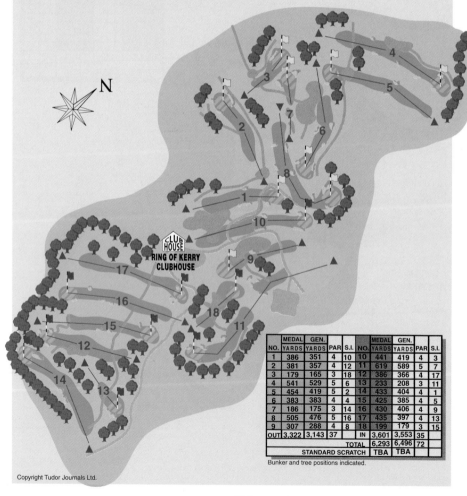

NO.	MEDAL YARDS	GEN. YARDS	PAR	S.I.	NO.	MEDAL YARDS	GEN. YARDS	PAR	S.I.
1	386	351	4	10	10	441	419	4	3
2	381	357	4	12	11	619	589	5	7
3	179	165	3	18	12	386	366	4	17
4	541	529	5	6	13	233	208	3	11
5	454	419	5	2	14	433	404	4	1
6	383	383	4	4	15	425	385	4	5
7	186	175	3	14	16	430	406	4	9
8	505	476	5	16	17	435	397	4	13
9	307	288	4	8	18	199	179	3	15
OUT	3,322	3,143	37		IN	3,601	3,553	35	
					TOTAL	6,293	6,496	72	
					STANDARD SCRATCH	TBA	TBA		

Bunker and tree positions indicated.

Copyright Tudor Journals Ltd.

West Barrow, Ardfert, Co. Kerry.
Tel: (066) 36379.
Fax: (066) 36008.

LOCATION: Barrow.
SECRETARY: Michael O'Brien.
HON. SECRETARY: Brendan Harney.
ARCHITECT: Arnold Palmer.
Tel: (066) 36379.

Challenging course with the first nine relatively flat holes, set on cliff top; the second nine by contrast are built on dunes. The course is set amidst the beautiful scenery associated with the Kerry region. Tralee is the first Arnold Palmer designed course in Europe.

Clubhouse Hours: 10.00am – 10.00pm (summer); 10.00am – 6.00pm (winter) Golf Shop open.
Clubhouse Dress: Casual – no beach wear or jeans.
Clubhouse Facilities: Lunch, dinner, snacks available all day everyday.

COURSE INFORMATION

Par 71; SSS 73; Length 6,252 metres.
Visitors: Welcome up to 4.30pm 1st April – 21st October. Limited green fees Weds / Weekends.
Avoid: Weekdays 1.30 – 2.30pm & 4.30pm onwards. Saturdays 11.00am – 1.30pm. Sundays 11.30am – 1.00pm.
Opening Hours: 8.00am – sunset (summer); 9.00am – sunset (winter).
Members: Wednesdays (June, July & August).
Green Fees: £45 Mon – Sat; Sun – members & guests only.
Juveniles: Welcome. Must be accompanied by an adult after 6pm. Caddy service available by prior arrangment; Handicap Certificate required. Telephone appointment required.

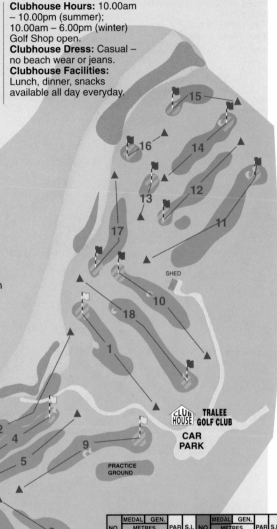

NO.	MEDAL METRES	GEN. METRES	PAR	S.I.	NO.	MEDAL METRES	GEN. METRES	PAR	S.I.
1	368	355	4	12	10	385	370	4	9
2	542	516	5	2	11	530	514	5	13
3	183	140	3	14	12	417	400	4	1
4	388	366	4	8	13	145	139	3	15
5	391	374	4	4	14	367	361	4	5
6	389	383	4	10	15	273	267	4	17
7	143	135	3	18	16	181	152	3	11
8	354	339	4	6	17	323	304	4	7
9	451	443	5	16	18	422	403	4	3
OUT	3,209	3,051	36		IN	3,043	2,910	35	
					TOTAL	6,252	5,961	71	
					STANDARD SCRATCH	73	71		

Bunker & tree positions indicated.
Copyright Tudor Journals Ltd.

Ring of Kerry, Waterville, Co. Kerry.
Tel: (066) 74102
Fax: (066) 74482.

LOCATION: One mile outside village.
SECRETARY: Noel J. Cronin. Tel: (066) 74102.
PROFESSIONAL: Liam Higgins. Tel: (066) 74237.
ARCHITECT: J. A. Mulcahy / E. Hackett.

Waterville features finely manicured fairways and greens with limited water on the course. Panoramic views from the back nine of the Atlantic Ocean and Kerry Mountains. Spectacular Par 3's. Driving Range on course. The course is long, however not hilly, so a pleasant 18 hole walk is enjoyed. Each hole has individual characteristics and every club in the bag will be needed.

COURSE INFORMATION

Par 72; SSS 74;
Length 7184 yards.
Visitors: Welcome any day.
Opening Hours: 7.00am – 7.30pm.
Ladies: Welcome.
Green Fees: £45 inc VAT.
Juveniles: Welcome. Lessons available by prior arrangements; Club Hire available; Caddy service available (May – Sept); Handicap Certificate required for open competitions; telephone appointment advised.
Clubhouse Hours: 7.00am – 11.00pm; full clubhouse facilities.
Clubhouse Facilities: Breakfast on request; Dining room facilities available from 11.30am – 7pm. Snacks served everyday in the bar.
Open Competitions: Open Week June / July by invitation.

NO.	MEDAL YARDS	GEN. YARDS	PAR	S.I.	NO.	MEDAL YARDS	GEN. YARDS	PAR	S.I.
1	430	395	4	11	10	475	450	4	2
2	469	425	4	1	11	496	477	5	10
3	417	362	4	3	12	200	154	3	18
4	179	160	3	15	13	518	480	5	14
5	595	525	5	9	14	456	410	4	4
6	371	343	4	13	15	392	365	4	6
7	178	155	3	17	16	350	330	4	12
8	435	410	4	5	17	196	153	3	16
9	445	405	4	7	18	582	550	5	8
OUT	3,519	3,180	35		IN	3,665	3,369	37	
					TOTAL	7,184	6,549	72	
					STANDARD SCRATCH	74	72		

Adare Golf Club, Adare Manor Hotel, Adare, Co. Limerick.
Tel: (061) 396566.
Fax: (061) 396124.

ARHITECT: Robert Trent Jones Snr.
GOLF ADMINISTRATOR: Linda Cross.

New course opened in 1995 in the grounds of Adare Manor and separate (confusingly) to the older established Adare Manor. This new championship course measures 7,138 yards off the Championship tees. The design of the course with four tees on each hole (and the Maigue River which creates a sense of beauty and challenge) ensures that every level of golfer will enjoy their game.

COURSE INFORMATION

Par 72; Length 7,138 Yards.
Visitors: Welcome.
Opening Hours: 7.30am – Dark (summer). 8.00am –Dark (winter).
Green Fees: £36 per round & £55 per day (residents). £45 per round & £65 per day (non residents). Group rate; 20–39 £39: 40 plus £35 (VAT inc.). Lessons, Club Hire (£15 a set) and Caddy service (£16 per bag or £3 for trolley) available by prior arrangement.
Clubhouse Dress: Formal.
Clubhouse Facilities: Tack Room bar and restaurant in Adare Manor Hotel. Driving Range open 7 days a week, £3 for a bucket of 40 balls.

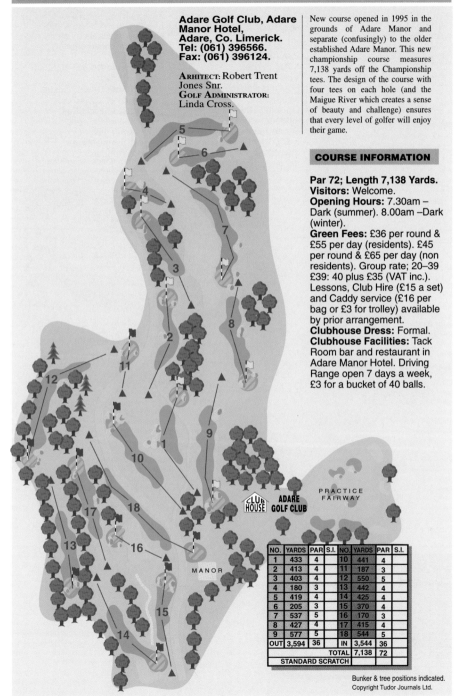

NO.	YARDS	PAR	S.I.	NO.	YARDS	PAR	S.I.
1	433	4		10	441	4	
2	413	4		11	187	3	
3	403	4		12	550	5	
4	180	3		13	442	4	
5	419	4		14	425	4	
6	205	3		15	370	4	
7	537	5		16	170	3	
8	427	4		17	415	4	
9	577	5		18	544	5	
OUT	3,594	36		IN	3,544	36	
				TOTAL	7,138	72	
STANDARD SCRATCH							

Bunker & tree positions indicated.
Copyright Tudor Journals Ltd.

319

Adare, Co. Limerick.
Tel: (061) 396204.

LOCATION: Ten miles from
Limerick City.
SECRETARY: Milo Spillane.
Tel: (061) 396204.

The original and more traditional
course in Adare, founded in 1900, is
called Adare Manor but is not the
new championship course in the
grounds of Adare Manor. Adare is a
parkland course, which is
particularly scenic. The Abbey and
Desmond Castle are unique features
to the course. There are three Par
5's and six Par 3's over the eighteen
holes. The fairways are narrow and
well maintained.

COURSE INFORMATION

**Par 70; SSS 69; Length
5,706 yards.**
Visitors: Welcome all days.
Booking required for
weekends.
Opening Hours:
9.00am – sunset.
Green Fees: £15 Mon – Fri.
& £20 Weekends.
Juveniles: Welcome, but
accompanied by an adult.

Club Hire available; Caddy
service available by prior
arrangements (summer
months).
Clubhouse Hours: 10.00am
closing time.
Clubhouse Dress: Casual –
no shorts or sports wear.
Clubhouse Facilities:
Snacks and Bar food
(booked in advance).
Open Competitions:
June & August.

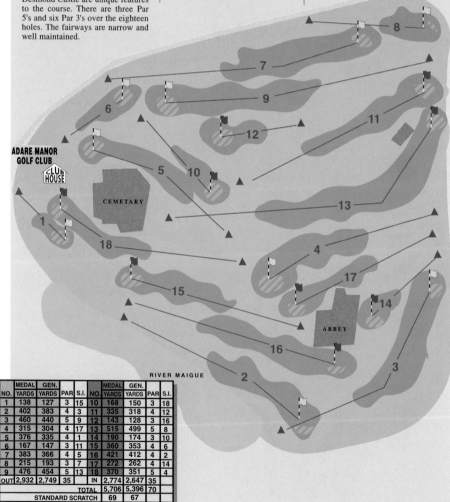

NO.	MEDAL YARDS	GEN. YARDS	PAR	S.I.	NO.	MEDAL YARDS	GEN. YARDS	PAR	S.I.
1	138	127	3	15	10	168	150	3	18
2	402	383	4	3	11	335	318	4	12
3	460	440	5	9	12	143	128	3	16
4	315	304	4	17	13	515	499	5	8
5	376	335	4	1	14	190	174	3	10
6	167	147	3	11	15	360	353	4	6
7	383	366	4	5	16	421	412	4	2
8	215	193	3	7	17	272	262	4	14
9	476	454	5	13	18	370	351	5	4
OUT	2,932	2,749	35		IN	2,774	2,647	35	
					TOTAL	5,706	5,396	70	
	STANDARD SCRATCH		69	67					

CASTLETROY

Castletroy,
Co. Limerick.
Tel: (061) 335261.

LOCATION: Less than three miles from Limerick City on N7 to Dublin.
SECRETARY: Laurence Hayes.
Tel: (061) 335753.

Parkland course with out of bounds on the left for the first two holes. Well maintained fairways are tree lined demanding accuracy off the tee. The long Par 5 10th features a narrow entrance to the green with a stream to catch the more adventurous. The par 3 13th features a panoramic view from the tee while the picturesque 18th is a stern test to finish with the green guarded by bunkers on both sides.

COURSE INFORMATION

Par 71; SSS 71; Length 6,335 yards, 5,793 metres.
Visitors: Welcome most weekday mornings. Some afternoons may be booked by societies (check in advance).
Avoid: Thursday afternoon; Weekends; Tuesday is Ladies Day (some restriction).
Green Fees: £22 (£12 with a member). Group rate of 12+ £15.
Juveniles: Must be accompanied by an adult. Club Hire available; Caddy service available by prior arrangement.

Clubhouse Hours:
8.00am – 11.30pm.
Clubhouse Dress:
Casual but neat.
Clubhouse Facilities: Bar snacks available all day everyday; last orders for full meals 9.30pm. Bar service as per licencing hours. Recently built clubhouse.

NO.	METRES	PAR	S.I.	NO.	METRES	PAR	S.I.
1	339	4	4	10	458	5	11
2	323	4	10	11	326	4	9
3	337	4	8	12	306	4	5
4	335	4	12	13	159	3	15
5	396	4	2	14	312	4	13
6	420	5	18	15	407	4	1
7	134	3	16	16	116	3	17
8	330	4	6	17	367	4	7
9	329	4	14	18	399	4	3
OUT	2,943	36		IN	2,850	35	
					TOTAL	5,793	71
				STANDARD SCRATCH		71	

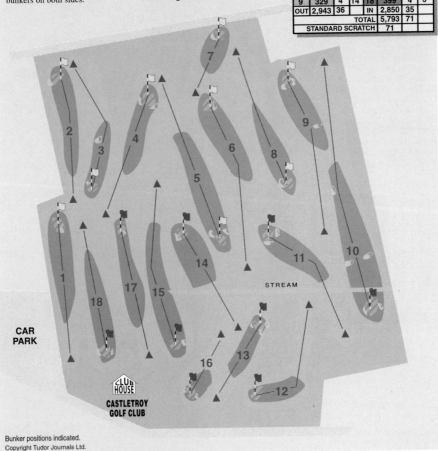

CAR PARK

STREAM

CLUB HOUSE

CASTLETROY GOLF CLUB

Bunker positions indicated.
Copyright Tudor Journals Ltd.

Killeline golf Club, Cork Road, Newcastle West, Co. Limerick.
Tel: (069) 61600.

LOCATION: 25 miles from Limerick City, off Killarney Road.
SECRETARY: John McCoy.
Tel: (069) 61600.

Killeline is an 18 hole parkland course. Wooded with over 3000 decidious trees giving all fairways a clear definition, two good par '5's and four challenging par '3's. In process of reconstructing the course up to championship link par 72.

COURSE INFORMATION

Par 70; SSS 68; Length 6,007 yards.
Visitors: Welcome, Sundays by arrangement only.
Opening Hours: 9.00am – sunset.
Avoid: Sundays.
Ladies: Welcome.
Green Fees: £11 Mon – Fri. £12 Sat/Sun.
Juveniles: Welcome but accompanied by adult.
Clubhouse Hours: 10.00am – closing time.
Clubhouse Dress: Casual, no shorts.
Clubhouse Facilities: Bar food, full meals (booked in advance) & pro-shop.
Open Competitions: June, July & August.

NO.	YARDS	PAR	S.I.	NO.	METRES	PAR	S.I.
1	282	4	17	10	331	4	9
2	127	3	15	11	361	4	7
3	290	4	18	12	341	4	6
4	336	4	8	13	470	5	13
5	425	4	3	14	144	3	16
6	451	5	10	15	330	4	11
7	409	4	4	16	180	3	14
8	432	4	2	17	408	4	1
9	160	3	12	18	407	4	5
OUT	2,912	35		IN	2,972	35	
				TOTAL	5,884	70	
	STANDARD SCRATCH				68		

TO DROMCOLLOGHER

CAR PARK   CLUB HOUSE

KILLELINE CLUBHOUSE

NEWCASTLE WEST
1/2 KM

Bunker and tree positions indicated.

Ballyclough, Limerick.
Tel: (061) 414083/415146.

LOCATION: Three miles South
of Limerick City.
SECRETARY: Declan
McDonogh.
Tel: (061) 415146.
PROFESSIONAL: John Cassidy.
Tel: (061) 412492.

A parkland course with tree lined
fairways. Pleasant surroundings,
situated on a hill overlooking the
city of Limerick.

COURSE INFORMATION

Par 72; SSS 71; Length
6,551 yards; 5,656 metres.
Visitors: Welcome up to
4.00pm Mon, Wed, Fri;
Thurs am only.
Opening Hours: 8.30am –
sunset.
Avoid: Tuesday and
weekends.
Ladies: Welcome Tuesdays.
Lessons available by prior
arrangements; Club Hire
available; Caddy service
available by prior
arrangements; telephone
appointment advisable.
Green Fees: £22.50 (with
member £13).
Clubhouse Hours: 9.30am –
11.00pm; full clubhouse
facilities.
Clubhouse Dress: Casual.
Clubhouse Facilities: Full
service from 12.00 noon.
Open Competitions: Mainly
holiday weekends.

NO.	MEDAL METRES	GEN.	PAR	S.I.	NO.	MEDAL METRES	GEN.	PAR	S.I.
1	326	309	4	9	10	397	379	4	2
2	439	426	5	15	11	341	328	4	11
3	427	419	4	1	12	372	370	4	6
4	349	337	4	5	13	280	273	4	17
5	158	153	3	16	14	140	132	3	14
6	466	456	5	7	15	344	297	4	4
7	378	369	4	3	16	305	287	4	10
8	122	110	3	18	17	344	318	4	8
9	450	438	5	13	18	318	312	4	12
OUT	3,115	3,017	37		IN	2,841	2,696	35	
					TOTAL	5,956	5,713	72	
					STANDARD SCRATCH	71			

Bunker positions indicated.
Copyright Tudor Journals Ltd.

REAR
ENTRANCE

CLUB
HOUSE

LIMERICK
GOLF CLUB

MAIN
ENTRANCE

Limerick County Golf & Country Club, Ballyneety. Co. Limerick.
Tel: (061) 351881.
Fax: (061) 351384.
E-Mail: lcgolf@iol.ie
WEBSITE:
www.golfclubireland.com/
www.golfing-ireland.com

LOCATION: 5 miles south of Limerick City on the R512, direction Kilmallock.
SECRETARY: Tony Larkin.
Tel: (061) 351881.
PROFESSIONAL: Philip Murphy.
Tel: (061) 351784.
ARCHITECT: Des Smyth & Associates.

18 hole championship standard golf course, set on 230 acres of undulating sand-based terrain, ensuring that it is playable 12 months of the year. The course boasts many interesting sand and water hazards. A uniquely-shaped circular clubhouse provides panoramic views of over 50% of the course and the surrounding countryside. Other facilities include driving range, three hole short-game area, 4 star luxury holiday cottage accommodation.

COURSE INFORMATION

Par 72; SSS 74; Length 6712 yards, 6137 metres.
Visitors: Welcome at all times.
Opening Hours: 7.00am to sunset.

Ladies: Max. handicap 36.
Green Fees: Mon – Fri £22. Sat / Sun £25.
Juveniles: Welcome.
Clubhouse Hours: 8.00am – 12.00pm.
Clubhouse Dress: Neat Dress.
Clubhouse Facilities: Full bar & restaurant services. Clubhouse tuition available. Clubs, Caddy cars and caddies on request.

NO.	MEDAL METRES	GEN. METRES	PAR	S.I.	NO.	MEDAL METRES	GEN. METRES	PAR	S.I.
1	373	352	4	7	10	330	307	4	6
2	158	131	3	15	11	444	438	5	16
3	367	354	4	3	12	304	285	4	12
4	489	452	5	5	13	448	420	5	18
5	408	384	4	1	14	350	326	4	14
6	169	145	3	13	15	178	164	3	4
7	283	261	4	17	16	370	349	4	8
8	386	364	4	9	17	346	330	4	10
9	379	353	4	11	18	409	381	4	2
OUT	3,012	2,796	35		IN	3,179	3,000	37	
					TOTAL	6,191	5,796	72	
					STANDARD SCRATCH	74	72		

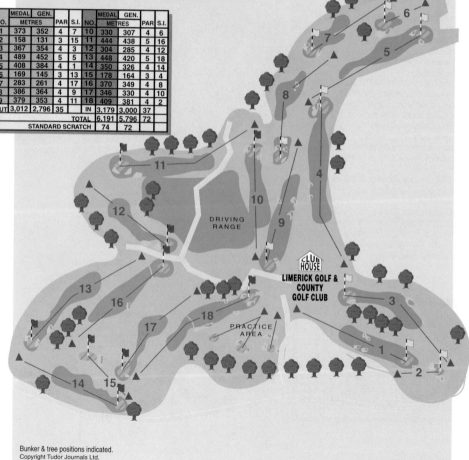

Bunker & tree positions indicated.
Copyright Tudor Journals Ltd.

Newcastle West Golf Club, Ardagh, Co. Limerick.
Tel: (069) 76500.
Fax: (069) 76511.

LOCATION: Three miles from Newcastlewest.
SECRETARY: Patrick Lyons.
ARCHITECT: A. Spring.
PROFESSIONAL: Available on request.

Set in 150 acres of unspoilt rolling West Limerick countryside.

Newcastle West comprises an 18 hole championship course built to the highest standards on sandy soil which is playable all the year round. A practice ground and driving range are included.

COURSE INFORMATION

Par 71; SSS 73; Length 5,905 metres.
Visitors: Welcome.
Opening Hours: 9.00am – sunset.

Avoid: Thursday afternoons and Sunday mornings.
Ladies Day: Play any day.
Green Fees: £15. Societies £10.
Clubhouse Hours: 10.00am – 11.00pm.
Clubhouse Dress: Casual.
Clubhouse Facilities: Full meals, snacks & Golf Shop.
Open Competitions: Open Week, June & Bank Holiday weekends.

	MEDAL	GEN.				MEDAL	GEN.		
NO.	YARDS	YARDS	PAR	S.I.	NO.	YARDS	YARDS	PAR	S.I.
1	456	465	5	17	10	170	185	3	14
2	345	356	4	12	11	352	399	4	3
3	166	191	3	10	12	303	358	4	7
4	303	330	4	13	13	303	310	4	16
5	372	412	4	2	14	500	507	5	11
6	163	187	3	4	15	320	335	4	18
7	338	381	4	8	16	377	407	4	1
8	495	506	5	15	17	167	183	3	9
9	345	370	4	6	18	411	435	4	5
OUT	2,983	3,198	36		IN	2,903	3,119	35	
					TOTAL	5,886	6,317	71	
	STANDARD SCRATCH		72			70			

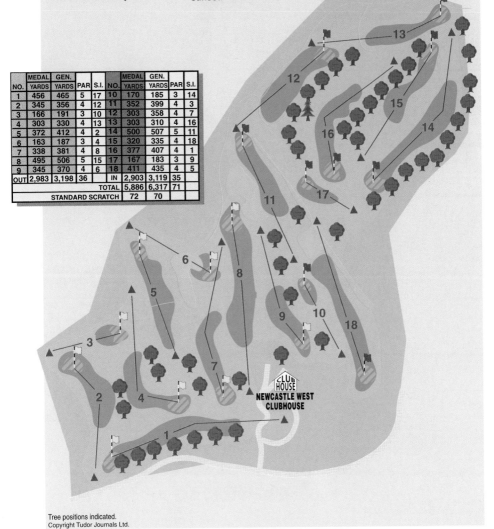

Tree positions indicated.
Copyright Tudor Journals Ltd.

Ballykisteen Golf Club, Monard, Co. Tipperary.
Tel: (062) 33333.
Fax: (062) 33668.

LOCATION: Centrally located on the M24 – two miles from Tipperary Town and within a twenty minute drive of Limerick City.
SECRETARY: Josephine Ryan. Tel: (062) 33333.
PROFESSIONAL: David Reddan.
ARCHITECT: Ryder Cup star Des Symth.

A parkland course, nestled in emerald green countryside in the heart of the Golden Vale. A very interesting and clever design has made this a course suitable to the high and low handicap golfer.

COURSE INFORMATION
Par 72; SSS 74; Length 6,765 yards.
Green Fees: £20

Juveniles: Club Hire available, Caddy service available by prior arrangement. Fully equipped Professional Shop, group and individual tuition and a floodlit Driving Range.

Clubhouse Facilities:
Elegant restaurant and bar – open to the general public all day everyday.

NO.	CHAMP YARDS	MEDAL YARDS	PAR	S.I.	NO.	CHAMP YARDS	MEDAL YARDS	PAR	S.I.
1	371	353	4	6	10	415	392	4	1
2	446	409	4	2	11	417	393	4	3
3	171	171	3	18	12	509	493	5	15
4	534	510	5	8	13	169	155	3	13
5	395	345	4	10	14	394	354	4	11
6	513	490	5	12	15	226	168	3	7
7	394	357	4	14	16	389	346	4	17
8	335	314	4	4	17	371	362	4	5
9	170	156	3	16	18	546	516	5	9
OUT	3,329	3,105	36		IN	3,436	3,179	36	
					TOTAL	6,765	6,284	72	
	STANDARD SCRATCH		74				72		

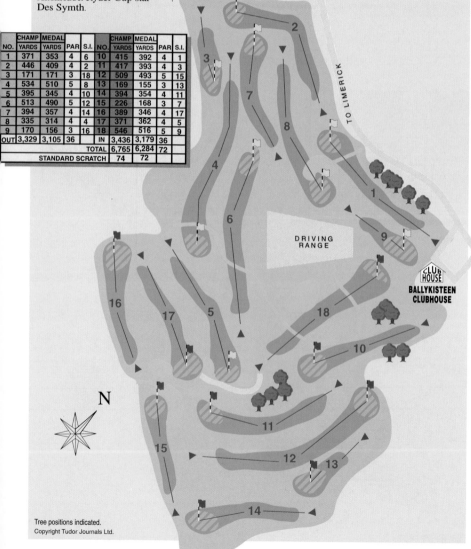

TO LIMERICK

DRIVING RANGE

BALLYKISTEEN CLUBHOUSE

N

Tree positions indicated.
Copyright Tudor Journals Ltd.

**Kilcommon,
Cahir,
Co. Tipperary.
Tel: (052) 41474.**

LOCATION: One mile from town centre.
SECRETARY: Imelda Dilleen.
Tel: (052) 41680.
PROFESSIONAL: Dominic Foran.
Tel: (062) 62111.
ARCHITECT: E. Hackett.

Prime parkland, part of old Cahir Park Estate. Sloping down to River Suir which runs along the right hand side of the 7th hole, this hole is rated as one of the most difficult on the course.

COURSE INFORMATION

Par 71; SSS 71; Length 5,805 metres.
Visitors: Welcome.
Opening Hours: Sunrise – sunset.
Avoid: Major club competition days. Sat / Sun in June / Aug.
Green Fees: £15 daily.

Juveniles: Welcome at times when course is available.
Clubhouse Hours: 10.30am – 11.00pm.
Clubhouse Dress: Casual.
Clubhouse Facilities: Full clubhouse facilites, tea coffee and snacks most days. Meals by prior arrangement.
Open Competitions: Open week May; Bank holiday weekends.

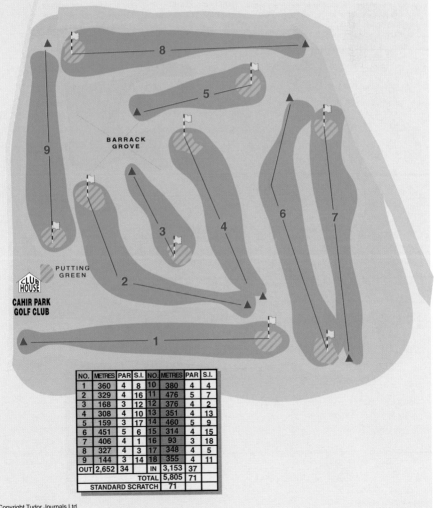

CAHIR PARK
GOLF CLUB

NO.	METRES	PAR	S.I.	NO.	METRES	PAR	S.I.
1	360	4	8	10	380	4	4
2	329	4	16	11	476	5	7
3	168	3	12	12	376	4	2
4	308	4	10	13	351	4	13
5	159	3	17	14	460	5	9
6	451	5	6	15	314	4	15
7	406	4	1	16	93	3	18
8	327	4	3	17	348	4	5
9	144	3	14	18	355	4	11
OUT	2,652	34		IN	3,153	37	
				TOTAL	5,805	71	
		STANDARD SCRATCH			71		

CARRICK-ON-SUIR   M U N S T E R   **TIPPERARY**

Garravoone,
Carrick-On-Suir
Co. Tipperary.
Tel: (051) 640047.

LOCATION: 1 mile from
Carrick-On-Suir on
Dargarvan Road.
SECRETARY: Michael Kelly.
Tel: (051) 95323.
ARCHITECT: E.Hackett.

Carrick on Suir is a scenic 18 hole
course on elevated ground close to
the town. The Comeragh Mountains
are on one side as a backdrop to the
first five holes and the River Suir in
the valley winds its way to the sea at
Waterford. The scenery will keep the

golfer occupied if the game is not
going to plan.

COURSE INFORMATION

**Par 70; SSS 68; Length
5,948 yards.**
Visitors: Welcome Mon –
Sat.
Opening Hours: Sunrise –
sunset.
Avoid: Mon – Wed in
summer after 5.00pm; Wed
Ladies Day.
Ladies: Welcome. Caddy
service available; Handicap
Certificate required.
Green Fees: £12 Mon – Fri;

£14 weekends (group
discounts available).
Juveniles: Welcome,
telephone appointment
required.
Clubhouse Hours:
10.00pm –11.00pm Mon –
Fri; 9.00am – 11.00pm Sat /
Sun (summer); Thurs
2.00pm – 7.00pm; Sat / Sun
9.00am – 9.00pm (winter).
Clubhouse Dress:
Casual but neat.
Catering Facilities: Full
meals and snacks available
by prior arrangement.
Open Competitions:
Tipperary Crystal Open
Week, August .

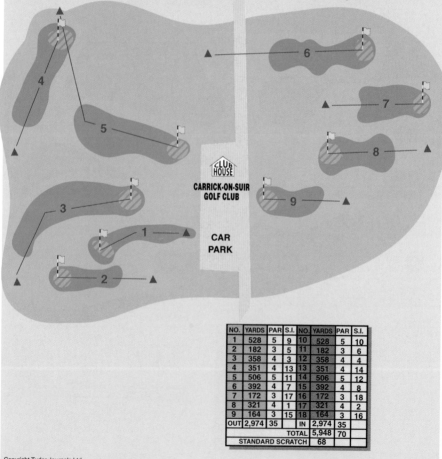

NO.	YARDS	PAR	S.I.	NO.	YARDS	PAR	S.I.
1	528	5	9	10	528	5	10
2	182	3	5	11	182	3	6
3	358	4	3	12	358	4	4
4	351	4	13	13	351	4	14
5	506	5	11	14	506	5	12
6	392	4	7	15	392	4	8
7	172	3	17	16	172	3	18
8	321	4	1	17	321	4	2
9	164	3	15	18	164	3	16
OUT	2,974	35		IN	2,974	35	
				TOTAL	5,948	70	
				STANDARD SCRATCH	68		

Lyneanearla, Mountain Road, Clonel, Co. Tipperary.
Tel: (052) 21138.

LOCATION: 3 miles from Clonmel.
SECRETARY / MANAGER: Aine Myles-Keating.
Tel: (052) 24050.
PROFESSIONAL: Robert Hayes.
ARCHITECT: Eddie Hackett.

Clonmel is a very pleasant inland course with lots of open space and plenty of variety. There is a stream that crosses three fairways and has the advantage of a picturesque setting on the scenic slopes of the pine and fir covered Comeragh Mountains overlooking the plains of Tipperary.

COURSE INFORMATION

Par 72; SSS 71; Length 5,845 metres.
Opening Hours: 8am – 10pm.
Visitors: Welcome.
Green Fees: £18 Mon – Fri ; £20 Sat,Sun & Bank Hols (with member £14 anytime).
Ladies: Welcome Mondays.
Juveniles: Welcome. Lessons by prior arrangement. Club Hire available. Telephone appointment required for societies. Motorised buggy available.
Clubhouse Hours: 8.30am – 11pm.
Clubhouse Dress: Casual.
Clubhouse Facilities: Bar open everyday; Catering – soup and sandwhiches. Lunch and dinner by prior arrangements.

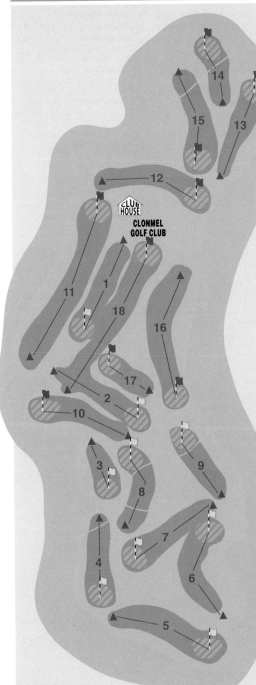

NO.	MEDAL METRES	GEN. METRES	PAR	S.I.	NO.	MEDAL METRES	GEN. METRES	PAR	S.I.
1	343	332	4	12	10	355	344	4	11
2	368	357	4	4	11	456	441	5	13
3	131	120	3	18	12	273	262	4	17
4	448	429	5	14	13	385	370	4	1
5	341	322	4	10	14	174	163	3	3
6	344	333	4	6	15	347	317	4	7
7	306	295	4	16	16	382	371	4	5
8	347	317	4	2	17	170	159	3	9
9	167	137	3	8	18	448	415	5	15
OUT	2,795	2,642	35		IN	2,990	2,824	36	
					TOTAL	5,785	5,484	71	
					STANDARD SCRATCH	70			

**Beechwood, Nenagh,
Co. Tipperary.
Tel: (067) 31476.**

LOCATION: 4 miles from
Nenagh town.
SECRETARY: Pat McGrath.
Tel: (067) 26145.
ARCHITECT: R. Stillwell/J.
Paramour.

This course features panoramic views
from some tees, and requires driving
and approach shots to several sloping,

two tier greens. It is playable all year
except in extremely adverse weather
conditions.

COURSE INFORMATION

**Par 69; SSS 68; Length 5,491
metres.
Visitors:** Welcome Mon – Fri
Avoid: Weekends.
Opening Hours: Sunrise –
sunset.
Ladies: Welcome Thursdays.

Green Fees: £15 all week and
the weekend. £5 for students
and juveniles.
Juveniles: Welcome.
Clubhouse Hours: 10.00am –
11.00pm.
Clubhouse Dress: Casual.
Clubhouse Facilities: All
catering facilities available.
Open Competitions: Open
week – 1st week in June;
Semi-opens – most Bank
Holiday Weekends.

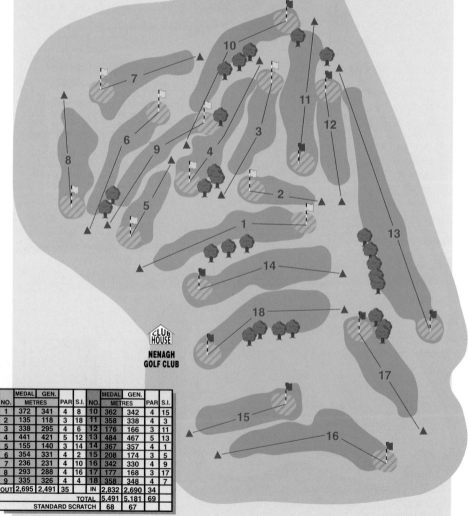

NENAGH
GOLF CLUB

NO.	MEDAL METRES	GEN.	PAR	S.I.	NO.	MEDAL METRES	GEN.	PAR	S.I.
1	372	341	4	8	10	362	342	4	15
2	135	118	3	18	11	358	338	4	3
3	338	295	4	6	12	176	166	3	11
4	441	421	5	12	13	484	467	5	13
5	155	140	3	14	14	367	357	4	1
6	354	331	4	2	15	208	174	3	5
7	236	231	4	10	16	342	330	4	9
8	293	288	4	16	17	177	168	3	17
9	335	326	4	4	18	358	348	4	7
OUT	2,695	2,491	35		IN	2,832	2,690	34	
					TOTAL	5,491	5,181	69	
					STANDARD SCRATCH	68	67		

Tree positions indicated.

Derryvale, Roscrea.
Co. Tipperary.
Tel: (0505) 21130.

LOCATION: 2 miles east of
Roscrea on the N7.
SECRETARY: Nora McDonnell.
Tel: (0505) 21130.

A fine 18 hole course with some
excellent Par 3's. The last six holes are
particularly challenging.

COURSE INFORMATION

**Par 71; SSS 70; Length
5,708 metres.**
Visitors: Welcome Sundays by
arrangement.
Opening Hours: 8am to dusk.
Ladies: Welcome Thurdays.
Green Fees: £12 Mon – Fri.
£15 Sat / Sun.
Juveniles: Welcome although
must be accompanied by an
adult. Club Hire and Caddy
trolleys available.
Clubhouse Hours:
10.30am – 11.30pm.
Clubhouse Dress:
Casual but neat.
Clubhouse Facilities: Full bar
and catering.
Open Competitions: Open
week, June. Bank Holiday
weekends.

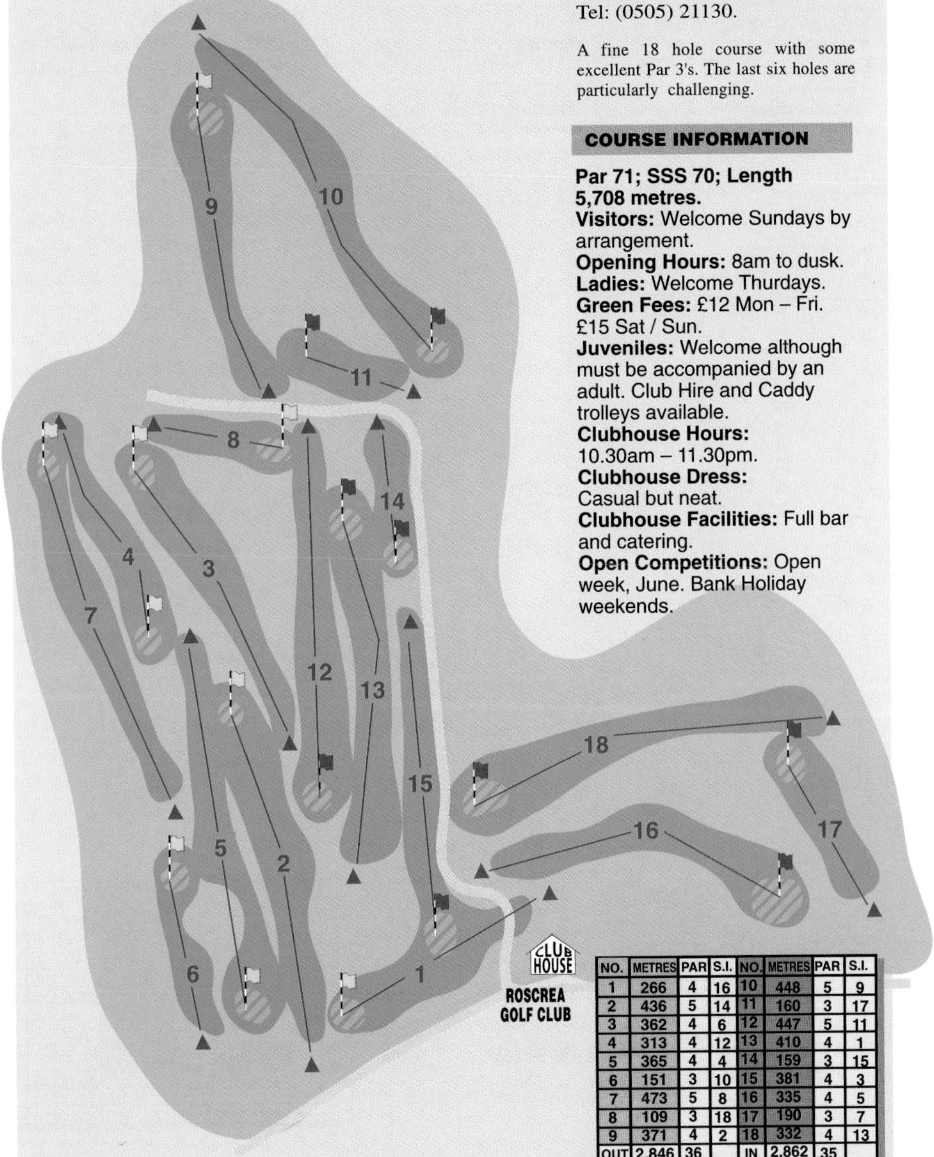

**ROSCREA
GOLF CLUB**

NO.	METRES	PAR	S.I.	NO.	METRES	PAR	S.I.
1	266	4	16	10	448	5	9
2	436	5	14	11	160	3	17
3	362	4	6	12	447	5	11
4	313	4	12	13	410	4	1
5	365	4	4	14	159	3	15
6	151	3	10	15	381	4	3
7	473	5	8	16	335	4	5
8	109	3	18	17	190	3	7
9	371	4	2	18	332	4	13
OUT	2,846	36		IN	2,862	35	
				TOTAL	5,708	71	
				STANDARD SCRATCH		70	

**Manna South,
Templemore.
Co Tipperary.
Tel: (0504) 31400.**

LOCATION: 1/2 mile from
town centre beside N62S.
SECRETARY: John Moloughney.
Tel: (0504) 31522/31720 or
(086) 245 1072

This course provides a pleasant test
of golf, starting with a 442 metre

Par 5. The course has five Par 3's,
finishing with a very good Par 5 at
the 9th and 18th. It has a very
compact layout requiring only short
walks from green to tees.

COURSE INFORMATION

**Par 68; SSS 67; Length
5,112 metres.
Visitors:** Welcome Mon –
Sat.

Opening Hours: 8.00am –
sunset.
Ladies: Welcome
Green Fees: £8 Mon – Sat.
£12 Sun & Bank Holidays.
Juveniles: Welcome, new
members welcome, apply
Honorary Secretary.
Clubhouse Hours: 8.00am –
sunset.
Clubhouse Dress: Casual.
Clubhouse Facilities: By
prior arrangement.
Open Competitions: Open
week July.

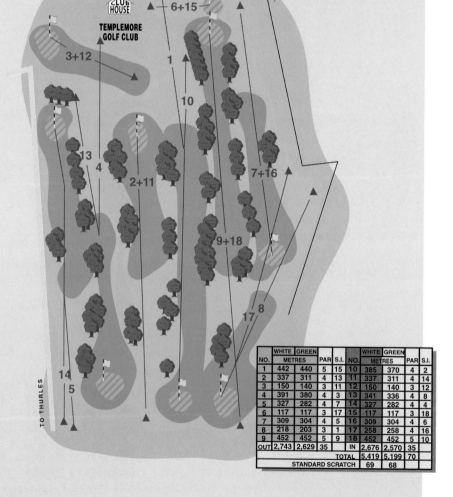

NO.	WHITE METRES	GREEN METRES	PAR	S.I.	NO.	WHITE METRES	GREEN METRES	PAR	S.I.
1	442	440	5	15	10	385	370	4	2
2	337	311	4	13	11	337	311	4	14
3	150	140	3	11	12	150	140	3	12
4	391	380	4	3	13	341	336	4	8
5	327	282	4	7	14	327	282	4	4
6	117	117	3	17	15	117	117	3	18
7	309	304	4	5	16	309	304	4	6
8	218	203	3	1	17	258	258	4	16
9	452	452	5	9	18	452	452	5	10
OUT	2,743	2,629	35		IN	2,676	2,570	35	
					TOTAL	5,419	5,199	70	
					STANDARD SCRATCH	69	68		

Turtulla, Thurles.
Co. Tipperary.
Tel: (0504) 22466.

LOCATION: 1 mile from Thurles town.
HON. SECRETARY: John Smith.
Tel: (0504) 21983.
PROFESSIONAL: Sean Hunt.
Tel: (0504) 21983.
ARCHITECT: Lionel Hewson.

Fine parkland course, with the main features being the four excellent Par 3 holes and the fearsome 18th with the out-of-bounds all the way down the left. Unusual beginning to your round with two Par 5's in a row.

COURSE INFORMATION

Par 72; SSS 71; Length 6,456 yards, 5,904 metres.
Visitors: Welcome.
Opening Hours: 9.00am – 11.30pm.
Ladies: Welcome.
Avoid: Limited availablity at weekends.
Green Fees: £18 (£9 with member).
Juveniles: Welcome, Club Hire available; caddy service and lessons available by prior arrangement, telephone appointment required.

Clubhouse Hours: 10.00am – 11.00pm. Full clubhouse facilities which include two championship squash courts. Limited availability at weekends.
Clubhouse Dress: Casual.
Clubhouse Facilities: Snacks at all times; full meals as ordered.
Open Competitions: Open Week, 24th July–3rd Aug; Junior Scratch Cup, 10th May; Inter. Scratch Cup, 6th Sept.

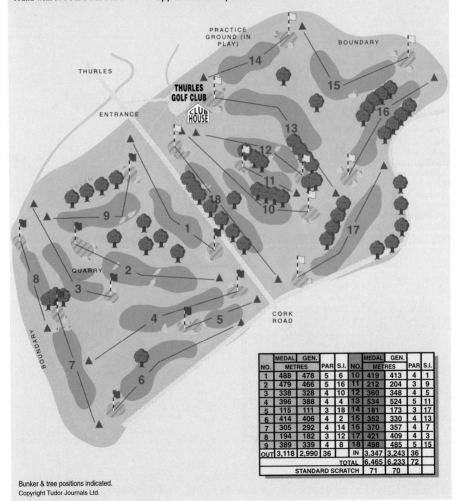

NO.	MEDAL METRES	GEN.	PAR	S.I.	NO.	MEDAL METRES	GEN.	PAR	S.I.
1	488	478	5	6	10	419	413	4	1
2	479	466	5	16	11	212	204	3	9
3	338	328	4	10	12	360	348	4	5
4	396	388	4	4	13	534	524	5	11
5	115	111	3	18	14	181	173	3	17
6	414	406	4	2	15	352	330	4	13
7	305	292	4	14	16	370	357	4	7
8	194	182	3	12	17	421	409	4	3
9	389	339	4	8	18	498	485	5	15
OUT	3,118	2,990	36		IN	3,347	3,243	36	
					TOTAL	6,465	6,233	72	
					STANDARD SCRATCH	71	70		

Bunker & tree positions indicated.

**County Tipperary Golf &
Country Club,
Dundrum, Co. Tipperary.
Tel: (062) 71116.
Fax: (062) 71366.**

DIRECTOR OF GOLF: William
Crowe.
Tel: (062) 71116.
SECRETARY: William Crowe.
PROFESSIONAL: Available on
request.

An attractive parkland course
playable all year round that has some
interesting holes.

COURSE INFORMATION

**Par 72; SSS 72; Length
6,709 yards, 6,150 metres.
Visitors:** Welcome anytime
(societies included).
Opening Hours: 8am –
sunset.
Ladies: Welcome.
Weekends: Advisable to book
in advance.
Green Fees: £20 midweek,
£24 weekends.
Juveniles: Welcome. Club
and Buggy Hire available.
Clubhouse Hours: 11.00am –
11.00pm.
Clubhouse Dress: Informal
but neat.
Clubhouse Facilities:
Restaurant and bar everyday.
62 bedroom hotel.
Open Competitions: Open
Week, 27th July–3rd Aug.

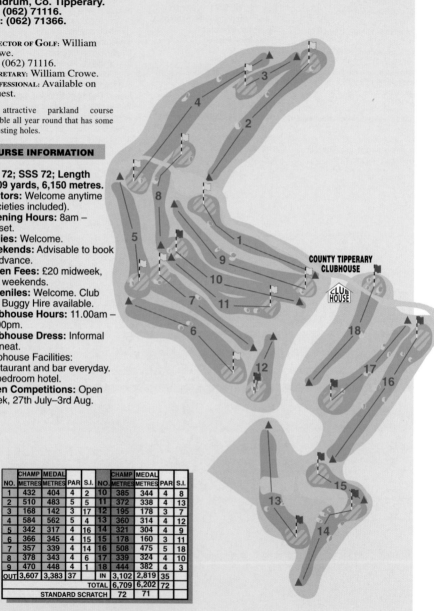

COUNTY TIPPERARY
CLUBHOUSE

NO.	CHAMP METRES	MEDAL METRES	PAR	S.I.	NO.	CHAMP METRES	MEDAL METRES	PAR	S.I.
1	432	404	4	2	10	385	344	4	8
2	510	483	5	5	11	372	338	4	13
3	168	142	3	17	12	195	178	3	7
4	584	562	5	4	13	360	314	4	12
5	342	317	4	16	14	321	304	4	9
6	366	345	4	15	15	178	160	3	11
7	357	339	4	14	16	508	475	5	18
8	378	343	4	6	17	339	324	4	10
9	470	448	4	1	18	444	382	4	3
OUT	3,607	3,383	37		IN	3,102	2,819	35	
					TOTAL	6,709	6,202	72	
					STANDARD SCRATCH		72	71	

Bunker and tree positions indicated.
Copyright Tudor Journals Ltd.

**Knocknagranagh,
Co. Waterford.
Tel: (058) 41605/43310.
Fax: (058) 44113.**

LOCATION: Dungarvan 2 miles.
On N25 route.
AMINISTRATOR: Tom Whelan.
Tel: (058) 41605 / 43310.
Fax: (058) 44113.
ARCHITECT: Maurice Fives.

Dungarvan Golf Club is set against the backdrop of the Comeragh Mountains and runs adjacent to

Dungavan Bay. This 6,700 yd Par 72 championship course has been architecturally designed with nine lakes and man-made hazards strategically placed to test all levels of golfer.

COURSE INFORMATION

**Par 72; SSS 73; Length
6,708 yards; 6,134 metres.
Visitors:** Welcome.
Opening Hours: 7.00am – sunset.
Ladies: Welcome.

Green Fees: Weekdays £15;
Sat, Sun and Bank Hols £20.
Society outings are welcome.
Special offer for mid-week reservations.
Juveniles: Welcome.
Clubhouse Hours: 9.00am – 12.00pm.
Clubhouse Dress: Neat at all times.
Clubhouse Facilities: Include light meals & full dining room service.
Open Competitions: Open weeks, July and September.

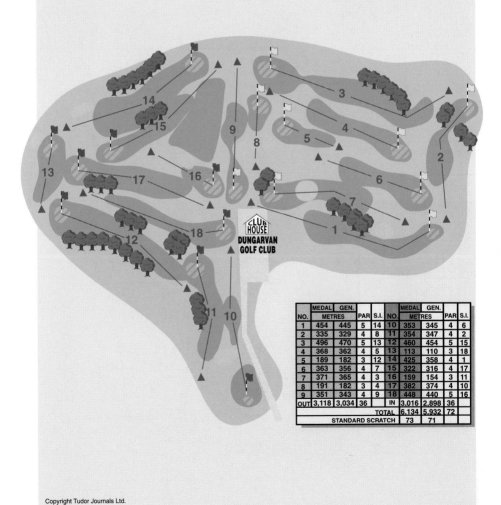

NO.	MEDAL METRES	GEN. METRES	PAR	S.I.	NO.	MEDAL METRES	GEN. METRES	PAR	S.I.
1	454	445	5	14	10	353	345	4	6
2	335	329	4	8	11	354	347	4	2
3	496	470	5	13	12	460	454	5	15
4	368	362	4	5	13	113	110	3	18
5	189	182	3	12	14	425	358	4	1
6	363	356	4	7	15	322	316	4	17
7	371	365	4	3	16	159	154	3	11
8	191	182	3	4	17	382	374	4	10
9	351	343	4	9	18	448	440	5	16
OUT	3,118	3,034	36		IN	3,016	2,898	36	
					TOTAL	6,134	5,932	72	
					STANDARD SCRATCH	73	71		

Dunmore East Golf & Country Club,
Dunmore East,
Co. Waterford.
Tel: (051) 383151.

LOCATION: Ten miles from Waterford City in Dunmore East village.
SECRETARY: Mary Skehan.
Tel: (051) 383151.
ARHITECT: William Henry Jones.

This 18 hole course overlooks the village of Dunmore East with panoramic views of the bay and harbour. The course offers challenging golf, in idyllic surroundings, with five holes on the waters edge.

COURSE INFORMATION

Par 72; Length 6,655 yards.
Visitors: No restrictions.
Opening Hours: Dawn – Dusk.
Ladies: Welcome no restrictions.
Juveniles: Welcome.
Green Fees: £10 Weekdays; £14 Weekends.

Clubhouse Hours: 10am – 12pm.
Clubhouse Dress: Neat / casual.
Clubhouse Facilities: Full bar, light snacks and full meals available all day. Club Hire available, Caddy trolleys by prior arrangement.
Open Competitions: Foursomes every Tuesday. Open Week 29th June & 5th July.

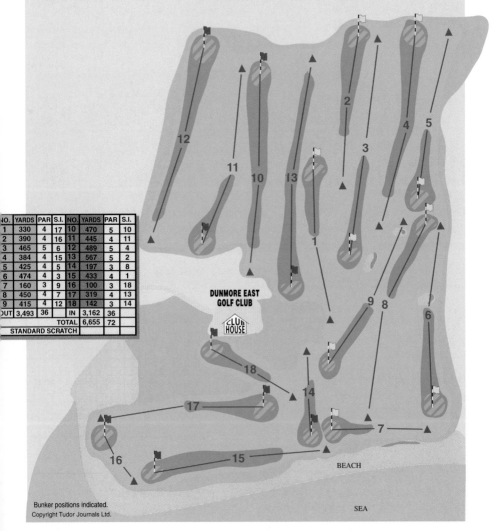

NO.	YARDS	PAR	S.I.	NO.	YARDS	PAR	S.I.
1	330	4	17	10	470	5	10
2	390	4	16	11	445	4	11
3	465	5	6	12	489	5	4
4	384	4	15	13	567	5	2
5	425	4	5	14	197	3	8
6	474	4	3	15	433	4	1
7	160	3	9	16	100	3	18
8	450	4	7	17	319	4	13
9	415	4	12	18	142	3	14
OUT	3,493	36		IN	3,162	36	
				TOTAL	6,655	72	
STANDARD SCRATCH							

DUNMORE EAST GOLF CLUB

CLUB HOUSE

BEACH

SEA

Bunker positions indicated.
Copyright Tudor Journals Ltd.

Faithlegg Golf Club,
Faithlegg House.
Co. Waterford.
Tel: (051) 382241.
Fax: (051) 382664.

LOCATION: Six miles from Waterford City, from Waterford take Dunmore East road for Cheekpoint village
SECRETARY: Ted Higgins.
Tel: (051) 382241.
PROFESSIONAL: Ted Higgins.
Tel: (051) 382241.
ARCHITECT: Patrick Merrigan.

Some wicked slopes and borrows on the greens and a dog-legged approach to the two tier 18th green are just some of the novel features incorporated into the course. The architect sensitively integrated the course into a landscape textured with mature trees, flowing parkland and no less than five lakes. This is a golfing tour-de-force.

COURSE INFORMATION

Par 72; SSS 72; Length 6,720 yards; 6,057 metres.
Visitors: Welcome. Societies always welcome.
Opening Hours: 7.30am – sunset.

Ladies: Welcome.
Green Fees: £15 Monday & Tuesday; £22 Wednesday & Thursday; £25 Friday, Saturday & Sunday.
Juveniles: Permitted.
Clubhouse Hours: 8.00am – 11.30pm.
Clubhouse Dress: Casual but neat (no jeans).
Clubhouse Facilities: Full bar and catering facilities available, mens & ladies locker rooms, Pro-Shop. Club, Caddy cars and trolleys available for hire.
Open Competitions: Dunmore Classic April. Open Week 8th – 16th August; Canada Life Pro-Am June; Open parent & child foursomes July.

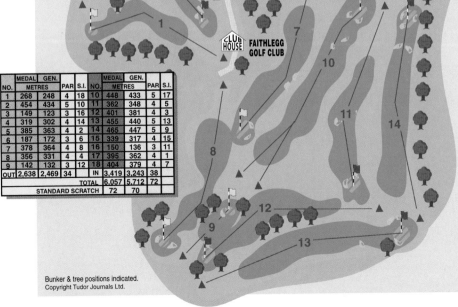

NO.	MEDAL METRES	GEN.	PAR	S.I.	NO.	MEDAL METRES	GEN.	PAR	S.I.
1	268	248	4	18	10	448	433	5	17
2	454	434	5	10	11	362	348	4	5
3	149	123	3	16	12	401	381	4	3
4	319	302	4	14	13	455	440	5	13
5	385	363	4	2	14	465	447	5	9
6	187	172	3	6	15	339	317	4	15
7	378	364	4	8	16	150	136	3	11
8	356	331	4	4	17	395	362	4	1
9	142	132	3	12	18	404	379	4	7
OUT	2,638	2,469	34		IN	3,419	3,243	38	
					TOTAL	6,057	5,712	72	
					STANDARD SCRATCH	72	70		

Bunker & tree positions indicated.
Copyright Tudor Journals Ltd.

**Gold Coast Golf Club,
Ballinacourty,
Dungarvan.
Co. Waterford.
Tel: (058) 42249/44055.
Fax: (058) 43378.**

LOCATION: Three miles East of
Dungarvan.
PRESIDENT: Thomas Fennell.
SECRETARY: Eugene Collins.
CAPTAIN: James Veale.
ARCHITECT: Moss Fives.

A parkland course bordered by
Atlantic Ocean with a scenic
background of Dungarvan Bay and
Comeragh Mountains.

COURSE INFORMATION

**Par 72; SSS 72; Length
6,171 metres.**
Visitors: Welcome.
Opening Hours: Sunrise –
sunset.
Avoid: Advisable to book in
advance for weekends.

Ladies: Welcome.
Green Fees: Mon–Fri £15;
Sat/Sun £18.
Juveniles: Welcome. Club
and trolley hire available.
Clubhouse Hours: 8.00am –
12.00pm.
Clubhouse Dress: Casual,
neat.
Clubhouse Facilities: Hotel
& catering services, including
leisure centre & swimming
pool on site.

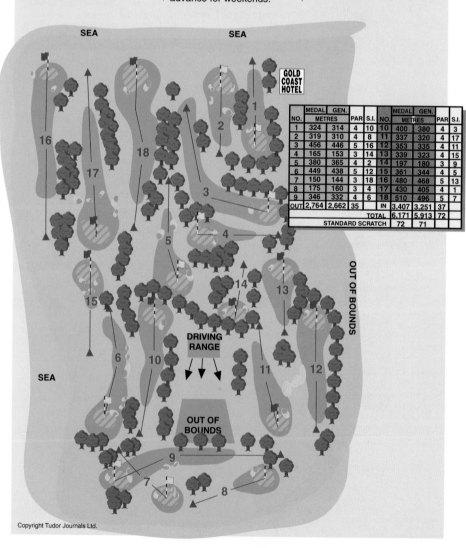

NO.	MEDAL METRES	GEN. METRES	PAR	S.I.	NO.	MEDAL METRES	GEN. METRES	PAR	S.I.
1	324	314	4	10	10	400	380	4	3
2	319	310	4	8	11	337	320	4	17
3	456	446	5	16	12	353	335	4	11
4	165	153	3	14	13	339	323	4	15
5	380	365	4	2	14	197	180	3	9
6	449	438	5	12	15	361	344	4	5
7	150	144	3	18	16	480	468	5	13
8	175	160	3	4	17	430	405	4	1
9	346	332	4	6	18	510	496	5	7
OUT	2,764	2,662	35		IN	3,407	3,251	37	
					TOTAL	6,171	5,913	72	
					STANDARD SCRATCH	72	71		

LISMORE

M U N S T E R **WATERFORD**

Lismore Golf Club,
Ballyin,
Lismore,
Co. Waterford.
Tel: (058) 54026.

LOCATION: 1Km north of town,
off R.666.
SECRETARY: Stephen Hales.
Tel: (058) 54026.

Undulating parkland course with mature
hardwood trees, on the estate of Lismore
Castle, in the Blackwater Valley.

NO.	METRES	PAR	S.I.	NO.	METRES	PAR	S.I.
1	289	4	14	10	335	4	7
2	326	4	8	11	330	4	9
3	123	3	18	12	123	3	17
4	326	4	6	13	326	4	5
5	135	3	16	14	135	3	15
6	357	4	4	15	462	5	13
7	368	4	2	16	368	4	3
8	317	4	10	17	352	4	1
9	300	4	12	18	317	4	11
OUT	2,541	34		IN	2,748	35	
				TOTAL	5,289	69	
	STANDARD SCRATCH				67		

COURSE INFORMATION

Par 69; SSS 67; Length
5,790 yards.
Visitors: More than welcome.
Opening Hours: Dawn – dusk.
Avoid: Sundays.
Ladies: Welcome Wednesdays.
Green Fees: £10 daily.
Juveniles: Accompanied by
an adult.
Clubhouse Hours:
9.00am – close.
Clubhouse Dress:
Neat / Casual.
Clubhouse Facilities: Bar, tea /
coffee, snacks, changing rooms.
Open Competitions: Open day
every Thurs,
1st Open Week ending Whit
weekend – May/June,
2nd Open Week ending August
Bank Holiday weekend.

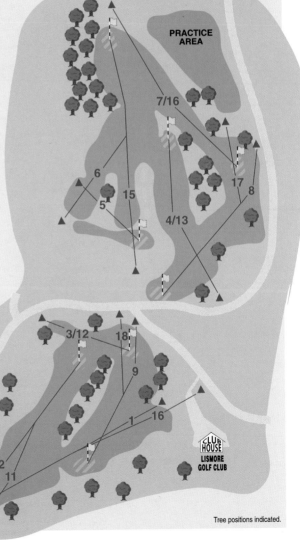

PRACTICE AREA

7/16

6

15

5

17 8

4/13

3/12 18

9

1 16

CLUB HOUSE

LISMORE GOLF CLUB

2

11

Tree positions indicated.

Copyright Tudor Journals Ltd.

339

**Newtown Hill,
Tramore.
Co Waterford.**

LOCATION: On the Dungarvan
coast road.
SECRETARY: James Cox.
Tel: (051) 386170.
PROFESSIONAL: Derry Kiely.

Eighteen hole championship course
with generous fairways. In a recent
survey, by Sports Columnist John
Cowyn, two holes — the 4th and the
6th were rated in the top eighteen in
Ireland.

COURSE INFORMATION

**Par 72; SSS 73; Length 6,055
metres.
Visitors:** Welcome.
Ladies: Welcome Mondays.

Green Fees: £25 Mon – Fri.
£30 Weekends.
Juveniles: Welcome, lessons
available by prior
arrangements; Club Hire
available; Caddy service
available by prior
arrangements; telephone
appointments required.
Clubhouse Hours:
11.00am – 11.30pm;
Clubhouse Dress:
Casual but neat.
Open Competitions: Open
Weeks 22nd Aug – 6th Sept
(1st week gents; 2nd week
ladies).

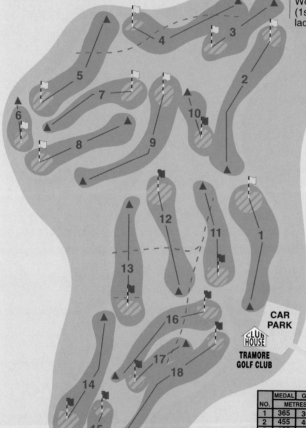

ANNESTOWN

CAR PARK

CLUB HOUSE

TRAMORE GOLF CLUB

NO.	MEDAL METRES	GEN. METRES	PAR	S.I.	NO.	MEDAL METRES	GEN. METRES	PAR	S.I.
1	365	365	4	6	10	174	174	3	16
2	455	455	5	15	11	366	333	4	4
3	155	155	3	11	12	315	315	4	10
4	344	344	4	3	13	366	325	4	7
5	294	294	4	12	14	406	367	4	1
6	159	159	3	17	15	117	117	3	18
7	367	367	4	8	16	500	500	5	9
8	371	371	4	2	17	346	322	4	5
9	506	506	5	13	18	449	449	5	14
OUT	3,016	3,016	36		IN	3,039	2,902	36	
					TOTAL	6,055	5,918	72	
					STANDARD SCRATCH	73	72		

Waterford Castle Golf Club, The Island, Ballinakill, Waterford.
Tel: (051) 871633.
Fax: (051) 871634.

LOCATION: Waterford City.
SECRETARY: Dick Brennan.
Tel: (051) 871633.
ARHITECT: Des Smyth & Associates.

Attractive parkland, wooded course with, four artificial lakes, surrounded by River Suir. Sand based Tees & greens.

An excellent test of golf in most enjoyable surroundings. Heated swimming pool & tennis available.

COURSE INFORMATION

Par 72; SSS 73; Length 6,209 Metres.
Visitors: Welcome.
Opening Hours: 8am – dusk.
Avoid: 8.30am – 10.30am (members times).
Ladies: Welcome.

Juveniles: Permitted with adult.
Green Fees: £24 midweek. £27 weekends.
Clubhouse Hours: 8.00am – dusk.
Clubhouse Dress: Casual, no jeans etc.
Clubhouse Facilities: Limited bar food – soup, sandwiches, tea/coffee. Full meals with pre-booking.
Open Competitions: July.

	MEDAL	GEN.				MEDAL	GEN.		
NO.	MTRS	MTRS	PAR	S.I.	NO.	MTRS	MTRS	PAR	S.I.
1	385	361	4	7	10	160	152	3	18
2	176	154	3	15	11	346	318	4	6
3	372	346	4	3	12	415	397	4	2
4	356	338	4	5	13	463	427	5	12
5	476	432	5	13	14	343	306	4	10
6	315	303	4	17	15	468	454	5	14
7	193	176	3	9	16	187	173	3	8
8	452	443	5	11	17	368	344	4	4
9	381	360	4	1	18	353	326	4	16
OUT	3,106	2,913	36		IN	3,103	2,897	36	
					TOTAL	6,209	5,810	72	
	STANDARD SCRATCH					73	71		

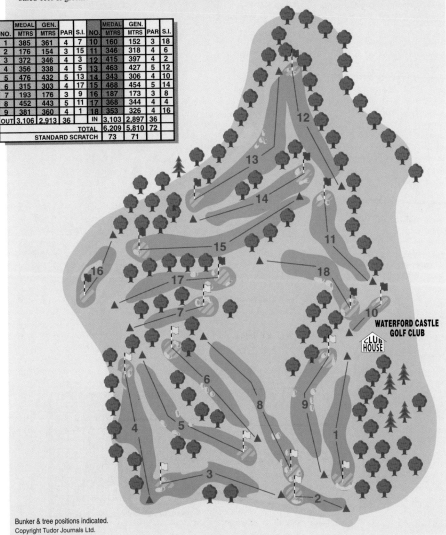

WATERFORD CASTLE GOLF CLUB

CLUB HOUSE

Dungarvan.
Co. Waterford.
Tel: (058) 43216.
Fax: (058) 44343.

LOCATION: 3 miles from
Dungarvan, 30 miles from
Waterford city.
SECRETARY: Austin Spratt.
ARCHITECT: Eddie Hackett.

The course extends over 150 acres of
magnificent rolling topography taking
in the beautiful panoramic views of
Co. Waterford. An interesting feature
of the course is that the first nine
holes are laid out on a large plateau
featuring a lovely stream which
comes into play at the 3rd and 4th
holes. The course extends to 6802
yds, but it was built to suit a wide
range of players with a minimum
interference to the natural
characteristics and vegetation.
Playable all year round.

COURSE INFORMATION

Par 72; SSS 74: Length
6,802 yards.
Visitors: Welcome.

Opening Hours:
Sunrise – sunset.
Green Fees: £20 Mon – Fri.
£25 Sat – Sun. Discount for
societies.
Juveniles: Welcome. Clubs
and caddy cars available for
hire.
Clubhouse Hours:
8.00am – sunset.
Clubhouse Dress: Casual /
neat.
Clubhouse Facilities: Full
bar & catering facilities all day,
every day.

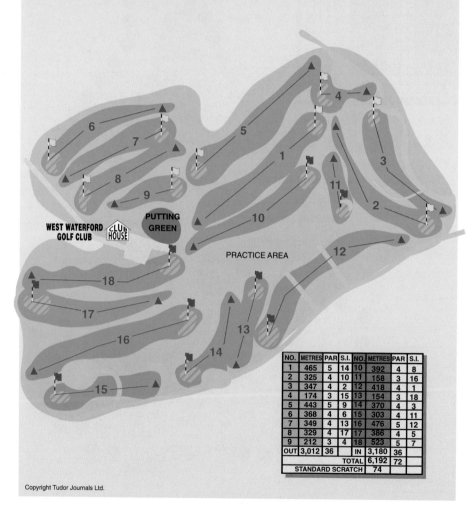

NO.	METRES	PAR	S.I.	NO.	METRES	PAR	S.I.
1	465	5	14	10	392	4	8
2	325	4	10	11	158	3	16
3	347	4	2	12	418	4	1
4	174	3	15	13	154	3	18
5	443	5	9	14	370	4	3
6	368	4	6	15	303	4	11
7	349	4	13	16	476	5	12
8	329	4	17	17	386	4	5
9	212	3	4	18	523	5	7
OUT	3,012	36		IN	3,180	36	
				TOTAL	6,192	72	
			STANDARD SCRATCH	74			

WEST WATERFORD
GOLF CLUB

PUTTING GREEN

PRACTICE AREA

CONNACHT

BY JACK MAGOWAN

Cecil Ewing was a big man — feisty, humorous, opinionated and hopelessly in love with golf. He wore an 'extra large' label in personality, and was the kind you thought would live for ever. When he died at 63, it was as though the game had lost a grand uncle.

Cecil had not only played in six Walker Cup teams and for Ireland over 90 times, he won the West of Ireland championship ten times and was beaten finalist on another eight occasions, a record almost without parallel in the days when the BBC of amateur golf, Burke, Bruen and Carr, were in their prime.

Ewing could play left-handed as well as right, and often did, usually for a happy wager.

Nobody loved an audience as much as he did, and his favourite party piece

would be to challenge somebody to a match over the last three holes of his beloved Rosses Point links.

If the reply was "no thanks, you're too good,", Cecil would propose a compromise "OK. I'll play left-handed and you right-handed," he would tease. And nine times out of ten the result would be the same — he won!

Like O'Connor Senior, he revelled, too, in wind and rough weather. "I learned the game in a good school," he used to say. "When it blows at Rosses Point, the only hiding place is in the clubhouse!"

Cecil had a gift for making the game look easy, and was 45, and over 17 stone, when he played against the United States for the last time in the Walker Cup at St Andrews. Three years later he was Irish Close champion again, a surprise winner over one of the toughest courses in the game, Ballybunion.

Ewing was also a Cup selector and captained Ireland to two European championship victories, one of them in Italy. The ball he used for an exciting win

against Ray Billows in Britain's historic Cup victory of 1938 is on display in Sligo's splendid new clubhouse and still sparks many potent memories, especially of some of the great names who've played under the shadows of Ben Bulben.

Like Walter Hagen, who took two days to get there from London. And Bobby Locke and Henry Cotton, and more recently Bernhard Langer. "I went there to play one round and stayed two weeks," says Langer of the 100 per cent links course that would almost surely covet a world rating were it not so isolated.

If it wasn't the sea air and scenery that captivated Langer, then it must have been the loudest silence in golf. Along the corridors of these exposed and barren fairways, all you hear is the grass growing!

Sligo can boast several star-studded holes, but the pick of them by far is the 17th. Tucked among high dunes, this classic hole spans 450 yards off the tiger tee, and in O'Connor Senior's book is

With views over Galway Bay and beyond, Galway Golf Club compliments a good challenge with superb scenery.

one of the finest two-shot holes in the country. "It carries a knock-out punch like Mike Tyson," smiles fight-fan O'Connor.

Ireland now has over 350 golf courses, and if there's a bad one anywhere, somebody once said, they're keeping it a secret. Inexpensive, underplayed and welcoming – that's how they beat the drums for Connacht courses, the cream of which are always special.

Nothing beats the birth of a new course, and if two here could be awarded a rosette for quality they are Carn, in Co. Mayo, and O'Connor Junior's wonderfully ambitious layout at Galway Bay.

Have you ever been to Belmullet? That's where Carn is – in the back of beyond. Or as *Golf World* so aptly put it in their choice of Britain's top – 10 new courses a couple of years ago, "it's not the sort of place you can pop in to on the way to somewhere else!"

Some holes there are truly majestic,

and there's the odd one or two that push the realms of respectability a bit too far. But it's a challenge and fun to play.

German and French golfers are drawn to Ireland's west coast like fruit flies to a ripening. The piano in the lounge at Connemara is a gift from a German diplomat who came for a fishing holiday some years ago, but never even got rod and line out of his car. Instead, he hired a set of clubs and had a ball in the company of some of the most remote, yet hospitable, people on earth.

Connemara, like Waterville, is an Eddie Hackett creation, and, like Waterville, the second nine there are better than the first. In fact, the last six holes at Clifden is as tough a finishing stretch as there is anywhere, a veritable no-man's land of sand and wilderness.

Westport course has an attractive mixture of tree-lined fairways and superb views

In May and June, the links are a tapestry of yellows, blues and purples.

It doesn't surprise me that Enniscrone is now in Ireland's top-30 rankings, for here, too, is a links course that can both exhilarate and terrify. It's about ten miles from Ballina on the shore of Killala Bay, and looks like a lunar landscape among dunes that dip and roll and disappear out of sight.

Eddie Power won the Irish title there in '93, beating Liam Higgins' son, David in a thrilling final, and calls Enniscore 'a sleeping giant'. It's the real thing, that's what he means!.

Westport has also hosted the Close championship and makes a fuss of visitors in a town where hotel beds are not expensive, and there are plenty of them.

After a benign start, Westport picks up momentum with the long 15th, the pinnacle hole. The tee-shot here is not for the faint-hearted, not with a carry over an inlet of Clew Bay that must be all of 170 yards. And just for added mischief, there's an out of bounds fence along the port side.

Again, the welcome at Westport has been known to trip up the unsuspecting, so go prepared.

No two golf courses play the same, and in the west of Ireland they are all different. From Achill to Athlone to the sylvan setting of Athenry—they're all nature's own design, a playground for those who like to compliment their golf with scenery and atmosphere. As Henry Longhurst once wrote, Irish golf has that indefinable something which makes you relive again and again the days you played there!

Athenry Golf Club,
Palmerstown, Oranmore,
Co. Galway.
Tel: (091) 794466.

LOCATION: 5 miles from Athenry town. 8 miles from Galway.
HON. SECRETARY: Mrs Eileen Burke. Tel: (091) 844502.
ARCHITECT: Eddie Hackett.

This eighteen hole parkland course sports two ruined forts amidst dense wooded backdrop. It was extended from a nine hole to an eighteen hole course in 1991 taking on a completely different layout, but not detracting from its sylvan setting.

COURSE INFORMATION

Par 70; SSS 69; Length 5,550 metres.
Visitors: Welcome.
Opening Hours: Sunrise – sunset.
Avoid: Sundays.
Green Fees: £15 Mon – Fri;£18 Sat/Sun.

Ladies: Welcome Wednesdays.
Juveniles: Permitted, must be accompanied by an adult after 5.00pm.
Clubhouse Hours: Flexible.
Clubhouse Dress: Casual.
Clubhouse Facilities: Full meals at all times.
Open Competitions: All bank holidays; Open Week, July 18th – 26th; Junoir and Intermediate Open, August 29th.Contact club for more details.

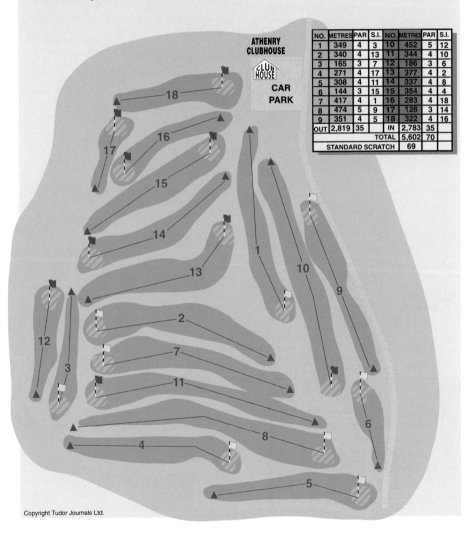

ATHENRY
CLUBHOUSE

CAR
PARK

NO.	METRES	PAR	S.I.	NO.	METRES	PAR	S.I.
1	349	4	3	10	452	5	12
2	340	4	13	11	344	4	10
3	165	3	7	12	186	3	6
4	271	4	17	13	377	4	2
5	308	4	11	14	337	4	8
6	144	3	15	15	354	4	4
7	417	4	1	16	283	4	18
8	474	5	9	17	128	3	14
9	351	4	5	18	322	4	16
OUT	2,819	35		IN	2,783	35	
				TOTAL	5,602	70	
				STANDARD SCRATCH		69	

Rossgloss, Ballinasloe, Co. Galway.
Tel: (0905) 42126,
Fax: (0905) 42538.

LOCATION: Off the Ballinasloe Portumna Road. Two miles from the town centre.
SECRETARY: Mr. John Millane. Tel: (0905) 42126.
ARCHITECT:
Eddie Connaughton.

Ballinasloe Golf Club was established on the Cloncarty Estate, now Garbally College, in 1894. Originally a nine hole parkland course, major redevelopment of the club was undertaken in 1970 and the course was extended to eighteen holes in 1984. The course is invariably playable all year round.

COURSE INFORMATION

Par 72; SSS 70; Length 5,865 Metres.
Visitors: Welcome.
Opening Hours: 8am – Dusk.
Avoid: Major Sunday competitions.

Ladies: Welcome Tuesdays.
Green Fees: £12 Mon–Fri. £12 Sat&Sun. Societies welcome. Golf Shop.
Clubhouse Dress: Neat and tidy.
Clubhouse Facilities: Full catering facilities Monday to Sunday.
Open Competitions: Open week 11th – 19th July; Opened Mixed Scramble 1st – 2nd August; other open days & weekends throughout the year.

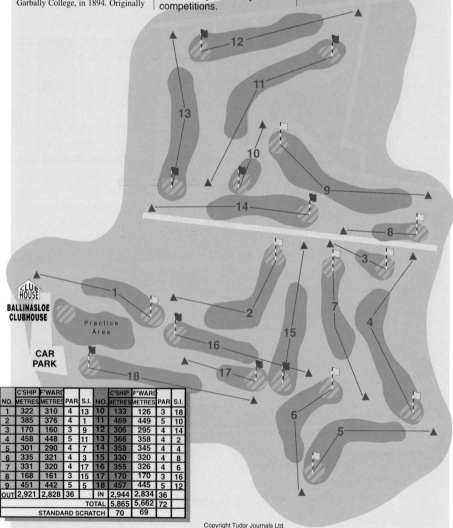

NO.	C'SHIP METRES	F'WARD METRES	PAR	S.I.	NO.	C'SHIP METRES	F'WARD METRES	PAR	S.I.
1	322	310	4	13	10	133	126	3	18
2	385	376	4	1	11	469	449	5	10
3	170	160	3	9	12	306	295	4	14
4	458	448	5	11	13	366	358	4	2
5	301	290	4	7	14	358	345	4	4
6	335	321	4	3	15	330	320	4	8
7	331	320	4	17	16	355	326	4	6
8	168	161	3	15	17	170	170	3	16
9	451	442	5	5	18	457	445	5	12
OUT	2,921	2,828	36		IN	2,944	2,834	36	
					TOTAL	5,865	5,662	72	
					STANDARD SCRATCH	70	69		

Ballyconneely, Co. Galway.
Tel: (095) 23502,
Fax: (095) 23662.

LOCATION: Nine miles from Clifden.
SECRETARY: John McLaughlin.
Tel: (095) 23503.
PROFESSIONAL: Hugh O'Neil.
ARHITECT: Eddie Hackett.

Situated on the edge of the Atlantic Ocean in a spectacular setting with the Twelve Bens Mountains in the background, this championship course is a challenge as good as any golfer would wish for. Established in 1973 the course has a popular reputation with big hitters, who relish the long meandering fairways.

COURSE INFORMATION

Par 72; SSS 73; Length 6,173 metres.
Visitors: Welcome.
Opening Hours: Dawn – Dusk.
Avoid: Sunday mornings.
Green Fees: £25 May – Sep, £16 Oct – April. Lessons available by prior arrangement (only Saturdays during summer). Club Hire and Caddy car available. Golf carts available.
Juveniles: Welcome but may not play weekends, Bank Holidays or Open Weeks. Handicap Certificate required.
Clubhouse Hours: 8am – 11pm.
Clubhouse Dress: Casual (no spikes).
Clubhouse Facilities: Bar Snacks and a la carte restaurant.
Open Competitions: Open Weeks,June 19th – 29th & Sept 4th – 13th. Handicap required for open competitions.

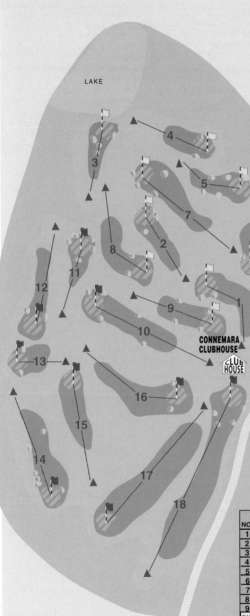

LAKE

CONNEMARA CLUBHOUSE

CLUB HOUSE

NO.	CHAMP METRES	MEDAL METRES	PAR	S.I.	NO.	CHAMP METRES	MEDAL METRES	PAR	S.I.
1	349	331	4	6	10	398	383	4	7
2	385	366	4	8	11	171	151	3	17
3	154	145	3	18	12	416	399	4	1
4	358	335	4	14	13	196	180	3	5
5	360	342	4	12	14	483	460	5	15
6	193	175	3	10	15	367	349	4	9
7	531	482	5	16	16	417	370	4	3
8	438	418	4	2	17	491	468	5	11
9	408	344	4	4	18	496	475	5	13
OUT	3,176	2,938	35		IN	3,435	3,235	37	
					TOTAL	6,611	6,173	72	
					STANDARD SCRATCH	75	73		

Bunker positions indicated.

**Connemara Isles Golf Club,
Eanach Mheain,
Leitir Moir,
Connemara.**

LOCATION: Annaghvaan Island, Leitir Moir via Causeway from Beal A'Daingin.
SECRETARY: Padraic O'Conghaile
Tel: (091) 572 498 / 572 348.
ARCHITECT: Craddock & Ruddy.

Unique Island course located in the heart of the Connemara Gaeltacht. The course is distractingly beautiful – where ocean inlets and rocky outcrops provide natural hazards, demanding steady nerves. After the game relax in the friendly atmosphere of Ireland's only thatched clubhouse, which is warmed by an open fire.

COURSE INFORMATION

Par 70; SSS 67; Length 5,042 yards; 4,700 metres.
Visitors: Welcome (appreciated if able to contact office).
Opening Hours:
9.30am – 11.30pm.
Avoid: Sunday afternoon.
Ladies: Welcome any day.
Green Fees: £10.

Clubhouse Hours:
9.30am – 11.30pm.
Clubhouse Dress:
Informal / casual.
Clubhouse Facilities:
Full bar, catering available by arrangement.

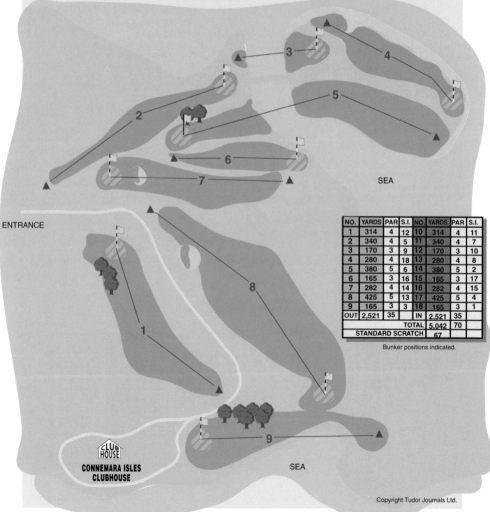

ENTRANCE

SEA

SEA

CONNEMARA ISLES
CLUBHOUSE

NO.	YARDS	PAR	S.I.	NO.	YARDS	PAR	S.I.
1	314	4	12	10	314	4	11
2	340	4	5	11	340	4	7
3	170	3	9	12	170	3	10
4	280	4	18	13	280	4	8
5	380	5	6	14	380	5	2
6	165	3	16	15	165	3	17
7	282	4	14	16	282	4	15
8	425	5	13	17	425	5	4
9	165	3	3	18	165	3	1
OUT	2,521	35		IN	2,521	35	
				TOTAL	5,042	70	
			STANDARD SCRATCH		67		

Bunker positions indicated.

Copyright Tudor Journals Ltd.

350

Galway Golf Club, Blackrock, Galway.
Tel: (091) 521827.

LOCATION: 3 miles west of Galway city.
SECRETARY: Padraic Fahy.
Tel: (091) 522033 (office).
PROFESSIONAL: Don Wallace.
Tel: (091) 523038.

A tight tree lined course. Some tiered greens make it very important to accurately place your drives and a good short game is necessary to score well. The course has excellent views of Galway Bay, the Burren and the Arran Islands.

COURSE INFORMATION

Par 70; SSS 71; Length 5,816 Metres.
Visitors: Welcome.
Opening Hours: 8am – Dusk.
Avoid: Tuesday, Saturday and Sunday.
Ladies: Welcome.

Green Fees: £18 weekdays, £23 weekends; Group rate (minimum 25) £15. **Clubhouse Hours:** 11am – 11pm.
Clubhouse Dress: Informal.
Clubhouse Facilities: At all times.
Open Competitions: May 13th – June 1st: Guinness Open; June 5th – 15th: Festival of Golf; July 27th – 31st: Race Week; Aug 1st – 3rd: Open Weekend.

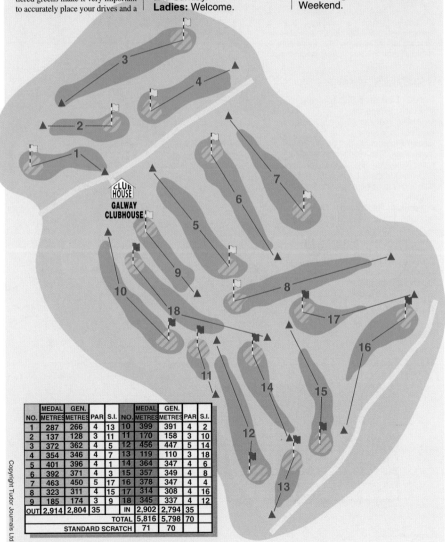

NO.	MEDAL METRES	GEN. METRES	PAR	S.I.	NO.	MEDAL METRES	GEN. METRES	PAR	S.I.
1	287	266	4	13	10	399	391	4	2
2	137	128	3	11	11	170	158	3	10
3	372	362	4	5	12	456	447	5	14
4	354	346	4	7	13	119	110	3	18
5	401	396	4	1	14	364	347	4	6
6	392	371	4	3	15	357	349	4	8
7	463	450	5	17	16	378	347	4	4
8	323	311	4	15	17	314	308	4	16
9	185	174	3	9	18	345	337	4	12
OUT	2,914	2,804	35		IN	2,902	2,794	35	
					TOTAL	5,816	5,798	70	
					STANDARD SCRATCH	71	70		

Galway Bay Golf & Country Club, Renville, Oranmore, Co. Galway.
Tel: (091) 790500.
Fax: (091) 790510.

LOCATION: Six miles south of Galway City.
DIRECTOR OF GOLF: Eamonn Meagher.
Tel: (091) 790500.
PROFESSIONAL: Eugene O'Connor.
Tel: (091) 790503.
ARCHITECT: Christy O'Connor Jnr.

Christy O'Connor Jnr, Ryder & world cup player, designed this 18 hole course to highlight and preserve the ancient historic features of the Renville Peninsula. The spectacular setting on Galway Bay is distractingly beautiful and the cleverly designed mix of holes presents a real golfing challenge which demands total concentration.

COURSE INFORMATION

Par 72; Length 6,533 metres.
Visitors: Welcome.
Opening Hours: 7am – 7.30pm.
Ladies: Welcome.
Green Fees: Apr–Oct 98 – £30 weekdays, £35 weekends & bank hols; Nov–Mar 98 – £25 weekdays, £30 weekends & bank hols. Group discounts available, phone for details.
Juveniles: Restricted – Before 8.30am, 11am – 12 noon & 3pm – 4pm (weekdays).
Clubhouse Hours: 7am – 11pm.
Clubhouse Dress: Informal.
Clubhouse Facilities: Restaurant, Spike Bar & Cocktail Bar – all day.
Open Competitions:
June / July – by invitation.

NO.	MEDAL METRES	GEN. METRES	PAR	S.I.	NO.	MEDAL METRES	GEN. METRES	PAR	S.I.
1	506	486	5	14	10	411	367	4	5
2	409	362	4	2	11	377	356	4	7
3	387	370	4	10	12	400	372	4	1
4	155	136	3	16	13	158	148	3	15
5	336	363	4	8	14	501	464	5	9
6	481	434	5	12	15	172	160	3	17
7	138	126	3	18	16	496	481	5	11
8	418	386	4	6	17	349	323	4	13
9	400	374	4	4	18	439	423	4	3
OUT	3,230	2,997	36		IN	3,303	3,094	36	
					TOTAL	6,533	6,091	72	
					STANDARD SCRATCH	73	71		

GALWAY BAY CLUBHOUSE | CLUB HOUSE

Bunker positions indicated.

**Gort Golf Club,
Castlequarter,
Gort, Co. Galway.
Tel: (091) 632244.**

LOCATION: Kilmacduagh
road, Gort.
HON. SECRETARY: Sean Devlin.
Tel: (091) 631281.
ARCHITECT: Christy
O'Connor Jnr.

A parkland course with out-of-bounds
areas on numerous holes. The course
has several unusual features and has

only recently been upgraded to an 18
hole course. Set in an area of rare beauty,
the course provides the visitor with a
true but fair challenge.

COURSE INFORMATION

**Par 71; SSS 69; Length
5,705 metres.
Visitors:** Welcome to play
everyday.
Opening Hours: Dawn to dusk.
Avoid: Sunday mornings
to 11.00am.

Ladies: Welcome Tuesdays.
Juveniles: Welcome before
6.00pm.
Green Fees: £12 daily. Four
ball – £40 Mon – Fri.
Clubhouse Hours: 10.00am
– 11.30pm.
Clubhouse Hours:
10.00am – 11.30pm.
Clubhouse Dress: Casual.
Clubhouse Facilities:
Light meals.
Open Competitions: Open
Week – 29th June – 6th July.

NO.	METRES	PAR	S.I.	NO.	METRES	PAR	S.I.
1	339	4	9	10	298	4	6
2	397	4	5	11	360	4	2
3	373	4	3	12	295	4	8
4	325	4	7	13	160	3	14
5	126	3	15	14	482	5	16
6	271	4	17	15	303	4	10
7	407	4	1	16	156	3	18
8	151	3	13	17	440	5	12
9	478	5	11	18	344	4	4
OUT	2,867	35		IN	2,838	36	
				TOTAL	5,705	71	
	STANDARD SCRATCH				69		

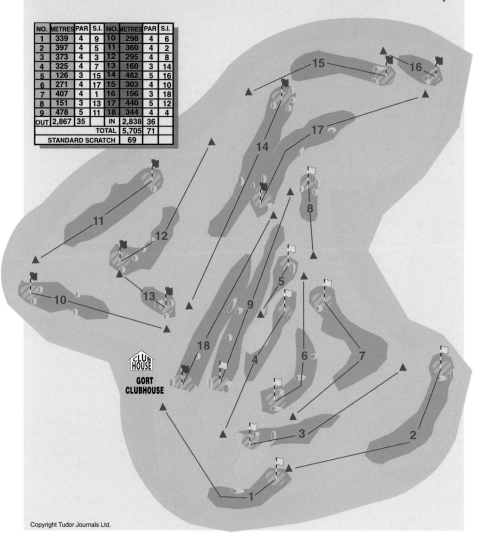

**GORT
CLUBHOUSE**

NO.	MEDAL METRES	GEN. METRES	PAR	S.I.	NO.	MEDAL METRES	GEN. METRES	PAR	S.I.
1	336	330	4	11	10	368	351	4	2
2	375	347	4	8	11	146	124	3	12
3	392	381	4	3	12	445	427	5	7
4	187	178	3	9	13	307	291	4	6
5	388	383	4	1	14	134	121	3	18
6	354	340	4	5	15	267	242	4	4
7	260	243	4	14	16	421	415	5	13
8	120	105	3	15	17	160	135	3	16
9	259	242	4	17	18	342	332	4	10
OUT	2,671	2,549	34		IN	2,590	2,438	35	
					TOTAL	5,261	4,987	69	
		STANDARD SCRATCH				69	69		

Loughrea Golf Club, Craigu, Loughrea, Co. Galway.
Tel: (091) 841049.

LOCATION: One mile south east on the Loughrea to Bullaun road.
SECRETARY: David McGann.
Tel: (091) 841049.
ARCHITECT: Eddie Hackett.

The course has wide grassy fairways with smooth greens and has a generally quiet atmosphere. The main course difficulties are the lush rough and the fact that second shots need great accuracy.

COURSE INFORMATION

Par 69; SSS 67; Length 5,261 metres.
Visitors: Welcome.
Opening Hours: 9am – Dusk.
Avoid: Sundays & major competition days.
Green Fees: £12 daily.
Juveniles: Welcome (before 6pm). Lessons available by arrangement.
Clubhouse Hours: Open all day.
Clubhouse Dress: Casual.
Clubhouse Facilities: New clubhouse, full catering facilities all day.
Open Competitions: Most Bank Holiday weekends and Open Weeks in June and August.

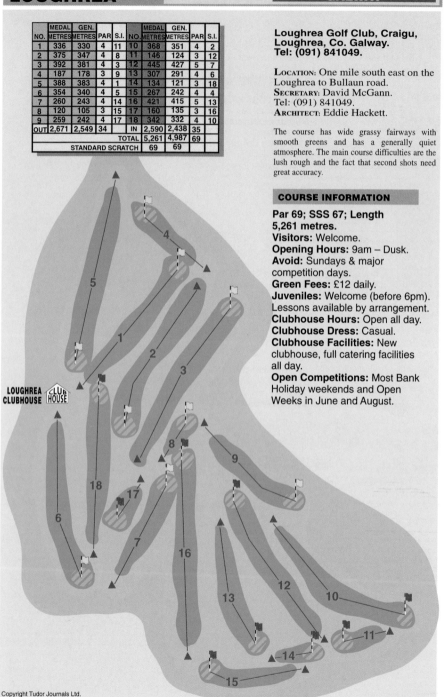

LOUGHREA CLUBHOUSE

**Mountbellew Golf Club,
Mountbellew, Ballinasloe,
Co. Galway.
Tel: (0905) 79259.**

LOCATION: Ballinasloe 17 miles,
Galway 30 miles and Roscommon
20 miles.
CAPTAIN: Noel Flesk.
HON. SECRETARY: Joe Clarke.
Tel: (0905) 79306.

Parkland course in sylvan setting. Ideal
for a casual, leisurely round or a day of
golf. Generous fairways on all

holes with the greens always in good
condition.

COURSE INFORMATION

**Par 69; SSS 66; Length
5,143 metres.
Visitors:** Wecome to play, no
special arrangements required.
Opening Hours:
Daylight hours.
Avoid: Saturday afternoons
(Ladies competitions). Sunday
all day (Mens competitions).

Green Fees: £7 every day;
£30 per weekly ticket.
Clubhouse Hours:
3.00pm – 9.00pm.
Clubhouse Dress: Informal.
Clubhouse Facilities: Light
snacks in bar. Outings catered
for by arrangement.
Open Competitions:
Open Week – June.

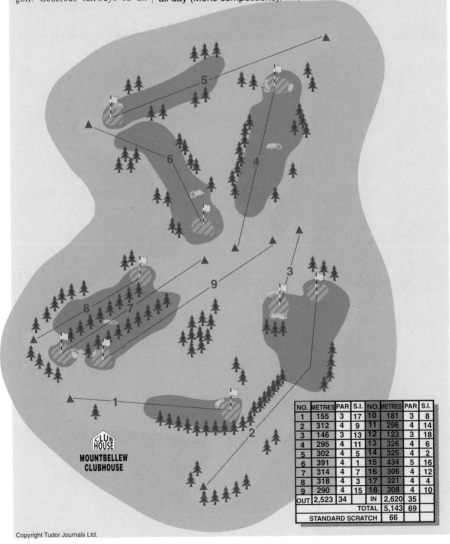

MOUNTBELLEW
CLUBHOUSE

NO.	METRES	PAR	S.I.	NO.	METRES	PAR	S.I.
1	155	3	17	10	181	3	8
2	312	4	9	11	296	4	14
3	146	3	13	12	123	3	18
4	295	4	11	13	326	4	6
5	302	4	5	14	325	4	2
6	391	4	1	15	434	5	16
7	314	4	7	16	306	4	12
8	318	4	3	17	321	4	4
9	290	4	15	18	308	4	10
OUT	2,523	34		IN	2,620	35	
				TOTAL	5,143	69	
STANDARD SCRATCH		66					

Gortreevagh, Oughterard, Co. Galway
Tel: (091) 552131.
Fax: (091) 552733.

LOCATION: Fifteen miles west of Galway City en route to Connemara.
SECRETARY: John Waters.
Tel: (091) 552131,
PROFESSIONAL: Michael Ryan.
Tel: (091) 552626.
ARCHITECT: Dr Harris/E Hackett.

A beautiful and mature parkland course on the shores of Lough Corrib, Oughterard is renowned for its friendly and welcoming atmosphere. Always in pristine condition with a variety of trees and shrubs to punish wayward shots to otherwise generous and lush fairways.

COURSE INFORMATION

Par 70; SSS 69; Length 5,506 metres.
Visitors: Welcome. Restricted at weekends, due to competitions.
Opening Hours: Sunrise – sunset.
Avoid: Telephone in advance.
Ladies: Wednesday.
Green Fees: £15 Mon – Sun.
Juveniles: Welcome.

Clubhouse Hours: 8.00am –12.00pm (except Winter). Full clubhouse facilities.
Clubhouse Dress: Casual.
Clubhouse Facilities: Breakfast from 8.00am – 10.30am; full dinner menu everyday all day until 10.00pm.
Open Competitions: Open Week in June. Many Open Weekends throughout the year. Handicap Certificate required for Open Competitions.

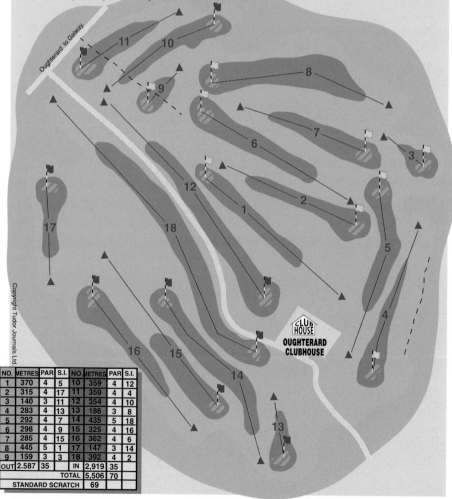

NO.	METRES	PAR	S.I.	NO.	METRES	PAR	S.I.
1	370	4	5	10	359	4	12
2	315	4	17	11	359	4	4
3	140	3	11	12	354	4	10
4	283	4	13	13	186	3	8
5	292	4	7	14	435	5	18
6	298	4	9	15	325	4	16
7	285	4	15	16	362	4	6
8	445	5	1	17	147	3	14
9	159	3	3	18	392	4	2
OUT	2.587	35		IN	2,919	35	
				TOTAL	5,506	70	
STANDARD SCRATCH					69		

Copyright Tudor Journals Ltd.

Portumna, Co. Galway.
Tel: (0509) 41059.

LOCATION: Less than two miles
west of Portumna on the
Woodford Road
HON. SECRETARY: Richard Clarke.
Tel: (0509) 41214.
CAPTAIN: P.J. Starr.
Tel: (067) 22046.

Located in Portumna Forest Park, this
is a very attractive woodland course
with plenty of mature trees. Deer can
sometimes be found on the course.
The finishing Par 3 hole is the most

difficult of the round, playing to an
elevated green.

COURSE INFORMATION

**Par 68; SSS 67; Length
5,474 metres.**
Visitors: Welcome to play
every day.
Opening Hours: 9am – Dusk.
Avoid: Sunday.
Ladies: Welcome.
Green Fees: £12.
Juveniles: Welcome.
Clubhouse Hours: 9.00am –

10.00pm. (Summer).
Clubhouse Dress: Casual.
Clubhouse Facilities:
Catering facilities by prior
arrangement.
Open Competitions:
Handicap Certificate required
for Open Competitions. Open
week – July.

NO.	METRES	PAR	S.I.	NO.	METRES	PAR	S.I.
1	406	4	3	10	241	4	2
2	166	3	13	11	350	4	10
3	405	4	1	12	332	4	4
4	300	4	15	13	149	3	8
5	140	3	17	14	368	4	6
6	327	4	11	15	453	5	16
7	374	4	5	16	161	3	18
8	235	4	9	17	362	4	7
9	345	4	12	18	160	3	14
OUT	2,798	34		IN	2,676	34	
				TOTAL	5,474	68	
	STANDARD SCRATCH				67		

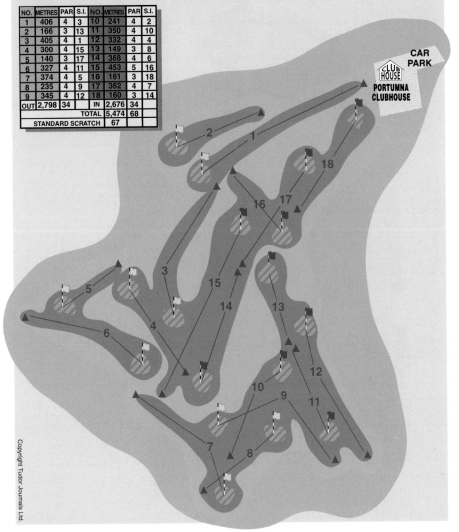

CAR PARK

CLUB HOUSE

PORTUMNA CLUBHOUSE

NO.	CHAMP METRES	MEDAL METRES	PAR	S.I.	NO.	CHAMP METRES	MEDAL METRES	PAR	S.I.
1	368	361	4	5	10	331	311	4	18
2	469	464	5	15	11	340	335	4	16
3	384	374	4	3	12	183	172	3	6
4	312	307	4	9	13	478	468	5	12
5	484	454	5	13	14	309	303	4	8
6	172	166	3	11	15	346	326	4	4
7	381	358	4	1	16	152	142	3	14
8	133	131	3	17	17	486	456	5	10
9	349	339	4	7	18	368	358	4	2
OUT	3,052	2,954	36		IN	2,993	2,871	36	
					TOTAL	6,045	5,825	72	
	STANDARD SCRATCH					71	70		

Tuam Golf Club, Barnacurragh, Tuam, Co. Galway.
Tel: (093) 28993.
Fax: (093) 26003.

LOCATION: Twenty miles north of Galway.
SECRETARY: Vincent Gaffney.
Tel: (093) 28993.
CAPTAIN: B.P.O. Brien.
HON. SECRETARY: John Davin.
PROFESSIONAL: Larry Smyth.
Tel: (093) 24091.

There is on-going development on this course. The fairways are guarded by plantations and trees, with greens well bunkered. Tuam recently completed their new clubhouse development.

COURSE INFORMATION

Par 72; SSS 69; Length 5,944 Metres.
Visitors: Welcome any weekday.
Opening Hours: 8.00am – Sunset.
Avoid: Saturday mornings and Sundays.
Ladies: Welcome.
Green Fees: £12 Mon–Fri; £15 Sat/Sun.
Juveniles: Must be accompanied by an adult after 5pm. Lessons available. Club Hire, Caddy service.
Clubhouse Hours: 9.00am – 12 midnight (except winter).
Clubhouse Dress: Casual / neat
Clubhouse Facilities: Bar and Catering facilities everyday (full restaurant).
Open Competitions: Open Weekends, 29th & 30th March / 19th & 20th July / 25th – 27th October. Open week, 15th – 22nd June.

Bunker positions indicated.

**Ballinamore Golf Club,
Ballinamore, Co. Leitrim
Tel: (078) 44346.**

LOCATION: Two miles north west of Ballinamore.
SECRETARY: Peter Duignan.
Tel: (078) 44163.

Members will confirm there is a large degree of difficulty with the course. Things are made interesting with a canal alongside the 3rd hole and the back of the 9th green. Also, 9 new holes from last year.

COURSE INFORMATION

**Par 66; SSS 63; Length
5,192 metres.**
Visitors: Welcome except on Captain's or President's Day.
Opening Hours:
8.00am – sunset.
Avoid: Sundays.
Ladies: Welcome.
Green Fees: £10 (£5 with a member). A Handicap Certificate is required.
Clubhouse Hours:
9.00am – 11.00pm.

Clubhouse Dress: Casual.
Clubhouse Facilities:
Catering facilities – soup and sandwiches.
Open Competitions: Open Week and certain weekends.

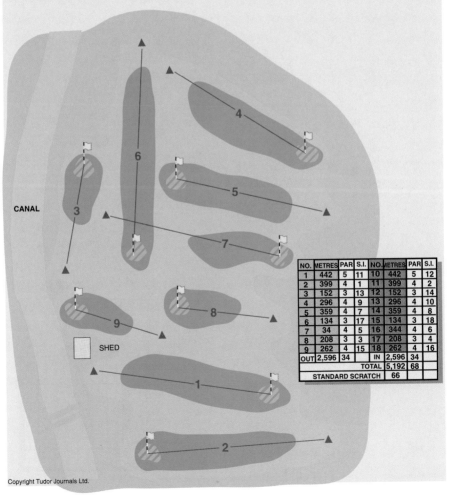

CANAL

SHED

NO.	METRES	PAR	S.I.	NO.	METRES	PAR	S.I.
1	442	5	11	10	442	5	12
2	399	4	1	11	399	4	2
3	152	3	13	12	152	3	14
4	296	4	9	13	296	4	10
5	359	4	7	14	359	4	8
6	134	3	17	15	134	3	18
7	34	4	5	16	344	4	6
8	208	3	3	17	208	3	4
9	262	4	15	18	262	4	16
OUT	2,596	34		IN	2,596	34	
				TOTAL	5,192	68	
				STANDARD SCRATCH		66	

Achill Golf Club, Keel, Co. Mayo.
Tel: (098) 43456.

Location: Keel, Achill.
Secretary / Manager:
P. Lavelle.

A scenic links course situated beside a large beach. Achill course is of a level and open nature – continuously grazed by sheep. Fairways marked by white stones.

COURSE INFORMATION

Par 70; SSS 67; Length 5,378 metres.
Visitors: Welcome.
Opening Hours: Dawn – Dusk.
Ladies: Welcome.
Green Fees: On application.
Juveniles: Must be accompanied by an adult.
Clubhouse Hours: Same as course.

Clubhouse Dress: Casual.
Open Competitions: Handicap Certificate required for open competitions.

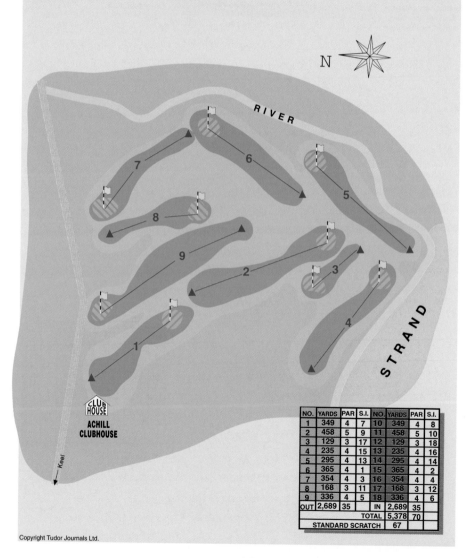

NO.	YARDS	PAR	S.I.	NO.	YARDS	PAR	S.I.
1	349	4	7	10	349	4	8
2	458	5	9	11	458	5	10
3	129	3	17	12	129	3	18
4	235	4	15	13	235	4	16
5	295	4	13	14	295	4	14
6	365	4	1	15	365	4	2
7	354	4	3	16	354	4	4
8	168	3	11	17	168	3	12
9	336	4	5	18	336	4	6
OUT	2,689	35		IN	2,689	35	
				TOTAL	5,378	70	
				STANDARD SCRATCH	67		

ACHILL CLUBHOUSE

Ballina Golf Club,
Mossgrove, Shanaghy,
Ballina, Co. Mayo.
Tel: (096) 21050.
Fax: (096) 21050.

LOCATION: Shanaghy, Ballina.

SECRETARY: V. Frawley.
Tel: (096) 21050.

A flat inland course, with fairways guarded by plantations.

COURSE INFORMATION

Par 71; SSS 69; Length 6,103 yards.
Visitors: Welcome.
Opening Hours: 8am –10pm (summer); 9am – 6pm (winter).
Avoid: Sunday mornings.
Ladies: Welcome.
Green Fees: Mon – Fri £12 per day; Sat / Sun / Bank Holidays £16; weekly ticket £35. H/Wife Mon – Fri £20; Sat / Sun / Bank Holidays £25; weekly £60.

Societies rates available.
Juveniles: Welcome.
Clubhouse Hours: 9.00am –11.00pm.
Clubhouse Dress: Neat / Casual.
Clubhouse Facilities: Catering and bar facilities available.
Open Competitions: Whit Weekend; Open Weekend – August. Handicap Certificate required for Open Competitions.

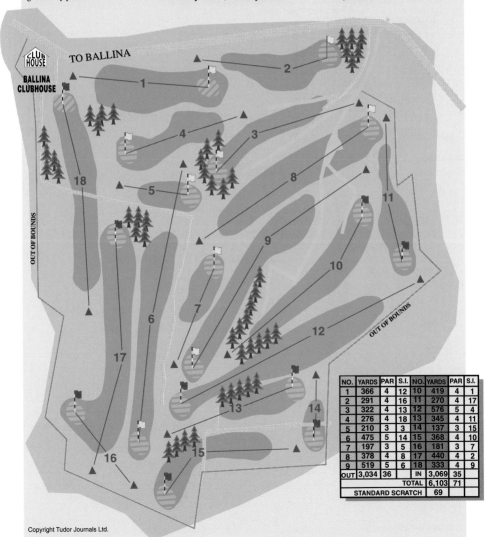

NO.	YARDS	PAR	S.I.	NO.	YARDS	PAR	S.I.
1	366	4	12	10	419	4	1
2	291	4	16	11	270	4	17
3	322	4	13	12	576	5	4
4	276	4	18	13	345	4	11
5	210	3	13	14	137	3	15
6	475	5	14	15	368	4	10
7	197	3	5	16	181	3	7
8	378	4	8	17	440	4	2
9	519	5	6	18	333	4	9
OUT	3,034	36		IN	3,069	35	
				TOTAL	6,103	71	
				STANDARD SCRATCH	69		

**Ballinrobe Golf Club,
Castlebar Road,
Ballinrobe, Co. Mayo.
Tel: (092) 41118.**

LOCATION: 30 miles from Galway. 20 miles from Castlebar and Westport.
SECRETARY: Tom Feerick.
Tel: (092) 41118.
ARCHITECT: Mr Eddie Hackett.

This scenic parkland course will offer a challenge to any golfer with its mature trees, man-made lakes, lush fairways and traditional stone walls. The greens are notable with their sweeping contours and good drainage.

COURSE INFORMATION

Par 73; SSS 73; Length 6,234 metres.
Visitors: Welcome.
Opening Hours: 7am – 8pm (summer) & 9am – 3pm (winter).
Avoid: Sunday and Tuesday evenings.
Ladies: Welcome.
Green Fees: £18 per round, £70 per week.

Juveniles: Welcome.
Clubhouse Hours: 10.00am – 6.00pm (June – August).
Clubhouse Dress: Casual.
Clubhouse Facilities: The clubhouse is a fully restored 250 year old estate house. Which offers golfers a restaurant with full bar, comfortable and well appointed changing rooms.
Open Competitions: Contact club for details.

NO.	METRES	PAR	S.I.	NO.	METRES	PAR	S.I.
1	336	4	15	10	365	4	2
2	410	4	1	11	364	4	8
3	175	3	9	12	348	4	10
4	478	5	11	13	156	3	12
5	354	4	7	14	491	5	16
6	484	5	5	15	348	4	6
7	158	3	13	16	156	3	14
8	490	5	3	17	376	4	4
9	302	4	17	18	443	5	18
OUT	3,187	37		IN	3,047	36	
				TOTAL	6,234	73	
				STANDARD SCRATCH	73		

Bunker positions indicated.

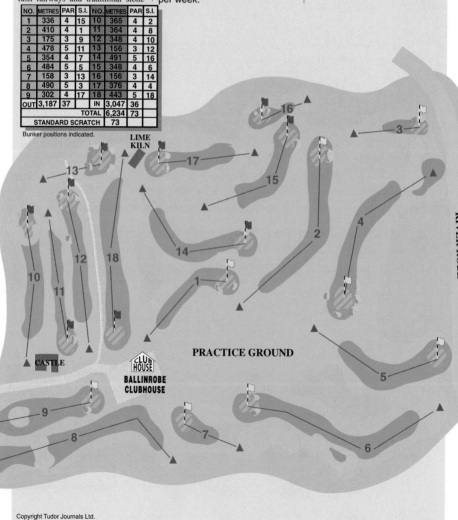

LIME KILN

PRACTICE GROUND

CASTLE

CLUB HOUSE
BALLINROBE CLUBHOUSE

RIVER ROBE

Ballyhaunis Golf Club, Coolnaha, Co. Mayo.
Tel: (0907) 30014.

LOCATION: 2 miles north of Ballyhaunis on the Charlstown Road. 7 miles from Horan International Airport.
HON. SECRETARY: Thomas McNicholas. Tel: (094) 81398 (day), (094) 81415 (evening).
CAPTAIN: Alex Caton.

An interesting parkland course situated close to the famous Knock Shrine. The main features of Ballyhaunis are its pleasant elevated greens protected with well positioned bunkers.

COURSE INFORMATION

Par 70; SSS 69; Length 5,801 yards, 5,413 metres.
Visitors: Welcome at all times.
Opening Hours: 9.00am – sunset.
Avoid: Members competitions on Sundays & Thursdays.
Ladies: Welcome Thursdays.
Green Fees: £10 per day.
Juveniles: Welcome (Handicap Certificate required). Must be off the course by 3.00pm unless accompanied by an adult. Caddy service available by prior arrangement summer only.
Clubhouse Hours: Licencing hours.
Clubhouse Dress: Casual. During presentations – jacket and tie.
Clubhouse Facilities: Full catering facilities by prior arrangement. Snacks available normally.
Open Competitions: Open Competition 5th July. Open Week 13th July. Handicap Certificate required.

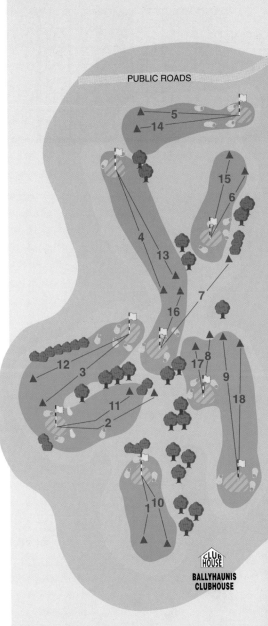

PUBLIC ROADS

BALLYHAUNIS
CLUBHOUSE

NO.	MEDAL METRES	GEN METRES	PAR	S.I.	NO.	MEDAL METRES	GEN METRES	PAR	S.I.
1	359	355	4	3	10	372	364	4	4
2	309	304	4	9	11	337	334	4	6
3	447	442	5	11	12	412	410	5	14
4	360	355	4	1	13	354	347	4	2
5	282	278	4	15	14	273	269	4	16
6	153	149	3	13	15	149	145	3	18
7	322	317	4	7	16	301	295	4	10
8	126	121	3	17	17	148	143	3	12
9	359	354	4	5	18	350	345	4	8
OUT	2,717	2,675	35		IN	2,696	2,652	35	
					TOTAL	5,413	5,327	70	
					STANDARD SCRATCH		69		

Bunker/hedge and tree positions indicated.
Copyright Tudor Journals Ltd.

Carne Golf Links, Carn, Belmullet, Co. Mayo.
Tel: (097) 82292.
Fax: (097) 81477.

LOCATION: On the Mullet Peninsula near Belmullet, Co. Mayo. 2.5KM from Belmullet.
SECRETARY: A.F. Valkenburg.
ARCHITECT: Eddie Hackett.

This new exciting links has a natural setting of considerable beauty. Splendid sand dunes on ancient commonage. Elevated tees and plateau greens exploit the magnificent backdrops over Blacksod Bay.

NO.	MEDAL METRES	GEN METRES	PAR	S.I.	NO.	MEDAL METRES	GEN METRES	PAR	S.I.
1	366	356	4	6	10	465	432	5	15
2	183	149	3	16	11	332	302	4	5
3	376	370	4	12	12	271	265	4	13
4	473	463	5	18	13	482	446	5	9
5	378	327	4	14	14	133	129	3	11
6	363	355	4	2	15	366	356	4	3
7	162	154	3	8	16	154	142	3	17
8	365	360	4	4	17	399	392	4	1
9	327	320	4	10	18	495	485	5	7
OUT	2,993	2,854	35		IN	3,097	2,950	37	
					TOTAL	6,090	5,804	72	
	STANDARD SCRATCH					73	72		

COURSE INFORMATION

Par 72; SSS 72; Length 6,090 metres.
Visitors: Welcome anytime.
Green Fees: £20.
Club Facilities: Practice range, Caddy and Car Hire.
Clubhouse Facilities: Bar and restaurant.

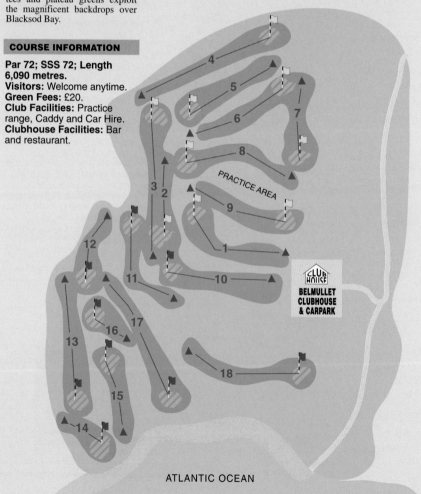

ATLANTIC OCEAN

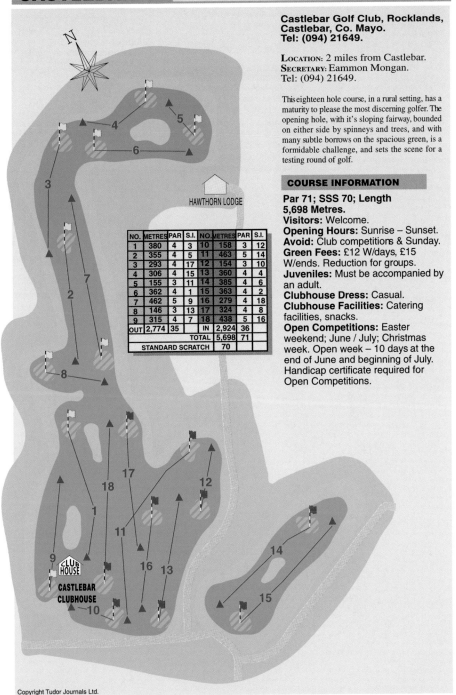

Castlebar Golf Club, Rocklands, Castlebar, Co. Mayo.
Tel: (094) 21649.

LOCATION: 2 miles from Castlebar.
SECRETARY: Eammon Mongan.
Tel: (094) 21649.

This eighteen hole course, in a rural setting, has a maturity to please the most discerning golfer. The opening hole, with it's sloping fairway, bounded on either side by spinneys and trees, and with many subtle borrows on the spacious green, is a formidable challenge, and sets the scene for a testing round of golf.

COURSE INFORMATION

Par 71; SSS 70; Length 5,698 Metres.
Visitors: Welcome.
Opening Hours: Sunrise – Sunset.
Avoid: Club competitions & Sunday.
Green Fees: £12 W/days, £15 W/ends. Reduction for groups.
Juveniles: Must be accompanied by an adult.
Clubhouse Dress: Casual.
Clubhouse Facilities: Catering facilities, snacks.
Open Competitions: Easter weekend; June / July; Christmas week. Open week – 10 days at the end of June and beginning of July. Handicap certificate required for Open Competitions.

HAWTHORN LODGE

CASTLEBAR CLUBHOUSE

NO.	METRES	PAR	S.I.	NO.	METRES	PAR	S.I.
1	380	4	3	10	158	3	12
2	355	4	5	11	463	5	14
3	293	4	17	12	154	3	10
4	306	4	15	13	360	4	4
5	155	3	11	14	385	4	6
6	362	4	1	15	363	4	2
7	462	5	9	16	279	4	18
8	146	3	13	17	324	4	8
9	315	4	7	18	438	5	16
OUT	2,774	35		IN	2,924	36	
				TOTAL	5,698	71	
				STANDARD SCRATCH	70		

Copyright Tudor Journals Ltd.

**Claremorris Golf Club,
Castlemagarrett,
Claremorris, Co. Mayo.
Tel: (094) 71527.**

LOCATION: Galway Road, 2
miles from town.
SECRETARY / MANAGER: Willy
Feely.
Tel: (094) 71868.

A difficult nine hole course. Very hilly
and usually very undercrowded except
for competitions which are played
mostly on Sundays. Claremorris Golf
Club was formed in 1918 and

some members still recall Christy
O'Connor Senior giving lessons in the
1940's at 2/6d (12 pence) per half hour.
Upgrading to a nine hole course in June.

COURSE INFORMATION

**Par 73; SSS 72; Length
6,300 metres.
Visitors:** Welcome to play at
any time.
Avoid: Competitions for members.
Ladies: Welcome.
Juveniles: Welcome
Green Fees: Weekdays – £12; £6

with a member. Weekends and
Bank Holidays – £14 ; £8 with a
member. Societies £10.
Clubhouse Dress: Casual.
Clubhouse Facilities:
Catering and bar facilities by
prior arrangement.

NO.	YARDS	PAR	S.I.	NO.	YARDS	PAR	S.I.
1	380	4	3	10	158	3	12
2	346	4	5	11	463	5	14
3	293	4	17	12	154	3	10
4	306	4	15	13	360	4	4
5	155	3	11	14	283	4	6
6	357	4	1	15	363	4	2
7	462	5	9	16	279	4	18
8	146	3	13	17	324	4	8
9	315	4	7	18	438	5	16
OUT	2,760	35		IN	2,822	36	
					TOTAL	5,582	71
				STANDARD SCRATCH		69	

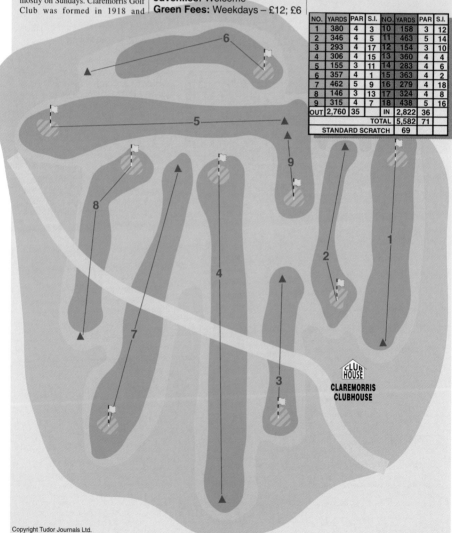

CLUB
HOUSE
**CLAREMORRIS
CLUBHOUSE**

**Swinford Golf Club,
Barbazon Park, Swinford,
Co. Mayo.
Tel: (094) 51378.**

LOCATION: Beside Swinford town.
HON SECRETARY: Tom Regan.
Tel: (094) 51502.
HEAD GROUNDSMAN: Michael Farrelly.

There are quite a number of trees on the course which adds considerably to the difficulty of wayward shots.

COURSE INFORMATION

**Par 70; SSS 68; Length 5,542 metres.
Visitors:** Welcome everyday.
Opening Hours: All day everyday
Ladies: Welcome.

Green Fees: £10 per day.
Juveniles: Permitted.
Clubhouse Hours: Open all day.
Clubhouse Dress: Casual.
Clubhouse Facilities: Bar.
Catering by request.
Open Competitions: Open weekends: 30th May – 1st June; 24th Oct – 26th Oct.
Open Week;1st week in August.
Handicap certificate required.

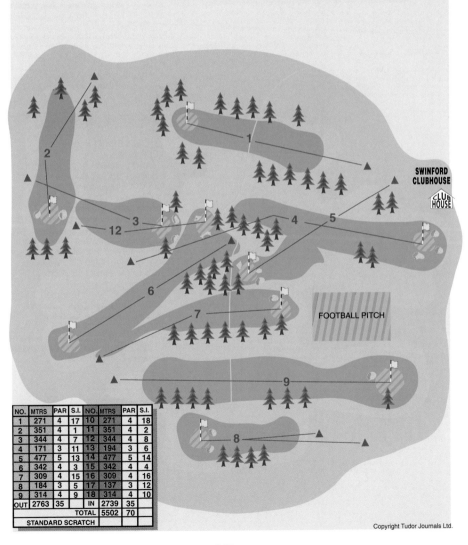

NO.	MTRS	PAR	S.I.	NO.	MTRS	PAR	S.I.
1	271	4	17	10	271	4	18
2	351	4	1	11	351	4	2
3	344	4	7	12	344	4	8
4	171	3	11	13	194	3	6
5	477	5	13	14	477	5	14
6	342	4	3	15	342	4	4
7	309	4	15	16	309	4	16
8	184	3	5	17	137	3	12
9	314	4	9	18	314	4	10
OUT	2763	35		IN	2739	35	
				TOTAL	5502	70	
STANDARD SCRATCH							

NO.	CHAMP YARDS	MEDAL YARDS	PAR	S.I.	NO.	CHAMP YARDS	MEDAL YARDS	PAR	S.I.
1	344	335	4	14	10	537	498	5	11
2	345	330	4	8	11	437	420	4	3
3	168	142	3	16	12	220	208	3	5
4	502	488	5	18	13	455	412	4	1
5	360	343	4	10	14	191	180	3	7
6	463	445	4	4	15	580	515	5	9
7	529	511	5	12	16	363	350	4	15
8	472	455	4	2	17	378	343	4	13
9	208	196	3	6	18	520	499	5	17
OUT	3,391	3,252	36		IN	3,695	3,401	37	
					TOTAL	7,086	6,653	73	
			STANDARD SCRATCH			72	73		

Westport Golf Club, Carrowholly, Westport, Co. Mayo.
Tel: (098) 28262/27070.

LOCATION: 2½ miles from Westport town.
MANAGER: Pat Smyth.
Tel: (098) 28262.
PROFESSIONAL: Alex Mealia.
Tel: (098) 28262.
ARCHITECT: Fred Hawtree.

Situated on the shores of Clew Bay and set in 260 acres of parkland, Westport offers golfers a memorable challenge. The course commands a wonderful view of Clew Bay and is dominated by the Holy Mountain, Croagh Patrick. The best known hole on this course is the Par 5 fifteenth which reaches 580 yards (535 metres) and features a long carry from the tee over an inlet of Clew Bay. Designed by the noted golf architect Fred Hawtree, who also designed the new course at St Andrews.

COURSE INFORMATION

Par 73; SSS 72; Length 6,653 yards.
Visitors: Welcome (phone first).
Opening Hours: Sunrise to sunset.
Avoid: Competition days.
Ladies: Welcome.
Green Fees: Weekdays – £18; weekends & Bank Holidays – £23. Special rates for societies.
Juveniles: Welcome. Lessons and Caddy service available by prior arrangement. Club hire available.
Clubhouse Hours: 9.00am – 11.30pm.
Clubhouse Dress: Informal.
Clubhouse Facilities: Catering facilities – meals available 9am – 10pm.
Open Competitions: Open week in August. Handicap Certificate required for Open Competitions.

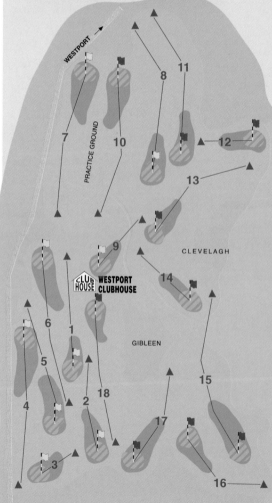

WESTPORT

PRACTICE GROUND

CLEVELAGH

CLUB HOUSE WESTPORT CLUBHOUSE

GIBLEEN

**Athlone Golf Club,
Hodson Bay, Athlone,
Co. Roscommon.
Tel: (0902) 92073/92235.**

LOCATION: Four miles from Athlone.
HON. SECRETARY: Tony Corry. Tel: (0902) 92073.
PROFESSIONAL: Martin Quinn. Tel: (0902) 92073 / 92868.
CAPTAIN: John Kinahan.

Athlone has a commanding view of Lough Ree from an elevated Clubhouse. Fairways are guarded by trees and a further large tree plantation recently undertaken should come into play soon. Out of bounds exists on the right of ten fairways. Course well equipped with strategically placed bunkers.

COURSE INFORMATION

Par 71; SSS 70; Length 5,935 metres.
Visitors: Welcome.
Opening Hours: 7.30am – 10.00pm.
Ladies Day: Tuesday.
Green Fees: £15 Mon – Fri; £18 Sat / Sun / Bank Holidays.
Juveniles: Must play with an adult before 3.30pm. Special times on noticeboard. Lessons available by prior arrangements. Club Hire available. Caddy service available by prior arrangements. Handicap Certificate required.

Clubhouse Hours: 7.30am – 11.30pm.
Clubhouse Dress: Casual – no shorts.
Clubhouse Facilities: Full catering facilities available, restaurant hours 9.30am – 10.00pm open all year round.
Open Competitions: Open Week first week in June; Lough Ree Open July and August.

NO.	MEDAL METRES	GEN. METRES	PAR	S.I.	NO.	MEDAL METRES	GEN. METRES	PAR	S.I.
1	348	339	4	7	10	332	322	4	10
2	155	149	3	11	11	457	447	5	12
3	268	261	4	15	12	404	392	4	3
4	380	372	4	4	13	326	316	4	8
5	503	493	5	9	14	300	291	4	16
6	432	421	5	17	15	171	163	3	14
7	392	382	4	5	16	412	397	4	1
8	381	373	4	2	17	120	111	3	18
9	176	166	3	13	18	378	365	4	6
OUT	3,035	2,956	36		IN	2,900	2,804	35	
					TOTAL	5,935	5,760	71	
			STANDARD SCRATCH			71	70		

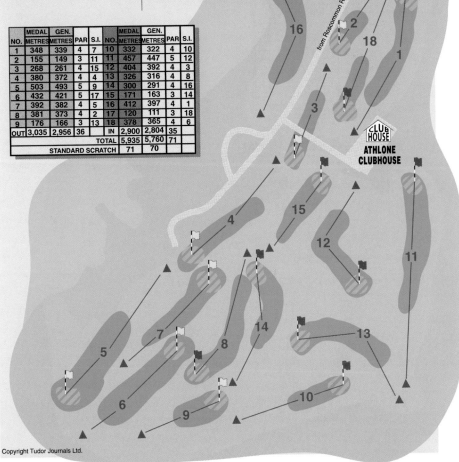

**Ballaghadereen Golf Club,
Aughalustia,
Ballaghadereen,
Co. Roscommon.
Tel: (0907) 60358.**

LOCATION: Three miles from
Ballaghadereen town.
SECRETARY: John Cawley.
Tel: (0907) 20544.

A relatively flat course but trees
which are maturing are becoming a
great asset both visually and also
coming into play. A trip to the rough
can quite easily cost a shot. The 2nd

hole in particular requires great
accuracy to a very small green, well
protected with bunkers.

COURSE INFORMATION

**Par 70; SSS 66; Length
5,180 metres.
Visitors:** Welcome at
all times.
Opening Hours: 9am – Dusk.
Ladies: Welcome.
Green Fees: £6 daily.
Handicap Certificate required
for open competitions.

Juveniles: Welcome. Must be
off course by 6pm. Caddy
service available by prior
arrangement.
Clubhouse Hours: Saturday
& Sunday evenings
Clubhouse Dress: Casual.
Clubhouse Facilities: Bar.
Catering by prior
arrangement.
Open Competitions: Open
week, 7th – 15th June.
Senoirs Open, last Thursday
of each month from May –
September.

NO.	METRES	PAR	S.I.	NO.	METRES	PAR	S.I.
1	342	4	3	10	335	4	4
2	145	3	9	11	105	3	18
3	426	5	16	12	367	4	1
4	150	3	10	13	150	3	11
5	238	4	17	14	284	4	13
6	313	4	7	15	313	4	8
7	353	4	2	16	421	5	12
8	304	4	14	17	305	4	15
9	314	4	5	18	315	4	6
OUT	2,585	35		IN	2,595	35	
				TOTAL	5,180	70	
			STANDARD SCRATCH		66		

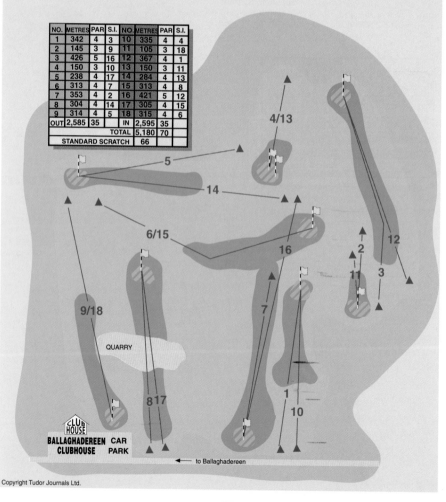

**Boyle Golf Club,
Knockadoobrusna, Boyle,
Co. Roscommon.
Tel: (079) 62594.**

LOCATION: One mile from
Boyle.
SECRETARY: Don Conlon.
Tel: (079) 62594.
HANDICAP SEC: Bartly Moran.
Tel: (079) 62102.

A feature of the course is the views of
Lock Key, Curlew Mountains, Sligo
Mountain and the Mayo Mountains
from the 8th green and 2nd tee. The
course is also within easy reach of
Loch Key and Forest Park, Boyle.

COURSE INFORMATION

**Par 67; SSS 66; Length 4,865
metres.**
Visitors: Welcome at all times.
Opening Hours:
Sunrise – sunset.
Ladies: Welcome Tuesdays.
Green Fees: £10 per round.
Special rate for families £12;
Gentleman & lady £10;
Juvenile £2.
Juveniles: Welcome. Must be
accompanied by an adult and
off the course by 5.00pm
during the summer. Restricted

at weekends, Sat mornings
10.00am – 12.00 noon only.
Club Hire available; Caddy
service available by prior
arrangement.
Clubhouse Hours:
4.00pm – midnight.
Clubhouse Dress: Casual.
Clubhouse Facilities:
Catering facilities: bar snacks.
Open Competitions: Open
Week July; 12 hole open
every Thurs from May – Dec;
Open Scramble every Friday
from May – Sept. Handicap
certificate required.

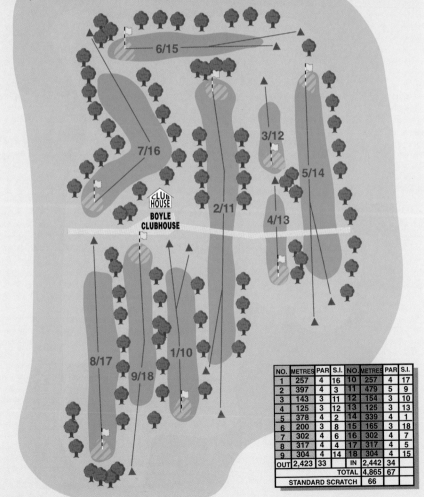

NO.	METRES	PAR	S.I.	NO.	METRES	PAR	S.I.
1	257	4	16	10	257	4	17
2	397	4	3	11	479	5	9
3	143	3	11	12	154	3	10
4	125	3	12	13	125	3	13
5	378	4	2	14	339	4	1
6	200	3	8	15	165	3	18
7	302	4	6	16	302	4	7
8	317	4	4	17	317	4	5
9	304	4	14	18	304	4	15
OUT	2,423	33		IN	2,442	34	
				TOTAL	4,865	67	
				STANDARD SCRATCH	66		

Copyright Tudor Journals Ltd.

**Carrick-on-Shannon,
Co Roscommon.
Tel: (079) 67015.**

LOCATION: Beside N4 route
four miles west of
Carrick-on-Shannon.
HOUSE SEC: Aiden McNally.
Tel: (079) 67015 or
(078) 20317.
CLUB SEC: Diarmuid Croghan.

A pleasant inland course overlooking
the River Shannon, that provides a
good test of golf for any low or high
handicappers.

COURSE INFORMATION

**Par 70; SSS 68; Length
5,545 metres.
Visitors:** Welcome to play at
any time (except
competitions).
Opening Hours: Daylight
hours.
Ladies: Welcome
Wednesdays.
Green Fees: £12 per day.
Juveniles: Welcome
(restricted at weekends).

Clubhouse Hours: 9.30am –
11.00pm.
Clubhouse Dress: Informal.
Clubhouse Facilities: Coffee
and snacks at bar plus full
meals.
Open Competitions: Open
Week – July. Open Weekends
April, June, July & August.
Handicap Certificate required
for Open Competitions.

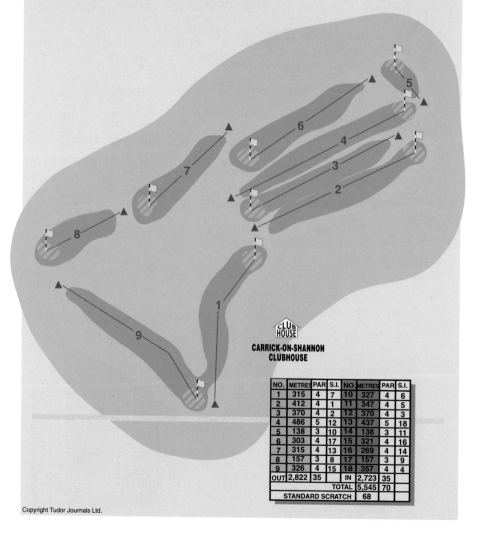

CARRICK-ON-SHANNON
CLUBHOUSE

NO.	METRES	PAR	S.I.	NO.	METRES	PAR	S.I.
1	315	4	7	10	327	4	6
2	412	4	1	11	347	4	5
3	370	4	2	12	370	4	3
4	486	5	12	13	437	5	18
5	138	3	10	14	138	3	11
6	303	4	17	15	321	4	16
7	315	4	13	16	269	4	14
8	157	3	8	17	157	3	9
9	326	4	15	18	357	4	4
OUT	2,822	35		IN	2,723	35	
				TOTAL	5,545	70	
STANDARD SCRATCH					68		

Castlerea Golf Club, Clonailis, Castlerea, Co. Roscommon.
Tel: (0907) 20068.

LOCATION: Town of Castlerea. Between Castlebar and Roscommon.
SECRETARY: Mr. J. Mulligan. Tel: (0907) 20203 / 20705.

This is a short parkland course with three Par 3 holes. River comes into play on 4th, 5th and 8th holes. Narrow fairways make accuracy important, although the light rough does not cause too much frustration for errant shots.

COURSE INFORMATION

Par 68; SSS 66; Length 4,974 metres.
Visitors: Welcome.
Opening Hours: Sunrise – sunset.
Ladies: Welcome.
Green Fees: £10.
Juveniles: Welcome. Caddy service available by prior arrangement. Trolleys for hire.
Clubhouse Hours: 10.30am to closing time. Bar open from 5pm weekdays and all day weekends.

Clubhouse Dress: Casual.
Clubhouse Facilities: By prior arrangment.
Open Competitions: Open Week June; Intermediate Scratch Cup July; Open Mixed Foursomes. Handicap Certificate required for Open Competitions.

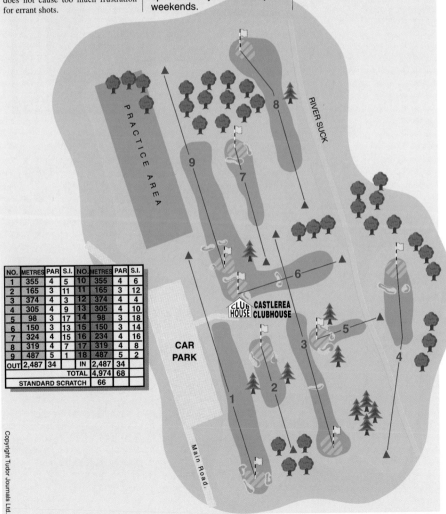

NO.	METRES	PAR	S.I.	NO.	METRES	PAR	S.I.
1	355	4	5	10	355	4	6
2	165	3	11	11	165	3	12
3	374	4	3	12	374	4	4
4	305	4	9	13	305	4	10
5	98	3	17	14	98	3	18
6	150	3	13	15	150	3	14
7	324	4	15	16	234	4	16
8	319	4	7	17	319	4	8
9	487	5	1	18	487	5	2
OUT	2,487	34		IN	2,487	34	
				TOTAL	4,974	68	
		STANDARD SCRATCH			66		

Roscommon Golf Club, Mote Park, Roscommon, Co Roscommon.
Tel: (0903) 26927.

LOCATION: Roscommon Town.
HON. SECRETARY: Brian Campbell.
Tel: (0903) 26927.
SECRETARY: Brian Campbell.
Tel: (0903) 26686.
CAPTAIN: Sean Kilroy.
Tel: (043) 21145.

Though a nine hole course, Roscommon is one of the more challenging golf tests in the Midlands and West. With a standard scratch score of 70, it requires long and

accurate hitting on some holes, while others will test the short game skills of the golfer. Extension to 18 holes due to open in Autumn '95.

COURSE INFORMATION

Par 71; SSS 71 Length 6,040 metres.
Visitors: Welcome to play any time except Tuesdays and Sundays.
Opening Hours: Sunrise – sunset.
Avoid: Summer evenings.
Ladies: Welcome Tuesdays.

Green Fees: £15.00 per day; £10.00 for Societies, weekly tickets on request.
Clubhouse Hours: 2.00pm – 11.30pm.
Clubhouse Dress: Informal.
Clubhouse Facilities: Bar and catering available everyday.
Open Competitions: Open
Weeks: June & Sept.

NO.	METRES	PAR	S.I.	NO.	METRES	PAR	S.I.
1	285	4	17	10	404	4	1
2	343	4	7	11	124	3	18
3	300	4	13	12	455	5	16
4	466	5	15	13	132	3	11
5	363	4	4	14	365	4	6
6	149	3	10	15	357	4	5
7	405	4	5	16	456	5	9
8	408	4	3	17	329	4	14
9	152	3	12	18	384	4	2
OUT	2,871	35		IN	3,006	36	
				TOTAL	5,877	71	
				STANDARD SCRATCH	71		

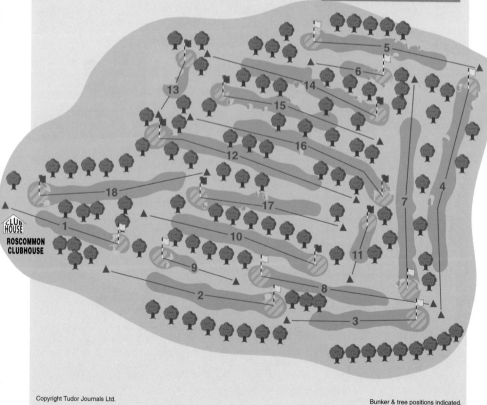

ROSCOMMON
CLUBHOUSE

Bunker & tree positions indicated.

County Sligo Golf Club, Rosses Point, Co Sligo.
Tel: (071) 77186/77134
Fax: (071) 77460.

LOCATION: Eight km. west of Sligo.
SECRETARY: Teresa Banks. Tel: (071) 77134.
PROFESSIONAL: Leslie Robinson. Tel: (071) 77171.
ARCHITECT: Colt & Allison.

Situated under the shadow of famous Benbulben, the County Sligo Golf Club, or Rosses Point as it is more popularly known, is one of Ireland's great championship links. Home of the West of Ireland Championship held each year since 1923. Set among vast sand dunes on the cliffs overlooking three large beaches. Constant winds are an added factor to its many challenges, not least of which are some of its elevated tees. A burn meanders through the course and comes into play on a number of holes.

COURSE INFORMATION

Par 71; SSS 72; Length 6,043 metres.
Visitors: Welcome to play, except during major championship competitions.
Opening Hours: Daylight.
Avoid: Advisable to check tee time available before travel.
Ladies: Welcome.
Green Fees: IR£27 weekdays; Sat / Sun / Bank Holidays IR£35; Societies: weekdays IR£23; weekend / Bank Holidays IR£31. Lessons available by prior arrangement. Club Hire available. Caddy service available by prior arrangement.
Clubhouse Hours: 8.00am - 11.30pm.
Clubhouse Dress: (Casual Neat).
Clubhouse Facilities: Full facilities. Snacks during day, a la carte after 6pm, and any other requirements by arrangement.
Open Competitions: Open week July / August. Handicap Certificate required for open competitions.

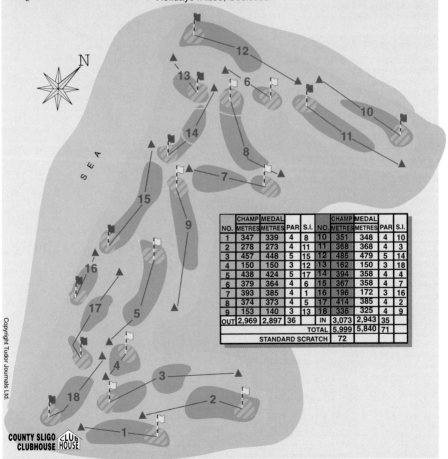

NO.	CHAMP METRES	MEDAL METRES	PAR	S.I.	NO.	CHAMP METRES	MEDAL METRES	PAR	S.I.
1	347	339	4	8	10	351	348	4	10
2	278	273	4	11	11	368	368	4	3
3	457	448	5	15	12	485	479	5	14
4	150	150	3	12	13	162	150	3	18
5	438	424	5	17	14	394	358	4	4
6	379	364	4	6	15	367	358	4	7
7	393	385	4	1	16	196	172	3	16
8	374	373	4	5	17	414	385	4	2
9	153	140	3	13	18	336	325	4	9
OUT	2,969	2,897	36		IN	3,073	2,943	35	
					TOTAL	5,999	5,840	71	
					STANDARD SCRATCH	72			

N

S E A

COUNTY SLIGO CLUBHOUSE CLUB HOUSE

Enniscrone Golf Club, Enniscrone, Co. Sligo. Tel: (096) 36297. Fax: (096) 36657.

LOCATION: Ballina Road, south of Enniscrone.
HON. SECRETARY: John Fleming. Tel: (096) 36243/21472.
PROFESSIONAL: Charles McGoldrick.
ADMINISTRATION: Mrs. Anne Freeman.
ARCHITECT: E. Hackett.

This links, on the shore of Killala Bay, is one of the many marvellous tests of golf which can be found in Ireland. The quality of the golf is matched by the surroundings, with the Ox Mountains close at hand. Killala Bay reaches out to the broad Atlantic within miles of sandy beaches surrounding the course. *"This is certainly a course not to be missed... the club is very keen to encourage visitors, so a warm welcome is assured"* (Golf World). Enniscrone is also the venue for the Irish Close Championships and the West of Ireland Championship.

COURSE INFORMATION

Par 72; SSS 72; Length 6,620 yds.
Visitors: Always welcome. (telephone at weekends).
Opening Hours: Sunrise – sunset.
Avoid: Bank Holidays; Sundays 8.00am – 11.00am and 1.30pm – 3.30pm.
Ladies: Welcome.
Green Fees: £18 per day. £24 weekends. Mid-week / weekends £18 for societies (12 or more people).
Juveniles: Must be accompanied by an adult. Club Hire is available. Caddy service and lessons available by prior arrangements. Telephone appointment required for weekends.
Clubhouse Hours: Open at all times.
Clubhouse Dress: Casual but neat.
Clubhouse Facilities: Catering facilities: snacks at all times. Meals by arrangement.
Open Competitions: Open Week 29th June – 3rd July.

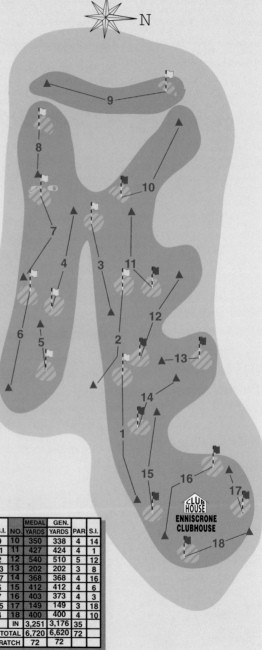

NO.	MEDAL YARDS	GEN. YARDS	PAR	S.I.	NO.	MEDAL YARDS	GEN. YARDS	PAR	S.I.
1	551	551	5	9	10	350	338	4	14
2	535	535	5	11	11	427	424	4	1
3	395	395	4	2	12	540	510	5	12
4	534	524	5	13	13	202	202	3	8
5	170	170	3	17	14	368	368	4	16
6	395	395	4	5	15	412	412	4	6
7	374	359	4	7	16	403	373	4	3
8	170	170	3	15	17	149	149	3	18
9	345	345	4	4	18	400	400	4	10
OUT	3,469	3,444	37		IN	3,251	3,176	35	
					TOTAL	6,720	6,620	72	
					STANDARD SCRATCH	72	72		

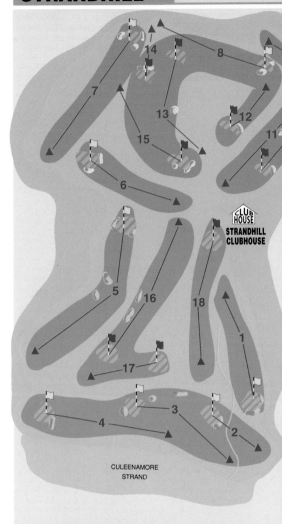

STRANDHILL CLUBHOUSE

**Strandhill Golf Club,
Strandhill, Co. Sligo.
Tel: (071) 68188.**

LOCATION: Five miles west of
Sligo City.
SECRETARY: Conal McGettigan.
Tel: (071) 68188.
ARCHITECT: E. Hackett

Strandhill is a links course, playable all
year round and situated in a most scenic
area with views of Knocknarea and
Benbulben Mountains. It has some very
interesting holes, with the final three
providing a sting in the tail.

COURSE INFORMATION

**Par 69; SSS 68; Length 6,032
yards, 5,516 metres.
Visitors:** Welcome.
Opening Hours:
8.30am – sunset.
Ladies: Welcome Thursday.
Green Fees: £15 Mon – Fri;
£20 Sat / Sun & Bank Hols;
£15 groups of 12 plus.
Juveniles: Welcome. Prior
arrangement is required for
groups.
Clubhouse Hours:
8.30am – 11.30pm.
Clubhouse Dress: Casual.
Clubhouse Facilities: Snacks at
any time, lunch by prior
arrangement.
Open Competitions: Most
weekends April – September.

CULEENAMORE
STRAND

NO.	MEDAL METRES	GEN. METRES	PAR	S.I.	NO.	MEDAL METRES	GEN. METRES	PAR	S.I.
1	397	380	4	2	10	304	285	4	14
2	158	155	3	8	11	300	263	4	12
3	375	330	4	17	12	304	260	4	16
4	291	270	4	10	13	338	305	4	7
5	480	460	5	18	14	132	111	4	13
6	355	336	4	11	15	306	270	4	3
7	352	335	4	5	16	386	362	4	6
8	308	275	4	15	17	178	141	3	9
9	186	140	3	4	18	384	329	4	1
OUT	2,902	2,681	35		IN	2,614	2,326	34	
					TOTAL	5,516	5,007	69	
					STANDARD SCRATCH	68	67		

Tubbercurry,
Co. Sligo.
Tel: (071) 86124.

LOCATION: 10 minutes walk from town centre.
SECRETARY: Billy Kilgannon.
Tel: (071) 86124.
ARCHITECT: Eddie Hackett.

A challenging nine hole parkland course with spectacular views of the Ox Mountains and surrounding countryside. It features a magnificent elevated 8th tee box to the difficult 185 yard par 3, (169metres).

COURSE INFORMATION

Par 70; SSS 69; Length 5,490 metres; 6,004 yards.
Visitors: Welcome everyday except Sundays.
Opening Hours: Dawn – dusk.
Avoid: Sundays.
Ladies: Welcome – active ladies committee.
Green Fees: £10.
Juveniles: £5.
Clubhouse Hours: 12.00 noon – 11.30pm (closed Tuesdays).

Clubhouse Dress: Neat dress.
Clubhouse Facilities: Newly built clubhouse – full bar and restaurant.
Open Competitions: Christmas, Easter, bank holiday weekends and Open Week in July.

TUBBERCURRY
CLUBHOUSE

NO.	METRES	PAR	S.I.	NO.	METRES	PAR	S.I.
1	336	4	6	10	336	4	6
2	282	4	15	11	282	4	15
3	327	4	11	12	327	4	11
4	145	3	17	13	145	3	17
5	347	4	3	14	347	4	3
6	389	4	1	15	389	4	1
7	321	4	7	16	321	4	7
8	169	3	13	17	169	3	13
9	429	5	9	18	429	5	9
OUT	2,745	35		IN	2,745	35	
				TOTAL	5,490	70	
	STANDARD SCRATCH				69		

GOLF CLUBS IN IRELAND
(NORTH & SOUTH – LISTED ALPHABETICALLY)

ADVERTISERS INDEX

GOLF DAYS GRATEFULLY ACKNOWLEDGES THE SUPPORT OF ADVERTISERS AND RECOMMENDS THAT READERS TAKE ADVANTAGE OF THEIR SERVICE WHEREVER POSSIBLE.

PUBLISHERS NOTE

THIS IS THE NINTH EDITION OF GOLF DAYS AND IN COMPILING THE INFORMATION WE ARE AWARE THAT IT IS NOT POSSIBLE TO ENSURE COMPLETE ACCURACY. WE WOULD WELCOME COMMENTS FROM READERS AND OBSERVATIONS FROM CLUB OFFICIALS TO ASSIST US IN OUR PROGRAMME OF CONTINUALLY UPDATING.

NOTES

12/12/98   87   + Mulraney Listowel. Clonlara   Glencullen
                   Seapoint ⑥ Old Field ⑦ Glenlo Abbey
① Powerscourt ② Old Head ③ Lisa Abbesty ④ Mt Blackstown ⑤ Killea Castle ⑥ Mont Juliet
25/7/99   93   + ⑦ ↑ + Lutterstown

23/4/03   112   + Watersreck + ⑦